CU00704514

The Design and Construction of British Warships 1939-1945

British Power Boat 70ft MGBs of the 6th MGB Flotilla in 1942

The Design and Construction of British Warships 1939–1945

The Official Record

Submarines, Escorts and Coastal Forces

Edited by

D K Brown

CONWAY
MARITIME PRESS

© Crown Copyright 1996
© Introduction and notes D K Brown 1996

First published in Great Britain in 1996 by
Conway Maritime Press,
an imprint of Brassey's (UK) Ltd,
33 John Street,
London WC1N 2AT

British Library Cataloguing in Publication Data
Design and Construction of British Warships, 1939-45:
Official Record – Vol. 2: Submarines, Escorts and Coastal Forces
 I. Brown, D. K.
 623.8250941

ISBN 0 85177 674 4

All rights reserved. Unauthorised duplication contravenes
applicable laws.

Typesetting and page make-up by TypeBright, Burton upon Trent
Printed and bound by Butler and Tanner Ltd, Frome

Contents: Submarines, Escorts and Coastal Forces

Introduction

At the end of World War I, the Naval Construction Department of the Admiralty produced a two-volume history of its wartime activities. Though originally 'Confidential', copies of this work can be found in a few libraries and have proved invaluable to historians. When World War II came to an end in August 1945 it was decided to produce a similar record but, though largely complete, it was never printed or issued, even internally. A number of chapters were slightly re-shaped and published as papers to the Institution of Naval Architects in 1947. In 1983 a carbon copy of the typescript came to light and a few copies were made for naval libraries and it is from these that the current work has been produced. There are indications on the original that one or two chapters were never completed, notably the introduction on the effect of naval limitation treaties (now covered briefly in the introduction to Volume I) and on wartime damage to ships. This book is published as it was written and no attempt has been made to correct any errors there may be (except obvious spelling mistakes), though manuscript notes suggest that it was very carefully checked. A limited number of footnotes have been added to supplement the information given, mainly as references to other sources. The second volume of a three-volume series, this book incorporates Chapters 9 to 16 of the original manuscript. Volume 1 covers Major Service Vessels, and Volume 3 covers Amphibious Warfare Vessels and the Fleet Train.

With rare exceptions, the text mentions only those designs which were actually built and the many designs progressed but abandoned are not mentioned. Few records remain of these designs which are frequently the 'missing link' between apparently unrelated ships which entered service.

ROYAL CORPS OF NAVAL CONSTRUCTORS IN 1945

Director of Naval Construction – C S Lillicrap, Esq, CB, MBE

Deputy Directors of Naval Construction – A P Cole, MBE (*act*) – (*a*) W G Sanders, MBE (*act*) and
L C Williamson (*act*), Esqrs

Director of Warship Production – S A McCarthy, Esq (*act*)

Director of Contract Work (Ships) – (*a*) C Hannaford, Esq, MBE (*act*)

Director of Contract Work (Supplies) – C J W Hopkins, Esq, MBE (*act*)

Assistant Directors of Naval Construction – F Hickey (*act*) and (*a*) A W Watson, MBE, Esqrs

Deputy Director of Dockyards – G A Bassett, Esq (*act*)

‡ *Senior Staff*

Bartlett J L (ADNC) (*act*),
Blackman, F T, MCD (*act*) (*tempy*),
Curphey, E S, MBE (Assistant D of D) (*act*),
Davies, W J A, OBE (*Assistant DWP*)
Forbes, W A D (ADNC) (*act*),
Gawn, R W L (Supt, Haslar),
Holt, N G, CBE (ADNC) (*act*),
Horley, A E (WPS NW Area)
Hudson, G, MBE (MCD) (*act*),

(*a*) Joughlin, J C, CBE (*Assistant DCW (s)*)
Kennett, E G (MCD) (*act*),
McCloghrie, G OBE (ADNC) (*act*),
Mathias, J E (*WPS Scottish Area*) (*act*),
Mathias, T L (ADNC) (*act*),
Merchant, C F (*Assistant D of D*) (*act*),
Moon, J E P (MCD) (*act*),
Offord, D E J, (*Superintendent, Undex, Rosyth*),
Payne, S, MBE (MCD) (*act*),

Pengelly, H S (ADNC) (*act*),
Shepheard, V G (ADNC) (*act*),
Stanley, H (*WPS North East Area*) (*act*),
Stantan, A G W (ADNC) (*act*),
Steed, F H (ADNC),
Sutcliffe, F (MCD) (*act*),
(*a*) Walker, J F, MBE (MCD)
Wallond, W H (*WPS NW Area*) (*act*),
(*a*) Woollard, L, MA (ADNC), Esqrs

‡ *Chief Constructors.*

(*a*) Adams, A (*act*),
Baker, R (*act*),
Bentley, T H (*act*),
(Bessant, J L, BSC (*act*),
Constr Capt F G Bogie, (*FNCO East Indies Station*),
Bryant, G (*act*),
Cannon, S R (*act*) (*Deputy WPS, Scottish Area*)
Carter, L T (*act*),
Chapman, J H B (*act*),
Constr Capt E F Craggs, BSC, *Lyness* (*act*),
Constr Capt V W Hall (*act*), (*tempy*) *For duty in Australia*
Hatchard W J (*act*),
Constr Capt S I Hill, *Colombo* (*act*),
Holt, W J (*act*),

W H Jackman, (*act*),
John, W G (*act*),
Johnson, H T (*act*),
King, I E, CBE (*act*),
Leddra, C H (*act*),
Lemmon, A T
McCammon, G W R MBE (*act*),
Mann, H R, OBE (*act*), (*tempy*),
May, H (*act*), (*Deputy WPS, NE Area*)
Constr Capt A J Merrington, OBE, BSC (*SCO Staff of ANCXF*) (*act*),
Monk, R J (*act*),
Narbeth, J H, BSC (*Eng*) (*act*),
Newnham, H E (*act*),
(*a*) Nicholls, A CBE, OBE,
(*a*) Noble, W E,
Constr Capt Paige, C V (*Bombay*) (*act*),

Constr Capt G W Pamplin (*Staff of RAFT*) (*act*),
Peake, H S (*act*), (*Deputy WPS NW Area*)
Perrett, W R (*act*),
Perry, C H, BSC (*act*),
Pound, F J A (*act*),
Richards, R H (*act*),
(*a*) Scott, C
Skinner, H E, OBE, BSC (*act*),
Sims, A J, OBE (*act*),
Constr Capt D W Smithers (*FNCO Mediterranean Fleet*) (*act*),
Stevens, L G (*act*),
Sutherby, F S (*act*),
Trevan, S N (*act*),
Watson, H J (*act*),
Watson, S H (*act*) Esqrs
Constr Capt R H Wright, *Kilindini* (*act*),

Tempy. Chief Constructors, H J Cox,

‡ *Senior Constructors*

Penwill, C H (*act*), Sherwin, C E (*act*), Esqrs
Pether, R P (*act*),

‡ *Tempy. Senior Constructors*

Mitchell, C C H P, P G Rouse, BA, MINA (*Supt of Conversions*), Whiting, W R G, MBE, MA Esqrs

‡ *Constructors.*

Andrew, W R, (*M Eng*) (*act*),
Barrett, L J (*act*),
Brooks, L J (*act*),
Chislett, H W J (*act*),
M C Dunstan (*act*),
Contr Com G S Ferris, BSC (ENG) (*act*) (*Lent to RIN*)
French, A W (*act*),
Gibbons, A J T (*act*),
Hancock, N (*act*),
Harrington, J W (*act*),
Constr Capt A N Harrison (*Lent to Royal Canadian Navy*),
Constr Com W R N Hughes (*Staff of VA(D)*) (*act*),

Constr Com L Kirkpatrick (*act*),
McCalin, E (*act*),
Mason, H R (*act*),
Matthews, F W (*act*),
Constr Com J R F Moss (*act*),
Mowatt, H M, BSC (*act*),
Newton, R N (*act*),
Constr Com S J Palmer, (*duty in Australia*) (*act*),
Perry, W G (*act*),
Constr Com T H Pilfold, (*duty at SHAEF*) (*act*),
Pound, E C, BSC (ENG) (*act*),
Purvis, M K (*act*),

Rayner, L W A (*act*),
Rogers, F C C,
Spanner, W F (*act*),
Constr Com J F Starks, (*Staff Admiral (S)*) (*act*),
Stewart, A, BSC (*act*),
Stunden, G J (*act*),
Tabb, H J (*act*),
Thorpe, T (*act*),
Tozer, R E (*act*),
Constr Com J E S Vincent, (*Freetown*) (*act*),
Vosper, A J (*act*),
Wood, R K, BSC (ENG) (*act*),

---

‡ *Arranged alphabetically*   (*a*) *Re-employed*   (*act*) *Acting*   (*tempy*) *Temporary*

‡ Temporary Constructors

Allen, T E,
Baker, D M,
Bedford, C A,
Constr Com J A Bonnyman, MBE (*duty in India*),
Boulton, T J,
Brookshaw, S W,
Bugler, A R,
Burrell, L W J,
Bush, F R,
Campaign, H H,
Chandler, C,
Coombes, L C,
Corfield, W A H,
Constr Com N J Coscoros,
Constr Com J Craig (*Staff of C-in-C, EIS*),
Constr Com R G Craig (*duty in Australia*),
Cross, T S,
Crossley, E,
(*a*) Cumbe, E. R,
(*a*) Daniels, S G,
Davey, S J,
Dwelly, E,
Eddey, J F J,
Grant, R C,

Constr Com F W Gray (*N Africa*),
Grinyer, A L,
Hankins, P H,
Constr Com A C Hardy,
Harris, C H L,
Hickish, J R,
Holloway, A H E,
Jago, E G,
Jeffery, W A,
Kicks, E,
King, P,
Langford, A T,
Littlejohns, F,
Constr Com C Lloyd-Roberts (*India*),
McMurray, M, BSC,
Mann, W J,
Martin, F J,
Matthews, A J,
Constr Capt J A Mavor (*PBCO, Italy*),
Mitchell, A BSC
Morley, F,
(*a*) Morris, R,
Constr Com H H Mutch (*Colombo*),
Nancarrow, G C,
New, H J C,

Norrington, E C,
North, D H,
O'Keeffe, W,
Osborne, A H,
Patridge, A,
Patterson, A P, BSC
Payne, R L,
Constr Com N H Perkin,
Phillips J,
Pitcher, H A
(*b*) Sears, F H,
Sedgwick, H E,
Smart, F J,
Constr Com W B Strang (*Staff of ANCXF (PH)*),
Thomas, A W,
Tillett, F L,
Turner, F,
(*a*) Turner, H A,
Constr Com A G Wearn (*Italy*),
Webb, W J,
Wolfe, A J M,
Wyatt, R,
Young, F, Esqrs

‡ Assistant Constructors, First Class

Constr Lieut-Com R Anscomb,
Constr Lieut-Com I McD Black, (*Staff of C-in-C, EIS*)
E C S Hepden, Esq

Constr Lieut-Com D R King,
Constr Lieut-Com R F Lofft, (*For special duty*),

Constr Lieut-Com E P Skinner (*Staff of C-in-C, BPF*),
Constr Lieut-Com W H Winn,

‡ Assistant Constructors, Second Class

Austin, A A,
Bell, L G,
Boulter, G J (*act*) (*tempy*),
Brinton, L J,
Brokensha, E A,
Chatten, H R P,
Cope, A J,
Dale, S D,
Constr Lieut-Com R J Daniel, (*Staff of RA(D), BPF*),
Davis, S M, M.ENG,
Evans, K G,
Constr Lieut-Com L H Evans, (*Staff of C-in-C, BPF*),

Farrell, K P,
Constr Lieut-Com J H Froud, (*For duty in Australia*),
Gibbons, E S,
Gundry, N E (*act*),
Hawkes, R,
Honey, N W,
Constr Lieut-Com R H Howorth,
Jolliffe, F V,
Constr Lieut-Com D B Kimber,
Constr Lieut J C Lawrence (*Staff of C-in-C, Med*),
Constr Lieut-Com C G Nace (*Staff of C-in-C, EIS*),

Constr Lieut A H Matthews (*duty in Australia*), (*act*),
North, E R (*act*),
Oldridge, C P (*act*),
Padbury, A E W,
Phillips, A E W,
Constr Lieut D S Radford (*Staff FOCT*),
Reeves, A E, (*act*),
Revans, J T,
Warren, W G,
Wood, E F,
Yearling, F H J, Esqrs

‡ Temporary Assistant Constructors

Blake, G D,
Crawford, J B,
Davies, J B,
(*a*) Froude, W,
(*a*) Hackney, G,

Lawson, D F,
Lees, J A H,
Constr Lieut L A Oliver,
Peel, R W,
Robinson, L M C,

Spanner, D C,
Lieut-Com P J Thornycroft,
Constr Lieut R J Tirard,
Watson, R H M,
Williams, F, Esqrs

‡ Temporary Acting Assistant Constructors

Constr Lieut-Com J P Allsopp,
Algate, E F,
Benoy, W H,
Chester, R,
Clews, C E,
Collecott, W B,
Davies, J J,
Dean, F D'A,
Dowden, A G,
Dunstall, J C,

Foot, F G,
Fuller, J V,
George, J,
Hastings, W A W,
Hosking, W H,
Jones, W,
King, J H,
Kingcome, F J,
Mason, T J,
(*a*) Merriman, T P,

Nightingall, V H,
Paradise, R,
Parsons, C H,
Price, J A,
Price, T L,
(*a*) Roberts, F C,
Rowe, J P,
Tippins, H G W,
Truscott, A G Esqrs

Honorary Member of the Corps
H B W Evans, Esq, MBE (*Assistant Constructor*)

---

‡ Arranged alphabetically   (*a*) *Re-employed*   (*b*) *On loan from other Government Departments*

(From Vol. III of the "Navy List" for July 1945 (corrected to 30 June)).

Key to Abbreviations and Terms

This book was written by naval constructors who probably expected that most readers would also be naval architects and other Admiralty officers who would be familiar with the many abbreviations and initials used. This glossary defines and explains most of them; though one or two sets of initials beat even the editor's 40 years of experience. Many of the entries relate to stability or strength and two short notes are included which explain the problems and define the terms used.

A   Aft

ACNS (W)   Assistant Chief of Naval Staff (Warfare)

Advance   The distance the ship moves in the direction of the original course during a turn.

AE   After End

AEW   Admiralty Experiment Works, at Haslar, near Portsmouth, where all hydrodynamic model testing was carried out.

Angle of max righting lever (GZ) See Stability note.

Angle of vanishing stability See Stability note.

AP   After perpendicular, at this date taken as the centre of the rudder stock.

AQ   Cannot be recognised. It clearly refers to cemented armour (C) and may be an error in the original.

BATM   British Admiralty Technical Mission – in Washington, USA.

BD   Between Deck. Of gun mounting refers to mountings, mainly twin 4.5in, worked from a gun bay between decks.

Bending Moment   See Strength note

BP   Between perpendiculars (of length) The fore perpendicular (FP) was the intersection of the design waterline with the stem, AP as above.

BTU   British Thermal Unit – an old, Imperial measure of heat.

Buster   A twin Bofors mount under development late in the war but never put into service, mainly because its weight of 20 tons was excessive.

C   Cemented, of armour. Armour with a very hard face produced by heating for a long period in contact with carbon.

Crush (of dock blocks)   During the war, most dock blocks were of timber which would compress (crush) under the weight of a ship.

D (quality), D1, D1HT   D Quality steel was a high strength steel introduced in the 1920s, D1 and D1HT were slight variations on D. It was not possible to make good, lasting welds on any of them.

DB   Double Bottom.

DC   Depth Charge.

DCHQ   Damage Control Headquarters, primary (1), secondary (2).

DCT   Director Control Tower.

Developed (blade) area   The total area of all blades outside the boss on the face of a propeller. (The face is the high pressure side, facing aft.)

Disc   The circle swept by the blades of a propeller.

Displacement   The total weight of a ship. Deep is fully laden, everything on board; standard is defined by the Washington Treaty,

roughly deep without all liquids, water, fuel etc.

DTSD   Director of Tactical and Staff Duties. Responsible for co-ordinating the views of naval staff divisions and issuing the Staff Requirement for a ship.

DW   A development of D quality steel which could be welded.

Endurance   Normally given with fouling corresponding to the average effect, six months out of dock in temperate waters. This conventionally added 1/4% per day to the frictional resistance (20-25% in six months). The effect was doubled in tropical waters. The quoted endurance was a comparative figure only, and true endurance was much less.

Expansion joint   A long superstructure will be strained by the flexing of the main hull in a seaway. It can either be made strong enough to accept the resulting load or the superstructure can be divided into short lengths. The joints between these lengths are known as expansion joints and will have a splash-proof cover.

F   Forward (sometimes used for Freeboard).

°F   Temperature, degrees Fahrenheit

(fl)   Fluid, refers to the effect of liquid movement on metacentric height, see Stability note.

g   The acceleration due to gravity – 32.2 ft/sec^2 – used as a measure of acceleration.

GM   Metacentric height. See Stability note.

HA   High Angle (gun mounting).

HADT   High Angle Director Tower

HA/LA   Combined High Angle/Low Angle mounting

Haslar   Site of AEW (*qv*), the ship model tanks.

Hogging   See Strength Note.

HP   High Pressure, as of a high pressure turbine stage or of a compressed air system

HT   High Tensile steel. Usually used in this book to describe high strength steels earlier than D quality.

Inclining (experiment)   See stability – an experiment to measure GM.

Inertia (in^{2}ft^2)   See Strength note

Lbs (Plate thickness)   Naval architects have to be very conscious of weight and to keep this in mind, the thickness of plates was given in lbs/sq ft. A 1 inch thick plate weighed 40lbs per sq ft (approximately) and was referred to as '40lb' plate. A similar approach was used for sections such as angle bars which were described by their weight ft run.

lbs/in^2   Pressure or stress in pounds per square inch, can also be written as psi.

Legend   In submitting a design for approval, DNC would complete a standard 4-page form setting out the main particulars of the design. This form was known as the Legend and quantities such as displacement given thereon became the Legend Displacement. After the Washington Treaty, the Legend Displacement would be the Standard (Washington) displacement. Prior to Washington the Legend displacement would include some fuel, usually one third.

Length (Between perpendiculars BP), (Overall)   See BP, length overall was from the furthermost points forward and aft (excluding the ensign staff but including stern galleries).

LP   Low pressure.

Maximum righting lever, Max GZ   See Stability note,

Metacentric Height   See Stability note.

ML   Middle Line.

NC   Non Cemented armour. Lacking the hard face of cemented armour which could not be made in thin plates. NC was generally preferred for turret roofs of any thickness because of its toughness.

NMMPP   Non Magnetic Protective Plating, used near the magnetic compass.

OB   Outer Bottom.

Peace Tanks   Fuel tanks carried high up in the machinery spaces of destroyers. Only used in peace because of the risk of fire in war.

Pitch   The face of a propeller of the type used in World War II was part of a helical screw – like a wood screw. The pitch of the propeller is the distance such a screw would move forward along its axis if turned through one revolution without slipping (again as in wood rather than water).

Propulsive coefficient (PC)   This is not an efficiency. It is the ratio of the power required to tow the hull, without appendages (bilge keels, shaft brackets etc) and without propellers to the power put into the shafts by the engines. It is a very useful shorthand to the naval architect, particularly in giving a first estimate of power for a new ship by comparison with a similar, existing ship. However, definitions and usage differ and it is a trap for the unwary.

psi   Pounds per square inch.

Rabbetted   Two plates slotted together at their edges in similar fashion to 'tongue and groove' floorboards.

Range (of stability)   See Stability note.

rpm   Revolutions (of shaft) per minute.

Sagging   See Strength note.

Speed   This may be given at deep displacement or standard. For a destroyer, there would be about 5 knots difference. Speed is quoted with a 'clean bottom' – no fouling.

STAAG   Twin Bofors mounting introduced late in the war. Acronym for 'Stabilised Tachymetric Anti Aircraft Gun'.

Standard   Displacement as defined by Washington; also used for corresponding draught and freeboard.

Stress   See Strength note.

SWL   Standard Water Line – see Standard.

Tactical Diameter   The diameter of the turning circle of the ship; unless otherwise stated, is full rudder angle.

Trim   Difference in draught between bow and stern. It was usual to design for about 2ft trim by the stern which would give good directional stability, sufficient draught for the propellers and would ensure that, in dry docking, the ship would settle on the blocks stern first, where the structure had been reinforced to take the heavy loads involved.

UD, UDk   Upper Deck.

UP   Unrotated Projectile. A rocket device which it was hoped would deter or even destroy attacking aircraft.

USK   Under Side of Keel.

Vote 8 cost   The cost without guns and stores.

WA   Warning Air (of Radar or, as it was then known, RDF – Radio Direction Finding).

WPS   Warship Production Superintendent.

WT   Wireless Telegraphy, radio using morse.

W/T   Water Tight.

Y   See strength note.

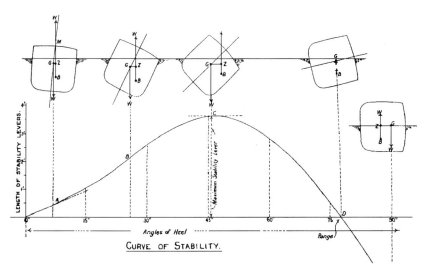

CURVE OF STABILITY.

Stability

To the naval architect, stability is a measure of the moment of force trying to bring the ship upright from a heeled position. The weight force acts downwards through the centre of gravity (G) which is (almost) a fixed point. The buoyancy force acts upwards through the centre of buoyancy (B) which is the centre of the underwater volume of the ship, which clearly moves as the ship is heeled.

The five small sections at the top of the diagram show how the centre of buoyancy B first moves outward as the ship is heeled, increasing the leverage bringing the ship upright and then, for extreme angles, moves back until the righting moment is zero and then becomes negative, causing capsize. Weight (W) equals buoyancy and hence the righting moment is measured by

Weight (W) x GZ

The stability characteristics were – and are – set out in the curve of stability or 'GZ curve' in which GZ, the righting lever, is plotted against angle of heel. The key parameters, which are given for each class in the text, are shown on the diagram.

Maximum stability lever, commonly called maximum GZ, defines the maximum steady heeling moment which the ship can withstand.

The angle at which the maximum GZ occurs is also important as if it is too small a sudden gust of wind may cause heel which exceeds the angle at which GZ is a maximum and lead to capsize (as in the loss of the *Captain* in 1870).

The extreme angle at which there is a positive righting moment is called the range. It is a less important parameter as, in a real ship, water will be pouring in down ventilators and other openings well before this angle is reached.

At small angles of heel (θ) GZ is given approximately by

GZ = GM. Sin(θ) – See Diagram

where GM is the metacentric height and θ is the angle of heel.

The values of most of the parameters used differ with changes in loading and are normally given for deep and light condition, the latter

usually giving the worst results since the weight of fuel low down in the deep condition acts as ballast. It was frequently necessary to add water ballast if the ship approached the light condition. During World War II it was customary to base design values of GM, GZ etc on previous practice rather than on rigid standards. With the experience gained from operating a large navy this was a perfectly acceptable procedure, shown by the fact that no British warship was lost due to stress of weather. The chosen values would have to be justified in formal debate with increasingly senior – and experienced – officers concluding with the DNC himself, who was not easily satisfied.

In the first paragraph it was said that the centre of gravity (G) was (almost) fixed. The effect of liquids, fuel or water, which are free to move in partially filled tanks does cause some movement of G except in the light condition where there are no liquids. This movement can be calculated and an effective position of G determined. This is known as G (fluid) usually written in this book as Gfl. Care would be taken in the design to minimise the possible movement of liquids and operators were warned to minimise the number of partially filled tanks.

It is possible to measure metacentric height directly in an inclining experiment. Known weighs (w) are moved a specified distance (x) across the deck and the heel (θ) measured. Then

w.x = W.GM.Sinθ

Since the position of M can be calculated precisely, that of G can be deduced.

Strength

Ships are loaded, even in still water, by the uneven distribution of weight and buoyancy along the length and this is made worse in waves. The worst case is when the ship is end on to waves of its own length and from a paper of 1870 by Edward Reed this was formalised into a standard calculation which was gradually refined. By World War II the waves considered were of the same length, crest to crest, as the ship with a height equal to 1/20 of the length.

Two conditions were considered:
Hogging with a wave crest amidships and the ends relatively unsupported and **Sagging** with crest at either end.

The loading of the ship – stores, fuel etc – would be adjusted to give a worst case in either condition. (Note, in some tables the different displacement used for Hogging and Sagging is given.) With the ship 'balanced' (weight = buoyancy) on the wave it was a simple, if lengthy, task to calculate the differential vertical force, the difference between weight and buoyancy, at each point along the length. This could be integrated to give the bending moment from which the stress (load per unit area of cross section) in deck and keel could be obtained with a knowledge of the properties of the structural section.

The resistance of the section to bending is given by the 'moment of inertia' in which the area (in²) of each longitudinally continuous member – plate or frame bar – is measured from the axis and multiplied by the square of this distance. Moment of Inertia (MI) or inertia has dimensions in² ft². In riveted ships 2/11 of the section in tension was deducted to allow for rivet slip.

When the ship is hogging, the deck will be in tension and the keel compressed whilst if sagging the deck will be compressed and the keel in tension. The neutral axis, roughly at half depth, is where there is no stress, either compressive or tensile, and the distance Y given in some tables is the distance of the deck or keel from this axis.

Such a calculation is an approximation to what happens in a real seaway but, given experience from many previous results for similar ships, its use can be quite reliable; indeed today's calculations, with a much greater theoretical background, are little different in principle. It was recognised that there were few long waves with a height of 1/20 their length and this was compensated for by accepting higher nominal stresses in long ships.

In ships of World War II the first warning of over-stressing was failure of rivets which was an all too common event, particularly in destroyers. However, there were no total failures of the structure of British ships as in some other navies. It should be noted that 'back breaking' was the commonest cause of sinking following action damage for destroyers and smaller ships. Appreciation of this problem led the designers to calculate stresses in battleships with all unarmoured structure destroyed.

For ships which are similar in both shape and loading it is reasonable to assume that bending moment is a constant fraction of Displacement x Length (= W.L/k where k is a constant derived from the previous ship) and reference will be found to estimates 'based on previous ships' in which this approximation has been used.

The tables usually give, both for hogging and sagging, values of bending moment and the stresses amidships in deck and keel. In one or two cases, stresses are calculated at other points along the length. There would also be a large number of calculations of the strength of detail portions of the hull and of items such as the rudder stock, shaft brackets, machinery seats etc but these are not reported in the book.

Starfish, *an early unit of the S class that was modified and improved throughout the 1930s and into the war.*

CHAPTER 9

Submarines

Editorial Note

The Royal Navy's operational submarines during World War II were of the S, T and U classes, (together with a few older vessels), designed before the war. In consequence they were somewhat old fashioned, with riveted hulls and a rather conservative approach to pressure hull design.[1] Welding was introduced during the war once a suitable steel became available giving an extra 50ft of diving depth. The other changes made during the war were of fairly minor nature suggesting that the original design was basically sound.

The war record of British submarines was remarkable considering that there were few targets and many A/S vessels in their operational areas. Their success was due primarily to the high standard of training of captains[2] and crews. The British torpedo was a simple design but reliable, unlike German and US torpedoes. It lacked the ability to angle the gyro and hence it was necessary to aim the whole submarine.

Submarine Construction 1919-1939

Submarine X1

At the latter end of 1920 it was decided to build a large submarine of experimental type.

In this submarine, called *X1*, the chief object in view was the development of a more powerful British design of diesel engine than the 100bhp per cylinder engine employed during the 1914/18 war. An 8-cylinder engine of 3000bhp, giving a total of 6000bhp for the two shafts was designed for ordinary surface propulsion. In addition, two German engines of 1200bhp (German rating) each driving a dynamo, were fitted as an auxiliary means of propulsion using the main motors, and for charging batteries.

It was also desired to ascertain the behaviour of a large submarine in so far as diving qualities and submerged control were concerned and the practicability of mounting and operating a relatively heavy armament.

X1 was expected to remain at sea for long periods and to be sufficiently well armed to engage a destroyer. For this latter purpose, two pairs of 5.2in guns, one pair forward and the other aft, were provided, and had a maximum range of 16,000yds.

Principal particulars were as follows:

Length overall	363ft 6in
Beam, maximum	30ft 5in
Draught, mean	18ft 10½in
Displacement, standard	2424 tons
Displacement, submerged	3580 tons
Bhp of main engines	6000
Bhp of auxiliary engines	2400
Bhp of motors	2600
Surface speed	19½kts
Submerged speed	9kts

X1 was a double-hull submarine, designed for a diving depth of 500ft, the pressure hull being 1in in thickness. The full fuel stowage was 452ton, giving an endurance of 16,000 miles at 7kts. Submerged full speed for 1½ hours was aimed at.

The torpedo armament consisted of six 21in bow tubes and twelve torpedoes in the stowages.

A pair of quick blowing and flooding tanks each having a Kingston valve were fitted both forward and aft in place of the two trimming tanks (one either end connected by a trim line), as fitted in previous submarines. These 'auxiliary' tanks, as they are now commonly known, were operated from the control room. The idea was quite new and claimed to greatly assist trimming and control.

The endurance depended upon the fresh water available and as only nineteen days' allowance could be stowed, as compared with ninety days' endurance of fuel at 7kts, a distilling plant on the lines of that then fitted in German submarines, in which the exhaust gas from the engines was used for vaporising water, was installed; the plant was not, however, a success.

Oberon

A conference was held in May 1922 to consider the various types of submarines which had been suggested by the C in C Atlantic Fleet, and it was decided to develop a submarine for distant patrol work, to be known as the Oversea Patrol Type.

The leading requirements were a surface displacement about 1200 tons, maximum surface speed 15kts with a cruising speed of 12kts, endurance 10,000 miles at economical speed, habitability and internal arrangements as necessary to enable vessel to operate in the tropics.

[1] D K Brown, 'Submarine Pressure Hull Design and Diving Depth between the Wars', *Warship International* 23 (3/1987).

[2] D K Brown, 'The Technology of Submarine Design', *Interdisciplinary Science Reviews*, 15/3, (September 1990). It is suggested that the training of the captain (Perisher's Course) was a vital factor in success. The German navy had a very similar course whilst the USN and Russian Navy did not have a specific course; Japan had a short course.

In April 1923 it was decided also that the control room should be silent (auxiliary machinery to be fitted elsewhere), the number of tanks should be reduced to a minimum, the main ballast tanks should flood in one minute, rapid flooding and blowing tanks should be fitted forward and aft for quick trimming, the supply of fresh water should be increased, HP blows should be fitted to all main tanks, evaporators off exhaust should be fitted so that vessel could add to fresh water supplies. These decisions were included in the design of *Oberon* in the 1923-24 Programme, which was laid down at Chatham Dockyard on 22 March 1924 and completed 24 August 1927.

The principal dimensions and particulars were:

Length overall	269ft 8in
Breadth extreme	28ft 0in
Draught, mean	15ft 6in
Displacement, standard	1311 tons
Displacement, submerged	1831 tons
Diving depth	500ft[3]
Oil fuel	186 tons
Surface endurance	11,400 miles at 8kts
Bhp of engines	2950
Surface speed	15kts
Bhp of main motors	1350
Submerged speed	9kts
Suberged endurance at full speed	2 hours

Armament

6 bow torpedo tubes 21in
2 stern torpedo tubes 21in
16 torpedoes
1-4in gun
2 Lewis guns

The submarine Oxley *built for the Australian Navy to a design modified from the Oberon.*

The external tanks were of a different form from those of the 'E' and 'L' class submarines. An increase in size of the external tanks was necessary to provide for the stowage of oil fuel in some of the spaces. Of the 186ton of fuel carried, about 180ton was in the external tanks and occupied the upper portions of the spaces between the two hulls, the ballast tanks being the lower portions, with branches for venting. The time of diving was reduced to a minimum.

A small pressure tank was provided on either side below the compensating tank in the externals, fitted with a Kingston valve and blowing arrangements. The purpose of these tanks was to ensure quicker diving by increasing the initial and subsequent rate of flooding of the main tanks and superstructure and the subsequent rate of changing depth.

Oxley and *Otway*

These two submarines were built for the Australian Government. The keels were laid down by Messrs Vickers Armstrong, Barrow on 24 August 1925 and completed 22 July 1927 and 9 September 1927 respectively.

The vessels were repeats of *Oberon* except for the following modifications:

(i) Increase in length due to increase in size of main motors, stowage of Asdic gear and battery cooling plant.
(ii) Increase in surface speed.
(iii) Auxiliary drive for low submerged speeds. The 60hp motor fitted primarily for driving the after low pressure blower was arranged to drive the propelling shafts through worm and worm-wheel on both shafts.

The principal dimensions and particulars were:

Length overall	275ft 0in
Breadth extreme	27ft 8in
Draught, mean	15ft 9in
Displacement, surface	1636 tons
Displacement, submerged	1872 tons
Diving depth	500ft
Oil fuel	195 tons
Surface endurance	12,300 miles at 8kts
Bhp of main engines	3000
Surface speed	15.19kts
Bhp of main motors	1350
Submerged speed	9kts
Suberged endurance at full speed	2 hours

Armament

6 bow torpedo tubes 21in
2 stern torpedo tubes 21in
16 torpedoes
1-4in gun
2 Lewis guns

Odin Class

These vessels, viz *Odin*, *Otus*, *Oswald*, *Osiris*, *Olympus* and *Orpheus*, were approved under the 1925-26 building programme and were of the Oversea Patrol Type.

The main difference between these vessels and *Oberon* was that the surface speed was increased from 15 to 17-17½kts and the bhp of engines raised from 2950 to 4400 to effect this.

Above water forward hydroplanes were introduced and also automatic inboard venting (AIV) to torpedo tubes. As the arrangement forward would not permit of an AIV tank being fitted the water was drained into the bilge.

Particulars of these vessels as completed were:

Length overall	283ft 6in
Breadth extreme	29ft 10½in
Draught, mean	16ft 1¼in
Displacement, surface	1781 tons
Displacement, submerged	2038 tons
Oil fuel	174 tons
Surface endurance	11,400 miles at 8kts
Bhp of main engines	4400
Surface speed	17½kts
Bhp of main motors	1320
Submerged speed	7¾kts
Diving depth	500ft

Parthian Class

Six submarines of this class, viz *Parthian*, *Proteus*, *Perseus*, *Pandora*, *Poseidon* and *Phoenix*, were ordered in the 1927 programme. They were generally similar to the *Odin* class except that the machinery spaces were rearranged to accommodate Vulcan clutches, the lower conning tower was enlarged to include a CO's cabin, power loading to the after torpedo tubes was dispensed with and the spare stern torpedoes were omitted, the main motor equipment was simplified, the shape of the bows was altered to give a better form for net-cutting, and No 7 P & S main ballast tanks were used as emergency oil fuel tanks. *Perseus* and *Proteus* were fitted with unbalanced rudders.

Particulars of these vessels as completed were as follows:

Length overall	289ft 2in
Breadth extreme	29ft 11in
Draught, mean	16ft 11in
Displacement, surface	1760 tons
Displacement, submerged	2040 tons
Oil fuel	159 tons
Surface endurance	10,750 miles at 8kts
Bhp of main engines	4337
Surface speed	17.94kts
Bhp of main motors	1635
Submerged speed	8.52kts
Diving depth	500ft

Rainbow Class

The 1928 programme included six submarines, viz. *Rainbow*, *Regent*, *Regulus*, *Rover*, *Royalist* and *Rupert*, but the last two of these were later cancelled. These vessels corresponded closely to the *Parthian* class.

The stowage of oil fuel external to the pressure hull was increased so as to avoid using a main tank for emergency oil fuel, and the plating to the fuel tanks was thickened from ¼in to ½in. The external tanks had an all-welded structure, following the practice being used in the reconstruction of the riveted external oil fuel tank structure in *Oberon*, *Oxley*, *Otway*, *Odin* and *Parthian* classes due to bad leaks in *Odin* class.

In view of the consideration being given to the salvage of sunken submarines at the time, an additional main bulkhead was introduced to give more complete subdivision. This necessitated a slight rearrangement of battery tanks and CO_2 machinery space.

The machinery was rearranged by putting the starting platform and controls at the after end of the engine room. This permitted the engine room to be shortened by 2ft as compared with *Parthian* class.

The particulars and dimensions of these vessels as completed were as follows:

Rover, *one of a number of large patrol submarines built between the wars.*

Length overall	287ft 2in
Breadth extreme	29ft 11½in
Draught, mean	16ft 1in
Displacement, surface	1763 tons
Displacement, submerged	2030 tons
Bhp of main engines	4100
Surface speed	17.88kts
Bhp of main motors	1670
Submerged speed	8.84kts
Surface endurance	10,900 miles at 8kts
Oil fuel	158 tons
Diving depth	500ft

S Class Submarines

This class was designed for the purpose of carrying out offensive patrols in narrow waters and to meet this purpose a standard displacement of 760ton was selected as being the optimum for operational efficiency.

The first two vessels of this class, *Swordfish* and *Sturgeon*, were ordered in the 1929 programme and were built at Chatham Dockyard.

The main particulars were as follows:

Length overall	202ft 2in
Breadth extreme	24ft 0in
Draught, mean	12ft 0in
Displacement, surface	735 tons
Displacement, submerged	935 tons
Bhp of engines	1550
Surface speed	13¾kts
Bhp of motors	1300
Submerged speed	10kts
Surface endurance	3800 miles at 9kts
Oil fuel carried	44.5 tons
Submerged endurance	1 hour at 10kts 32 hours at 2kts
Diving depth	300ft

Armament

1–3in HA gun
2 machine guns
6 torpedo tubes with 6 spare torpedoes

The 1930 programme included two vessels of S class, viz *Seahorse* and *Starfish*, built at Chatham. They were similar to *Swordfish* and *Sturgeon* except that a 3in gun on a fixed mounting replaced the 3in gun on a disappearing mounting as it was found that the resistance of the housing containing the disappearing gun was not appreciably less than that of a fixed mounting fitted on the casing and this arrangement was better for stability. The superstructure forward was lowered and the bow buoyancy tank was omitted to reduce yawing, and silhouette was reduced to improve diving time and stability.

The S class submarines in the 1931 programme, viz *Shark* and *Sealion*, included the above modifications together with the abolition of the non-compensated oil fuel tanks, which were incorporated with the compensated tanks as the compensating water capacity was found to be more than adequate. Also the external oil fuel tanks were omitted. This entailed new building drawings being prepared which, besides the above modifications, included two escape chambers, strengthened bulkheads and reduction in the number of main tanks.

Orders for these vessels were deferred with a view to embodying some further modifications put forward for the 1932 programme S class submarines, viz. *Snapper* and *Salmon*. These further modifications were to replace the single main motor on each shaft by twin motors, giving simpler control and doubling the rate of battery charging, and to replace the separate electrically driven HP air compressors or boosters by one HP compressor worked off each shaft, thus saving two

Starfish, *in July 1937, was one of the S class built in small numbers before the war and, slightly modified, in large numbers during the war.*

auxiliary electric motors with subsequent saving in complication and upkeep. The modified machinery arrangements enabled the accommodation arrangements aft to be considerably improved.

The new table of particulars for these vessels was as follows:

Length overall	208ft 8in
Breadth extreme	24ft 0in
Draught, mean	11ft 10in
Displacement, surface	760 tons
Displacement, submerged	960 tons
Bhp of main engines	1550
Surface speed	14¾kts
Bhp of main motors	1300
Submerged speed	10kts (designed)
Surface endurance	4700 miles at 8kts
Oil fuel	40 tons
Diving depth	300ft

Further repeats of *Shark*, embodying modifications found necessary in previous vessels, were *Seawolf* (1933 programme), *Sunfish* and *Spearfish* (1934 programme) and *Sterlet* (1935 programme).

Porpoise Class

These vessels were designed as minelaying submarines with laying arrangements at the stern and stowage for fifty mines in a single row through the casing. This principle of design was decided upon in preference to an internal minelaying arrangement which would entail considerable space being occupied by the mines within the pressure hull and necessitate a large increase in the displacement of the vessel.

Just prior to this time *M3* had been converted into an external minelaying submarine and the result of the trials had shown that as regards minelaying gear and compensating arrangements to maintain trim whilst minelaying, satisfactory results had been achieved. On these trials difficulties were caused by the long time taken to flood the mine casing and the distribution of buoyancy in the vessel which made *M3* heavy by the stern.

Trials carried out by *Vernon* indicated that mines would remain efficient for a month if subjected to alternate wetting and drying. Furthermore, the casing protecting the mines would keep them substantially dry on the surface and permit of access to them for maintenance, adjustments, etc thus obviating the disadvantages inherent with the continuously drowned mines in the L class, as adapted for minelaying, where the mines were in inaccessible tubes in the externals.

Porpoise was ordered in the 1930 programme and built by Messrs Vickers Armstrong, Barrow.

The time of diving from full buoyancy to periscope depth with mines on board was 1min 32sec ordinarily and 1min 14sec using Q tank. These times were similar to those for *Odin*, *Parthian* and *Rainbow* classes. The first of class trials of *Porpoise* showed that the tactical diameter on the surface with mines on board was less than, and the tactical diameter submerged approximately the same as, those of the *Rainbow* class. On the sea trials a surface speed of 16.16kts was obtained. The designed speed was 15kts.

Grampus and *Narwhal* were ordered in the 1933 programme, *Rorqual* in the 1934 programme, *Cachalot* in the 1935 programme, and *Seal* in the 1936 programme. *Grampus* was postponed from the 1932 programme to introduce certain features which had been decided upon since *Porpoise* was ordered.

In these ships, the bulkheads were designed to withstand a test pressure of 70lb/in², whereas in *Porpoise* they were designed to withstand a test pressure of 50lb/in² and in previous vessels of only 35lb/in². Escape chambers were fitted adjacent to bulkheads one forward and one aft.

To contain all the oil fuel within the main hull and so obviate the possibility of oil tracks, the pressure hull was built of 'keyhole' section and oil fuel carried low down in the middle line tanks. The main tanks were fitted on either side above these internal oil fuel tanks. To provide extra oil fuel capacity in an emergency the after main tanks, Nos 8 P & S, were constructed as main ballast-cum-oil-fuel tanks.

The magazine was designed to carry six warheads as well as 50% of the wartime ammunition stowage. A 4in gun was provided in these vessels (a 4in gun having been mounted after completion in *Porpoise* instead of the 4.7in gun originally mounted).

The main differences, other than those mentioned above, between these vessels and the *Porpoise* are indicated in the following table:

	Grampus Design	Porpoise
Length overall	293ft 0in	288ft 0in
Breadth, extreme	25ft 5in	29ft 10in
Mean draught	16ft 10in	16ft 0in
Standard displacement	1520 tons	1505 tons
Speed, surface	15.75kts	16.16kts
Speed, submerged	8.75kts	8.75kts

Thames Class

This class was intended for fast reconnaissance and offensive units to accompany the Battle Fleet, the main requirements being a surface speed of 21kts and standard displacement of 1760 tons. After much discussion the design was modified to a high speed overseas patrol type.

Increases in weight of machinery, oil fuel and lubricating oil and other small changes led to an increase in the standard displacement from 1760 tons quoted from the sketch design to 1805 tons for *Thames* as built.

Three vessels of the class, viz. *Thames*, *Severn* and *Clyde*, one in each of the 1929, 1931 and 1932 programme, were built at Messrs Vickers Armstrong, Barrow. They were fitted with supercharged engines. The external oil fuel tank structure was all-welded except for the connections to the pressure hull.

Results of first of class, diving and other trials showed manoeuvring, control and time of diving compared favourably with previous vessels. The actual maximum speed of *Thames* under trial conditions was 22.58kts, about 1½kts in excess of requirement.

Severn and *Clyde* were generally similar to *Thames*, the principal differences being a lengthening of the motor room, consequent on a change from the 330 volt battery grouping in *Thames* to a 220 volt grouping, the fitting of two escape chambers, main bulkheads to withstand a test pressure of 70lb/in² instead of 35lb/in², omission of the single internal fuel tank carrying 14 tons, and the strengthening of hull structure in way of the main engine room.

These changes involved an increase in standard displacement in these two latter vessels from 1805

Thames, whose design developed from a requirement for a large and fast submarine to accompany the battle fleet; she made over 22kts on trials.

tons to 1830 tons and a decrease of ½kt in maximum surface speed. The reduced surface endurance still exceeded the staff requirement of 10,000 miles at 8kts.

The main particulars of these vessels other than those mentioned were as follows:

	Thames	Severn & Clyde
Length overall	345ft 0in	345ft 0in
Breadth extreme	28ft 3in	28ft 3in
Surface displacement	2165 tons	2200 tons
Submerged displacement	2680 tons	2720 tons
Draught, mean	15ft 7½in	15ft 11in
Oil fuel	216 tons	202 tons
Diving depth	200ft	200ft[4]

General Remarks on the War Period 1939-1945

The London Naval Conferences of 1930 and 1936 limited the standard displacement of submarines to 2000 tons and their gun calibre to 5.1in with the exception that each contracting power could retain, build or acquire three vessels of 2800ton and gun calibre 6.1in. Britain never invoked this part of the agreements, X1 having been built before 1930, and France retained only one of her three large submarines, Surcouf, of 2880 tons.[5]

The design and development of British submarines took low priority in the meagre naval programme of the few years prior to the war. Design staff at the Admiralty and building, repair and maintenance staffs in the dockyards and private yards were kept to a bare minimum and in consequence the British submarine fleet at the opening of hostilities in September 1939 consisted largely of out-of-date types.

Each stage of the war brought new ideas and techniques with increased demands upon weight and space for the installation of new apparatus and equipment. The principal changes and innovations introduced during the war were:

(i)   *Gun Armament* – an Oerlikon gun for defence against air attack was fitted at the after end of the bridge in all vessels except U class.

(ii) *Torpedo Armament* – stern firing external torpedo tubes were introduced into the 1940 S and 1941 T classes. The S class had one tube at the after end of the casing and the T class had one at the after end of the casing and two amidships, these latter being reversed from their designed position of firing forward. In the 1943 A class, two internal and two external tubes were fitted at the after end.[6] Torpedo loading arrangements were greatly simplified in war-built vessels, the pre-war arrangement of transporting trolleys and rails being replaced by bracket stowage with hinged arms and the torpedoes being 'skidded' into the loading position.

(iii) *Minelaying by Patrol Submarines* – in the early stages of the war, T, S and U class submarines were equipped with transporting and loading gear to enable mines to be laid from the bow internal torpedo tubes, these mines being carried in lieu of torpedoes when necessary.

(iv) *Radar* – masts to carry air and surface warning aerials, both rotating, the former being telescopic and the latter periscopic, were introduced. Space in the control room being at a premium, the radar sets had to be accommodated in the already congested W/T office. In the war-designed A class a separate radar office was incorporated.

(v)   *Asdic* – type 129 was already fitted at the start of the war, but additional equipment was incorporated as the war progressed. Type 129 was sited in the fore end of the ballast keel and was consequently 'blind' for targets above and abaft the submarine. To overcome this deficiency, Type 138 was added early in 1943. This was sited on the after casting. Considerable difficulties were encountered in finding sufficient space inside the engine room for operation of the type 138.

(vi) *Air Conditioning* – early experience on submarine operations in the Far East indicated that the dehumidifiers already installed in some of the T and S class were inadequate for their purpose and possessed other disadvantages.[7] Urgent measures were taken to replace them with the more efficient Freon air conditioning plants, each T, S and U class submarine being finally equipped with two units. In consequence, the habitability of these submarines was so much improved that they were able to carry out patrols of up to forty-five days' duration or even longer in isolated cases. The associated ship ventilation system required to be extensively modified. In S and U class space for the Freon units could only be found by removing the A end of the VSG drive to the capstan.

(vii) *Air Purification* was brought into prominent by the experiences of several sub-

[4] Note the reduction in diving depth as the pressure hull was reduced in thickness to make weight available for the more powerful machinery.

[5] It is interesting that most navies at the end of World War I copied the unsuccessful German U-Cruiser concept. None of these later giant submarines was effective either.

[6] The need to increase stern fire may be seen as a consequence of the consequence of the inability to angle the gyro.

[7] It is reliably reported that one submarine in the Indian Ocean making routine reports of internal temperature and humidity was told that the conditions reported would not support human life.

marines when they were forced to remain submerged for much longer periods than were normal. During long submergences it is necessary to remove the excess carbon dioxide from, and replenish the oxygen in, the submarine's atmosphere. Special instructions regarding this were issued. Carbon dioxide was removed by absorbing it in soda lime or lithium hydroxide spread around the submarine on trays, and the oxygen was supplied from additional oxygen bottles. Tons of soda lime and lithium hydroxide were used. Later in the war, special apparati were developed and tried with success in HMS *Thule* under patrol conditions. That for removing carbon dioxide was a more scientific and efficient method of absorption, the air being drawn through canisters of carefully prepared soda lime. Oxygen was obtained by electrically burning a special candle. These apparati, however, were not brought into mass production until after the end of hostilities.

(viii) *Fresh Water* – stowage was increased in the T and S class by converting some of the compensating water tanks or by building additional tanks, to meet the longer patrols in the Far East. Distillers were installed to give increased capacity.

(ix) *Increased Oil Fuel Capacity* to enable them to cover the large distances involved in war patrols in the Pacific was provided in T and S class by converting some of the main tanks for emergency use as oil fuel tanks. In T class the increase in capacity amounted to 65% and in S class 35%, thereby improving the 'operational endurance' by some 40% and 16% respectively. Earlier in the war one of the main (ballast) tanks in U class submarines had been similarly converted.

(x) *Storecarrying* by submarines to Malta, when that base was besieged, introduced many problems of which one was the transport of aviation spirit in external tanks and in containers stowed in the casing which entailed careful preparation of the tanks, incidental pipe and valve work, and special precautions against the danger of explosion and fire. Perishable and other stores and provisions were carried in containers inside and outside the main hull and in some cases a battery section was landed to obtain the necessary storage space. Torpedoes and explosives were transported in special containers carried in the casing. The main bulk of the stores conveyed thus to Malta was carried by the larger, and older, type submarines of the O, P and R class, *Porpoise, Rorqual, Severn* and *Clyde*. S, T and U class were also used but their storage capacity was much less in comparison.

(xi) *Accommodation* – in almost every class of submarine the accommodation as designed to meet staff requirements became inadequate due to the continual

Valletta harbour during the war with Taku *in the foreground and the U class* Una *and* Unrivalled *beyond. Malta not only functioned as an important submarine base, but the siege of the island required vital stores to be brought in by submarine.*

additions of personnel required to operate new equipment such as radar, antiaircraft guns, stern torpedo tubes, asdic, etc and consequently modifications to the layout of mess spaces and to be made as building progressed during the war. Portable berths were fitted in the torpedo stowage compartments of T, S and U classes. In some classes the wardroom had been sited forward of the crews' mess space and to improve fighting efficiency it was moved to the fore end of the control room so that the officers were within easy reach of the bridge and control room. Similar remarks apply in the case of the CO's cabin.

(xii) *Sound Insulation* of auxiliary machinery became increasingly important as the war progressed. In the early stages of development the method of insulation consisted of mounting the machines on simple bonded rubber and steel 'sandwich' type mountings and of fitting flexible rubber pipe connections where necessary, each machine being treated separately. Later the types of mountings were standardised and a range of hexagonal pedestal type mountings developed. These were developed by ARL early in 1944 and combined both shock and sound insulating properties. No completely successful high pressure flexible piping had been developed by the end of the war although several designs were tried.

The progress of this work was largely made possible by the development of a successful noise range at Loch Goil, where each submarine underwent searching trials to determine the range of its separate items of machinery.

In the war-designed A class, as complete sound insulation arrangements as possible were incorporated. The ballast pump was specially designed to reduce the noise emission. In this class every machine so treated had a noise range of 500yds or less. As many machines as possible were insulated in the S and T class, during building or as they came in for refit.

(xiii) *Batteries* – early war experience showed that the battery cell containers were very liable to damage by the shock following a depth charge explosion. Exhaustive trials were carried out in a shock target – designated Job 9 – with various types of container and methods of support. As a result, the tank bearers, carrying the gratings on which the cells sat, were supported on 1in thick rubber pads and similar pads were fitted at the tank sides. Each cell was also encased in a rubber envelope to prevent leakage of acid earthing and evolution of chlorine, should the container become damaged. New types of cell containers were later developed which, combined with the rubber pads, enabled the rubber envelopes to be dispensed with.

(xiv) *Carriage of Small Craft* – the carriage of Chariots and Welman craft by parent submarines was advocated by the Naval Staff in 1943. This involved considerable design work, extensive trials and modifications, and would have involved appreciable topweight in many submarines had the idea been adopted generally. A few T class submarines carried out operations with Chariots in special pressure-tight containers on the casing but the later idea of carrying such craft at the side of the bridge and in the casing, exposed to the sea, did not reach the operational stage. Arrangements were, however, made for towing small craft.

(xv) *Struts to Torpedo Hatch* – it was reported at the end of 1941 that in several vessels which had been forced to go below the normal diving depth the torpedo hatches had leaked. This was ascribed to local distortion of the hull in way of the large opening and, to alleviate this, special transverse struts were fitted in all classes. These struts were carefully fitted so that they only began to take the compression load in the opening when the normal diving depth was reached, thereby ensuring that the structure took its full share of the load beyond the normal diving depth.

Towards the end of hostilities other major modifications such as the fitting of 'snort' gear, complete rearrangement of the control room to facilitate attack and using improved radar apparatus and plotting, automatic telemotor control, larger capacity air-loaded accumulators to the telemotor system and anti-radar and anti-asdic measures, were being put to trial for operational use. Some of these items and all of those noted above except (xiv) were incorporated in the war-designed A class submarine which, however, did not complete in time to be employed in actual operations.

The weight involved by these and other less important alterations and additions necessitated a

[8] The buoyancy from the sea must at all times be equal to the weight of the submarine – the buoyancy force being equal to the volume of the submarine times the density of water. If the submarine moved to water of a different density, weight had to be adjusted by taking in or discharging water from internal tanks. The additional weight of wartime additions meant that there was less scope for making density corrections.

very substantial reduction in the margin of stability and special instructions, such as the jettisoning of oil fuel in rough weather, had to be issued for the guidance of commanding officers should the circumstances demand action to improve seaworthiness or fighting efficiency, eg heavy motion in a seaway reducing navigational qualities to an unacceptable limit, leaks from oil fuel tanks leaving a track.

The second important effect of these modifications on operational qualities was to reduce the range of density of water in which the submarine could operate by at least one third and it was not surprising, therefore, when in 1944, in unusually fresh water near the mouth of large rivers, some submarines found difficulty in keeping diving trim.[8]

The steady grown of the number of As & As and the tendency towards mass production methods led, in 1942, to an investigation into the possibilities of simplification of design of equipment and, where acceptable, its deletion. Certain simplifications were introduced thereafter such as the main line being constructed of steel piping, direct telemotor operation of hydroplanes, reduction of number of telemotor pumps from three to two and the omission of spring-loaded accumulators to all main tanks. Guard rail stanchions, ensign and jackstaffs, flag lockers, indicator lamp and similar items of equipment not essential in war had been omitted earlier.

The adoption of all-welded pressure hulls in the later T and S class and the A class enabled a deeper operational diving depth to be obtained whilst accelerating the production rate by facilitating mass production methods. The advantages

of prefabrication, made possible by the introduction of welding of the hull and casings generally, became apparent in the larger ship-building firms towards the end of hostilities with Germany and, had the war continued longer, production would have reached a much higher rate than that previously possible by more orthodox methods. The early stages of the welding of pressure hulls were, as might be expected, marked by set-backs due to inefficient technique and lack of skilled personnel, but in a comparatively short time these difficulties were overcome, due in no small measure to the detailed examination of welded joints by radiography – a procedure which, experience has shown, pays handsome dividends.

The small submersible made its appearance during the war. Before the war proposals to built midget submarines were considered on more than one occasion, but it was the view of the Naval Staff that we had no requirements for craft of this type, and consequently no steps were taken to develop them. They came into prominence in 1942 and played an important part in crippling the German battleship *Tirpitz* and the Japanese cruiser *Takao*.

They were first used against Allied shipping in the Mediterranean in the form of the Italian two-man Chariot (or Human Torpedo). Then later they were used in the form of midget submarines by the Japanese. We then developed a series such as the Chariot, X Craft, Welman craft, Welfreighter and Mobile Floating Unit (MFU). The Germans developed several types such as the Linsen, Morder, Biber, Mölch, and Seehund. It is probable that the German craft were inspired by the successes of the British X Craft and Welman craft.

An X Craft running on the surface during a wartime demonstration for the press.

The offensive value of all such craft is primarily to attack ships in harbour. Secondary uses are for landing agents in enemy territory and for beach reconnaissances.

The development of these British submersibles was severely hampered by production under wartime conditions with lack of experienced staff. Many features had to be adopted which could certainly have been improved if development had taken place in peacetime.

For the Welman, Welfreighter and MFU, designers in outside industry were employed. Notwithstanding the ingenuity and resource they brought to bear on their problems, their lack of experience in submarine design resulted in delays and numerous difficulties which were left to DNC to solve.

Submarine Construction – 1938 Onwards

Minelaying and Storecarrying Submarine Designs

Several designs of minelaying submarines were developed from 1938 onwards, none of which were built, but a brief record of their main particulars is given below.

At a meeting called by the Chief of Naval Staff on 18 October 1938 it was decided to proceed with a new 1939 minelayer design with an endurance and speed not exceeding that of *Cachalot* with T class engines, the oil fuel being carried, however, inside the hull as far as practicable.

A sketch design and legend of particulars for a vessel of surface displacement 1755 tons, length 294ft 0in, speed 15¾kts surface, diving depth 300ft and carrying fifty mines, was prepared. The design incorporated a pressure hull of circular section instead of the 'keyhole' section previously adopted in *Grampus* and four submarines of the type were included in the 1939 building programme. They were afterwards cancelled, in favour of four of a smaller type.

This smaller type minelayer submarine, suitable for operations in the North Sea, was discussed at a meeting called by the First Sea Lord on 20 January 1939. It was contended that the larger design referred to above would be unable to lay mines in less than fifteen fathoms and their large complement constituted a disadvantage. On the question of the number of mines to be carried, it was noted that the superstructure method of carrying mines involved a longer submarine and it was agreed that eight to twelve mines per submarine would meet requirements. Admiral (Sub-

marines) expressed his opinion that all patrol submarines should be capable of carrying a few mines.

It was finally agreed to prepare a design on the same lines as the 1939 S class modified to incorporate the 'Sunfish' type of engine, with eight to twelve mines in the saddle tanks, increased fuel capacity to give 4000 miles endurance at 10kts, a maximum surface spread of 14kts and omitting the external torpedo tubes. The First Sea Lord recommended to the Board that a design of this type should replace the previous large type in the 1939 programme referred to above.

The approved staff requirements described this design as being a small combined patrol and minelaying type submarine capable of operations in Home (including Baltic) and Mediterranean waters of minelaying in depths down to twelve fathoms, the surface speed being the maximum possible with the 'Sunfish' type of engine but absolute reliability of 11kts under operational conditions being essential. Notable features in the requirements included noiseless operation of the hydroplanes and steering, the omission of escape chambers in favour of the twill trunk method of escape and a maximum suberged speed of 9kts. The design was later modified to provide for escape chambers instead of twill trunks.

The sketch design was of submerged displacement 1030 tons, surface displacement 820 tons, length overall 221ft 0in, diving depth 300ft, maximum surface speed 14kts, maximum submerged speed 9kts, endurance 4100 miles at 10kts on the surface and 120 miles at 3kts submerged and carried one 3in gun, six bow tubes and six reload torpedoes, and twelve mines.

Tenders were invited in the middle of 1939, but owing to the serious change in international affairs and on the instructions of the Controller, the building of these minelaying submarines was not proceeded with.

In October 1940, Admiral (Submarines) made proposals for replacing the minelaying submarines lost in action and stressed that the replacements should be repeats of the *Seal* (*Porpoise* class) with only such modifications as were necessary to bring them up-to-date. Accordingly an order was placed in January 1941 with Messrs Scotts S & E Co, Ltd, for three submarines of the 'Improved *Cachalot* type', the machinery to consist of two 8-cylinder T class engines each developing 1650bhp at 460rpm. These submarines were included in the 1940 supplementary building programme. It was not considered necessary to prepare a new sketch design, it being decided that that submitted to the Board on 19 December 1938 for the large type minelayer of the 1939 programme, described previously, was suitable for the purpose.

Building drawings and legend of particulars were approved by the Board in April 1941 and information for building forwarded to Messrs Scotts. At this time, however, a requirement for increased production of patrol-type submarines arose and at Controller's Meeting in June 1941 it was decided to cancel the three minelaying submarines placed with Messrs Scotts.

Towards the end of 1942 when plans for the war in the Far East were taking shape, Admiral (Submarines) put forward proposals for the design of a minelayer-cum-storecarrier submarine, the primary function of which would be minelaying. The broad staff requirement given by Admiral (Submarines) envisaged a submarine approximating to the T class in size with a surface speed of 18½kts, stowage space in external tanks for 120ton of aviation spirit and provision for carrying thirty-six torpedoes in containers in the casing. A start was made on drawing up the detailed staff requirements but work was stopped by a decision taken at Controller's Meeting in February 1943. It was agreed, however, at this meeting to investigate the practicability of converting old-type submarines to submarine supply ships.

Proposals to this effect were put forward in February 1942 by Admiral (Submarines) who stated that, owing to the inadequate endurance of T and 1940 S classes for the Far Eastern war, tanker/supply submarines would be of great operational value. Production at home was such that the existing submarine programme could not be interfered with and there was no possibility of getting the submarines built in the USA but the conversion of some of the older types of vessels might be classified as repairs.

At a meeting between DNC and FOS/M in February 1942, it was agreed to investigate a design to carry 600ton of fuel (sufficient for three T class submarines) additional to the requirements of the supply submarine itself, spare torpedoes to be carried in containers in the casing, all torpedo tubes, torpedoes and mines and one battery to be omitted.

Owing to the shortage of staff the necessary design work could not be carried out by DNC Department and Messrs Vickers Armstrong, Barrow, agreed to undertake the work. The first preliminary sketches and design calculations were forwarded by Messrs Vickers Armstrong in March 1943.

The staff requirements could not be fully met and the final design had a length on the WL of 289ft 2in, surface displacement 2494 tons, and submerged displacement 2914 tons. The surface speed was 14½kts with 8000 miles endurance at 2kts. The cargo load which could be carried was 430ton of oil fuel, 150ton of stores (including lubricating oil), twenty-four torpedoes and 150 rounds of 4in ammunition.

Owing, however, to the interference to refits of vessels in the USA if these conversions were undertaken, the conversion was dropped in July 1943.

U Class Submarines

This class, built under the 1936 building programme, was intended to replace the H class (see *Records of Warship Construction, 1914-1918*) as the useful life of the latter terminated. They were considered to be suitable for both submarine and anti-submarine training in addition to meeting the requirements for defensive patrol in the vicinity of the coasts of the UK or of bases in any part of the British Empire, and for short distance offensive patrol.

The legend of particulars and sketch design were approved by the Board in June 1936. The principal particulars were:

Length overall	186ft 6in
Breadth extreme	16ft 1in
Surface displacement	600 tons
Submerged displacement	700 tons
Shp of main engines	720
Bhp of main motors	825
Max speed, surface	11¼kts
Max speed, submerged, for 2 hours	10kts
Endurance on surface at 10kts ideal conditions	3600 miles
Endurance submerged at 2kts	120 miles
Oil fuel stowage	40 tons
Torpedo tubes 21in	4 bow internal
Torpedo tubes 21in	2 bow external
Reload torpedoes	4
Guns	1 Lewis gun
Diving depth	200ft

The design, which was of the single hull type, was such that a 3in gun and ammunition could be carried in lieu of two torpedoes and arrangements were made so that this could be effected at short notice.

Three vessels, *Undine*, *Unity* and *Ursula*, were ordered from Messrs Vickers Armstrong, Barrow, in November 1936 and completed in August, October and December 1938 respectively. They were the only vessels of the class available for operational use when hostilities commenced in September 1939. *Undine* carried out First of Class trials achieving a surface speed of 12.45kts and submerged speed of 8.58kts. *Undine* and *Unity* were equipped with Paxman engines and *Ursula* with Armstrong Whitworth engines. The length of these vessels, as completed, was 191ft 0in compared with the legend figure of 186ft 6in

Just prior to the outbreak of war and thereafter, several orders were placed and in all a total of seventy-four vessels were built, based upon the original 1936 design, modified in the light of war experience. The names of the vessels, builders, etc are given in a table at the end of this chapter. Vessels prior to *Venturer* were of riveted construction, those from *Venturer* onwards had thicker pressure hull plating and were partly welded.

In the early part of the war, the three pre-war *Unity* class proved difficult to handle at periscope depth in rough weather due to the bluffness of the bow arising from the incorporation of the two bow external torpedo tubes. This bluffness also caused a considerable bow wave and some loss of speed in a seaway. The building programme was by this time well progressed and consequently the earlier vessels to complete at Messrs Vickers Armstrong, Barrow, could not be modified to the full extent desirable as regards fineness of the bow which commenced from different positions abaft the fore end according to stage of completion and consequently their overall lengths varied slightly, being either 191ft 0in or 192ft 4in. Later vessels of riveted construction were fined even more and their overall length increased to 196ft 10in. In all these vessels, the two bow external tubes were omitted, and the 3in gun added instead.

Other early modifications to the class included the fitting of a quick diving tank ('Q' tank) of 1.9ton capacity (for use also as a salvo compensating tank), removal of the bow shutters which had introduced difficulties in connection with torpedo discharge and were difficult to maintain in satis-

factory working conditions – a general decision for all classes – the fitting of a 12pdr gun in lieu of a 3in gun, as these became available,[9] and omission of the drop keel – also a general decision for all classes. The incorporation of type 291 radar, to the exclusion of the existing W/T mast, took place in step with other classes.

To enable longer patrols to be carried out No 5 main tanks port and starboard were converted about 1942 for use as emergency fuel tanks thus increasing the total fuel stowage from 38.5ton to 55.0 tons. The fresh water capacity was also increased and a distilled water tank installed.

All vessels of the first group ordered during the war, and the three pre-war vessels, ie fifteen vessels in all, were constructed with the ward room at the forward end of the main flat over No 1 battery tank. War experience indicated that the more usual position, adjacent to the control room, was better and in consequence all later vessels were modified to this arrangement.

Modifications to improve resistance of battery cell containers to shock, sound insulation of auxiliary machinery and omission of the starboard anchor and cable equipment, etc took place in step with other classes, but it was not possible to fit an Oerlikon gun abaft the bridge owing to topweight limitations.

This class of submarine was used extensively in the Mediterranean theatre as well as in home waters and in 1941 a redesign was decided upon to bring them up-to-date with war experience at that time and at the same time attempt to cure the 'singing propeller', a common trouble with the class. This latter was mainly attributed to a less direct flow of water to the propellers than was usual and was cured by fining the stern. This, together with a further fining of the bow, brought the overall length to 204ft 6in. The opportunity

[9] The gun mounted in the U class is a complicated story. The three original boats were designed for the 3in but it was probably only fitted in *Ursula* . The boats of the Emergency 1940 and the short boats of the 1941 Programme had the 12pdr whilst later boats had the 3in (17lb shell). There may well be exceptions or even changes.

Ursula, *in January 1939, one of three U class built as training submarines which formed the basis for a very large number built during the war.* Ursula *has the original six tube arrangement in the bow, later reduced to four.*

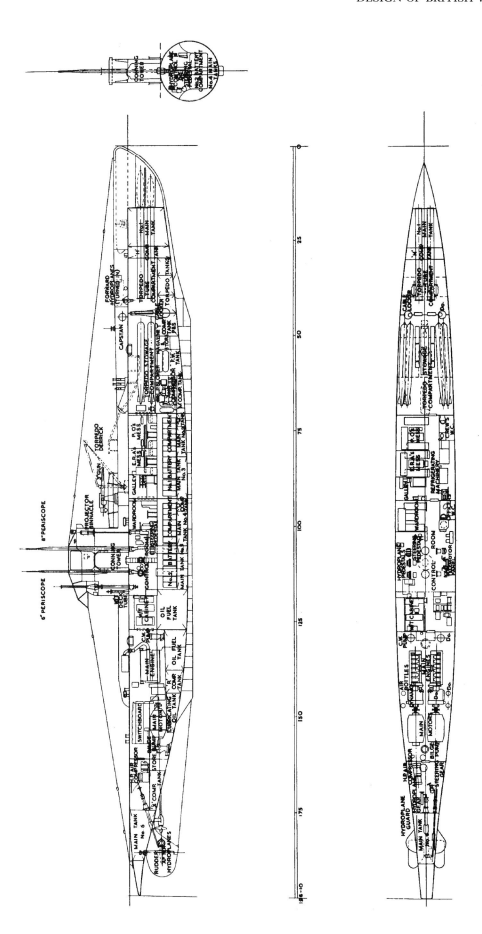

Internal arrangements of a U class submarine, as fitted for 3in gun

was taken to increase the diving depth by two methods: first by an increase in thickness of pressure hull plating from 20 to 25lb/ft^2 and the use of S quality instead of HST steel; secondly by the introduction of welded tee-bar framing and welded butts of the pressure hull plating, the weight saved in this, and other ways, being utilised to obtain the increased thickness. The result was an increase in diving depth from 200ft to 300ft. The surface displacement increased to 658 tons and the submerged displacement to 740 tons.

T Class Submarines

At the beginning of the war only three vessels of this class were completed, viz *Triton*, *Triumph* and *Thistle*, all built at Messrs Vickers Armstrong, Barrow. Eleven more in the 1936, 1937 and 1938 programmes had been ordered and were in course of construction (see the table at the end of this chapter). *Thetis*, which sank in Liverpool Bay during trials on 1 June 1939, was raised just after the beginning of the war and was later reconditioned by Messrs Cammell Laird and renamed *Thunderbolt*.

The design was a patrol type intended to replace the O, P and R classes for service in Far Eastern Waters. The legend of particulars was as follows:

Length overall	277ft
Breadth extreme	26ft
Surface displacement	1300 tons
Submerged displacement	1595 tons
Shp main engines	2500 tons
Bhp of main motors	1450
Oil fuel stowage	134 tons
Surface speed	15.25kts
Endurance at 11kt surface, ideal conditions	4500 miles
Submerged speed for 1½ hours	9kts
Submerged endurance at 2¼kts	55 hours
Submerged endurance (with auxiliary drive)	85 hours
Torpedo tubes, forward internal	6-21in
Torpedo tubes, forward external	6-21in
Torpedo tubes, amidships external	2-21in firing forward
Torpedoes (total)	16
Guns	1-4in, 2 Lewis
Diving depth	300ft

Triton, the first of the class, underwent satisfactory trials in September 1938 and attained a surface speed of 16.29kts.

In the early stages of the design of this class, consideration was given to the adoption of a 'fig-ure eight' shape of section for the pressure hull with the object of accommodating all the oil fuel internally and so avoiding the possibility of leakage of oil fuel from the effects of depth charging. The idea was discarded for various reasons, but it is notable that this 'figure eight' section was, in fact, adopted by the Germans in their latest types during the war, with a similar object. Model tests carried out by them indicated considerable weakness at the junctions of the upper and lower circles of the pressure hull, with consequent adverse effect upon diving depth. In the T class design, all the fuel was accommodated inside the hull (circular for most of the length) at some cost in tank space for trimming. The latter gave rise, later, to density range difficulties.

Earlier ships of the class were constructed with riveted Z-bar framing. Welded tee-bar framing was fitted in 1938 programme and later ships following experiments with the submarine shock target, Job 81.

The three vessels of the 1938 programme – *Tetrarch*, *Talisman* and *Torbay* – were modified to carry six mines P and S in the external tanks, in vertical wells. The minelaying equipment trials in *Tetrarch* were not entirely successful and the conversion also impaired performance. Surface speed was reduced by 1½kts when carrying mines. By blanking the recesses when not carrying mines this reduction of speed could almost be eliminated, but blanking entailed dry-docking. War experience had emphasised the importance of high surface speed and in view of this and the small number of mines carried, the requirement was cancelled and the vessels modified to their original shape. It was, however, approved for all 'U, T and S class submarines to be equipped for discharge of mines through the bow internal tubes for minelaying in shallow waters. Satisfactory trials were carried out in *Trusty* in August 1941, and subsequently all T class were equipped to carry six mines in the internal tubes and twelve in the stowages in lieu of torpedoes when necessary.

From the commencement of hostilities up to June 1942, orders were placed, from time to time, for further T class vessels. In all fifty-three vessels were built, of which the last twelve had all-welded pressure hulls. Details of builders, building times, etc are given in a table at the end of this chapter.

Vote 8 cost of a T class submarine was about £460,000.

To improve depth keeping and reduce the bow wave when on the surface caused by the rather blunt form of the bow above water, the bows of *Triumph* and *Thunderbolt* were modified and in the later war programme vessels the bow external tubes were moved 7ft aft to enable the bow to be

¹⁰ When the original
design was started, it was
thought that it might be
impossible to use the
periscope to attack heavily
escorted forces and that
torpedoes would be fired
on acoustic (Asdic)
information. Since this
would be less accurate,
more torpedoes would be
fired to ensure a hit.

Below top: *The outboard
boat is* Tigris, *as completed
with the midships external
torpedo tubes facing forwards.*
Below bottom: Thrasher, *a
T class submarine of the
second group, seen in May
1943. Note that she has the
three aft firing external tubes
of later boats. She has been
fitted with 291 radar and an
Oerlikon.*

fined still more. The width of the forward casing was reduced with the same object.

Complaints regarding the wetness of the bridge were received from sea early in the war, and in January 1940 it was decided to fit a partly enclosed or 'cab type' bridge to make the bridge more tenable and assist navigation on the surface in rough weather. This decision was later rescinded and the 'cab' removed in all submarines so fitted, improved wind deflectors being fitted at the same time. The shutters covering the fore-end openings to the bow internal torpedo tubes were removed in all vessels built and building, early in 1940, to obviate the risk of their being damaged by the force of heavy seas in rough weather, or jamming due to ice or other obstructions, the small reduction of maximum speed (from 16.3 to 16.0kts) being accepted.

As designed the class possessed ten torpedo tubes, all firing forward.[10] Later, to provide stern fire, consideration was given to reversing the two amidships external tubes. This was found practicable by moving the tubes aft a short distance and considerably widening the casing abaft the bridge, the latter being necessary to ensure that discharged torpedoes would not foul the external tanks before entry into the water. This modification, together with the fitting of an additional external stern firing torpedo tube at the after end of the casing, was incorporated in all vessels building in July 1940, subject to no delay in completion.

To improve diving depth, later vessels, as noted above, were constructed with all-welded pressure hulls of S quality steel of 30lb thickness instead of HST quality steel of 25lb. This increased thickness was made possible with the adoption of electric welding in lieu of riveting for the pressure hull, by saving the weight of buttstraps and edgestrips. The diving depth was increased from

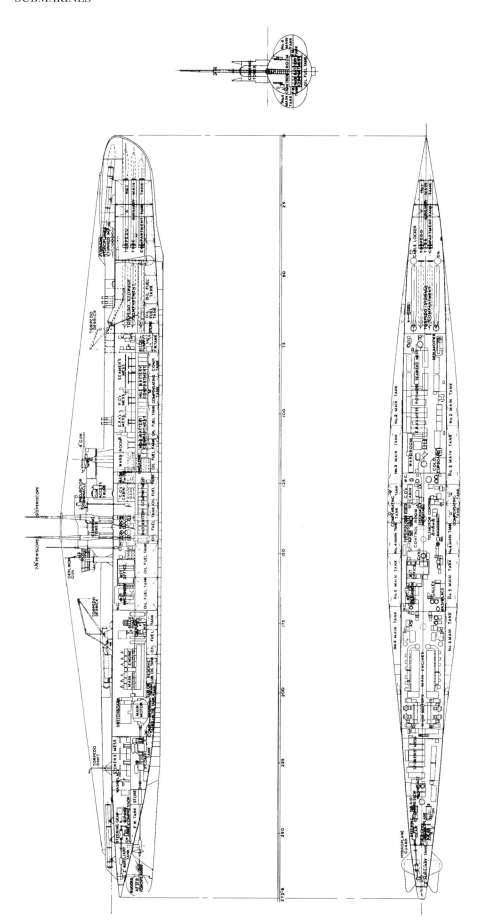

Internal arrangements of a T class submarine as modified during the war with three aft-firing torpedo tubes

300 to 350ft, the first vessel so constructed being satisfactorily test-dived to 400ft.

As with other classes, when attention was directed operationally to the Far Eastern theatre, the ability to operate at greatly increased distances from base in tropical water was improved in several ways. Nos 3 and 5 external main ballast tanks were converted to carry oil fuel, thus increasing the total fuel stowage from 134 to 215ton, the lubricating oil capacity being increased concurrently by converting W compensating tank for the purpose. Some of the first vessels so modified retained the riveted construction of the external fuel tanks but before proceeding East it was decided to weld up the tanks to obviate the risk of leaving an oil track. In later vessels, the converted tanks were all-welded at the beginning. Later, to prevent leakage from these external fuel tanks from small leaks due to 'working' of the structure, or from punctures by light fire from aircraft, a sub-pressure pump installation was fitted. This arrangement enabled a small suction pressure to be brought on to the leaking tank, up to 2lb/sq in below the sea pressure, which was effective in preventing leakage from a slot or crack ⅛in wide, and 8 to 12in long. This scheme was also installed in the later S class and war-designed A class.

The fresh-water stowage was increased in earlier ships of the class by converting H compensating tank to a fresh-water tank, bringing the total stowage capacity to 28 tons instead of 19½ tons. In later vessels, additional fresh-water tanks were incorporated abreast the battery tanks, bringing the total capacity to 23.4 tons and meeting the requirement laid down without converting H tank.

Two Freon air conditioning plants were installed, each of 55,000btu capacity, and the ventilation system modified accordingly, to improve habitability. The dehumidifiers previously fitted, having proved inadequate to meet tropical conditions, were removed. These extensive modifications were proved by experience on operations in the Pacific to be well worth while.

Other modifications, carried out in common with other classes of submarine, included the omission of the starboard anchor and cable equipment to reduce topweight, the fitting of an Oerlikon gun abaft the bridge for anti-aircraft defence and sound insulation of auxiliary machinery.

Rearrangement of the control room to include the latest equipment and to improve attack methods was carried out to the maximum possible extent in T class, so that finally the very late vessels compared well, in this respect, with the A class which were designed to carry the more mod-

ern equipment from the start. The ultimate arrangement was attained in stages marked by the continuous improvement in radar.

The many alterations and additions to this class, some of the more important of which are described above, inevitably involved additional weight, and a consequent reduction in margin of stability and density range. Special instructions were issued to Flotillas for the jettisoning of fuel in external tanks to improve surface stability should weather conditions make this desirable and arrangements were made to restore the greatly reduced density range to an amount acceptable for operations in the Far Eastern theatre, ie to be able to dive in water varying from 1.011 to 1.028 specific gravity in any condition of trim.

1940 S Class

At a meeting in January 1940, presided over by Admiral (Submarines), the suitability of the existing types of submarine for operation in the North Sea was discussed. The T class were considered to be too large and the U class too small and it was recommended that a design, primarily a repeat of the intermediate sized S class, but incorporating new features arising from trials of the shock target Job 81, increased diving depth and measures to eliminate rattle effect, should be progressed. The Controller gave approval to this proposal.

The legend particulars approved in April 1940 were as follows:

Length overall	217ft 0in
Breadth extreme	28ft 8¾in
Displacement, surface	805 tons
Displacement, submerged	995 tons
Shp for propulsion	1500
Bhp (max) of main engines	1900
Bhp of main motors (total)	1300
Maximum speed surface	14kts
Maximum speed submerged	
(1¼ hours)	9kts
Endurance, surface at 10kt	3800 miles
Endurance, submerged at 3kts	120 miles
Torpedo tubes	6-21in bow
Torpedoes (total)	12
Guns	1-3in and 1 automatic gun
Diving depth	300ft

Fifty vessels in all were ordered, the names and builders being given in the table at the end of this chapter.

Twill trunk escape arrangements were fitted to the hatches in the torpedo stowage compartment, engine room and after compartment.

The first vessel of the class, *Safari*, carried out satisfactory first of class trials and attained speeds of 14.8kts surfaced and 9kts submerged. This vessel was satisfactorily test dived to 50ft beyond the designed depth of 300ft.[11]

In earlier vessels of the class the pressure hull was constructed of riveted HST plating, with welded tee-bar framing. Later vessels were built with all-welded pressure hulls of a new steel known as S quality steel and possessing the necessary mechanical properties and suitability for electrical welding. The saving in weight thus made allowed the thickness of pressure hull to be increased and the diving depth raised to 350ft. A 4in gun was substituted for the 3in gun also.

In May 1941, Admiral (Submarines) requested that consideration be given to increasing the surface endurance of the class in view of the anticipated trend of the war and as a result the oil fuel stowage was increased by 22 tons by the conversion of part of No 4 and part of No 5 main tanks port and starboard to permanent oil fuel tanks. This increased the surface endurance at 10kts by some 37% to 5500 miles. The longer patrols anticipated for operations in the Far East demanded still more endurance and in the riveted vessels this was met by converting No 4 main tanks P & S to emergency oil fuel tanks, bringing the total oil fuel capacity to 92 tons and the endurance at 10kts (ideal conditions) to 8000 miles. In the all-welded vessels, then in course of building, the internal oil fuel capacity was maintained at 45 tons and No 3 main tanks, with a

capacity of 40 tons, were built as emergency oil fuel tanks, bringing the total fuel stowage to 85 tons and the endurance at 10kts to 7500 miles.

Other modifications made necessary by the long patrols in the Far East and the extreme climatic conditions encountered there included the provision of more fresh water and lubricating oil and the installation of two Freon units, each of 55,000btu capacity for cooling and drying the atmosphere in the submarine. This latter modification involved extensive modifications to the existing ventilation system and the sacrifice of the forward LP blower to obtain the necessary space for the Freon unit forward. In addition the VSG A end and motor for operating the capstan had to be removed and the B end driven direct from the telemotor system.

In July 1941 the provision of astern torpedo fire was approved, and it was decided to instal a stern external tube. This could not be done in the first vessel at Messrs Vickers Armstrong, Barrow, nor in the first vessel at Messrs Cammell Lairds, but later vessels were so modified until the necessity for additional radar and for a 4in gun, in place of the existing 3in gun, was given priority when the stern tube had to be omitted for reasons of stability.

The 1940 S class were adapted to enable the laying of mines from the internal torpedo tubes in the same manner as were the T class. The arrangements were such that eight mines could be

[11] It was normal in those days to test to a depth deeper than the nominal design figure. This was intended to allow for the possibility that a boat already near the maximum might inadvertently, perhaps due to hydroplane problems, go even deeper. Individual captains often went deep to give confidence to their crews – it seems unlikely that they realised how small was the margin of safety. See reference in note 1.

HM S/M Shakespeare *entering Algiers early in 1943. A 1940 S class boat with an additional stern tube but retaining the 3in gun.*

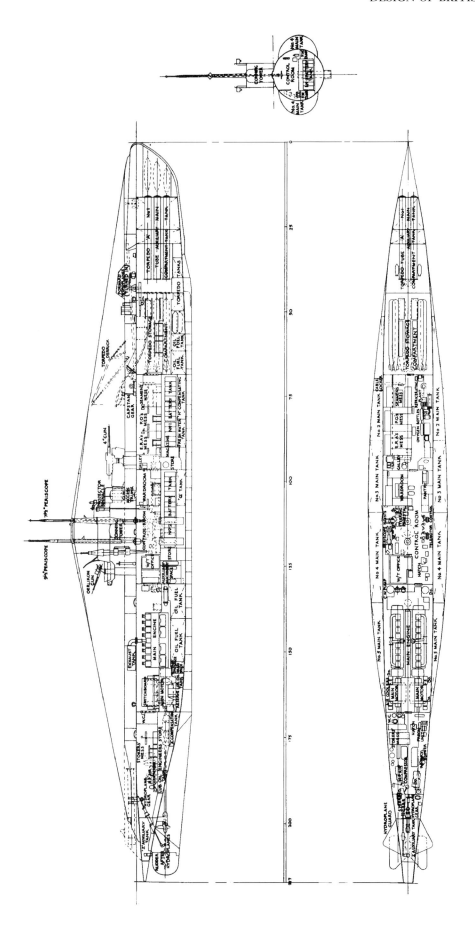

Internal arrangements of an S class submarine as modified during the war with 4in gun carried in the torpedo stowages in lieu of four re-load torpedoes and four mines could be carried in the tubes themselves in lieu of torpedoes.

The 3in gun was replaced in later vessels of the class (the all-welded vessels and one riveted vessel) by a 4in gun since it would be more effective against the small enemy craft engaged in submarine actions generally in the Far East. For stability reasons the stern torpedo tube then had to be removed. It had been approved to fit an Oerlikon gun at the after end of the bridge early in 1942 and to obtain additional space for the stowage of ammunition the slop drain tank was sacrificed and the space given up to ammunition stowage.

Only four vessels were completed with drop keels, a decision having been reached in November 1941 that these should be omitted in all new construction submarines.

Before and during the first two years of the war, some submarines had been fitted with a partly closed in or 'cab' type bridge. Experience under war conditions established that this type of bridge was inferior to the completely open type and in February 1942 approval was given for 'cab' type bridges in existing submarines to be converted to the open type and the latter type to be fitted in all new construction vessels.

The installation of radar and rearrangement of attack instruments in the control room took place in step with T class except that in the 1940 S class the difficulties encountered were more acute owing to the smaller control room and radio office. Even prior to installation of radar it was found necessary to interchange the periscopes and improve the layout of attack instruments to facilitate torpedo attack. By absorbing the ward room pantry and by further encroachment into the control room and auxiliary machinery space it was found possible to fit a modified version of the type 267W set, called type 267QW, served by two non-elevating masts to carry the arrays for surface and aircraft warning when surfaced.

Vote 8 cost of a typical S class submarine was £318,000.

A Class

In a personal minute to the Board of Admiralty dated 14 June 1941 the Prime Minister (Mr Winston Churchill) called for a new submarine programme to meet the turn of events which the war had taken. Numbers and speed of construction were to be the primary factors as the vessels would be required principally for short-range work to resist invasion and impose blockade. However, this first call for a war design submarine led eventually to the A class, a general purpose submarine capable of high surface speed and long endurance suitable for operations at home or abroad.

In late June 1941, Admiral (Submarines) requested DNC to give consideration to proceeding with a new design of a small submarine for attack on merchant ships, the intention being that the construction should not interrupt the existing submarine programme. The main requirements of the design were a maximum surface speed of 17kts with a cruising speed of 15kts under patrol conditions in order to overtake merchant ships.

Alliance and an A class sister at Portsmouth in December 1947 showing the general appearance as completed. The casing for the folding Snort mast can be seen on the port side just aft of the conning tower.

This was to be achieved with an existing and tried type of engine. Four bow internal torpedo tubes and a stern tube, internal or external, a 3in gun, diving depth 300ft and an endurance of 6000 miles at 10kts on the surface in ideal conditions were also to be provided. Three sketch designs were prepared closely resembling the 1940 S class but with the smaller torpedo armament.

The Controller also, about the same time, called for a new design intended for coast defence or anti-invasion purposes and three other designs were prepared. These were all about the same length 160ft, displacement 430-490 tons, 1000shp, surface speed 13½kts, submerged speed 7½kts and an endurance of 3000-3500 miles at 9kts.

All six sketch designs were considered by Controller and Admiral (Submarines) at a discussion in July 1941 and it was agreed that the latter three designs would be of little use as anti-invasion submarines owing to their limited operational scope and the former three designs offered little advantage over the 1940 S class and they were not progressed further.

At this meeting it was suggested that a new type (ML) diesel engine capable of 3300hp should be designed with the object of incorporating it, should the circumstances demand, in a new design of submarine capable of 18kts surface speed and superseding the S and T class.

The staff requirements for such a design were drawn up and approved in October 1942, the new class being designated A class. These requirements embodied improvements rendered necessary by war experience, eg: higher surface speed, up-to-date radar, improved habitability for operations in the Far East, including air conditioning and increased fresh water capacity, and much longer surface endurance to cover the distances from base to patrol area at high speed. To achieve the increased diving depth of 500ft which was required, circularity of hull was essential, and consequently only four bow internal tubes could be fitted, with two external tubes to make up the salvo of six that was also required. On the other hand, whereas the staff requirement for stern torpedo fire was laid down as two internal and one external tube, the final arrangement included two external tubes aft in addition to the two internal ones.

The ability to charge batteries whilst submerged was included in the requirements to counter the rapid improvement in radar taking place at that time, and consideration of the introduction of auxiliary diesel generators to achieve this was suggested. It was later decided that 'submerged dieseling' need not be arranged as it was considered to be of no operational value to British

submarines at that time. A requirement for such equipment under the name of 'Snort' arose later in the war when the earlier ships of the class were in production, the intention then being for it to be fitted by depot ships in the Far East, should the circumstances demand it.

The design proceeded with the utmost speed and was approved in February 1943. Increased endurance was obtained by carrying oil fuel in tanks under the forward battery compartment and arranging for a pair of main ballast tanks to be capable of carrying oil fuel as an emergency measure.

Legend particulars were as follows:

Length overall	277ft 9in
Breadth extreme	22ft 3in
Surface displacement	1360 tons
Submerged displacement	1590 tons
Shp main engines	4300
Max surface speed	19kts
Oil fuel Internal	61 tons
External	105 tons
Surface endurance	12,200 miles at 10kts
or	15,200 miles at 10kts with 48 tons fuel in No 4 main tank
Shp main motors (total)	1250
Max submerged speed for 1 hour	8kts
Submerged endurance at 4kts	20 hours
Torpedoes Forward:	4 internal, 2 external tubes, 6 reloads
Aft:	2 internal, 2 external tubes, 4 reloads
Guns	1-4in, 1 Oerlikon
Diving depth	500ft
Complement	60

(Surface endurance figures marked: Ideal Condition)

Arrangements were made for four of the class to be fitted with Admiralty 6-cylinder engines instead of 8-cylinder engines as for the rest of the class due to difficulties of supply. This reduced the shp to 3400 and the maximum surface speed to 18kts.

Bow shutters were fitted to the underwater torpedo apertures forward to enable the speed of 18½kts to be attained. They had to be sufficiently robust to withstand heavy weather.

Full attention was paid to the reduction of waterborne noise from the propellers and from auxiliary machinery, having regard to the great advances made in this field of detection.

As the design proceeded the after end was made slightly larger and the overall length increased to

279ft 3in. The submerged displacement increased during building to 1620 tons.

To ensure rapid production most of the submarine was mocked up, this mock-up being built at Messrs Vickers Armstrong, Barrow. The engine room for the Vickers 8-cylinder engined vessel was not mocked up and the mock-up of the engine room for the Admiralty 8-cylinder engined vessels was built at Messrs Cammell Laird. Arrangements were made for all shipbuilders to view these mock-ups and to work to the same drawings. Arrangements were also made to facilitate the supply of large hull items, usually subcontracted out, to the best advantage of all builders. This rested in a choice of sub-contractors suitable to all shipbuilders, having regard to capacity, transport, etc. The extent to which ships' fittings and pipe work could be sub-contracted out to the same firms by all shipbuilders was investigated. Arrangements were made by all the main shipbuilders to introduce a degree of prefabrication into the construction of these vessels.

Forty-six vessels were at first ordered, viz. twenty-one from Messrs Vickers Armstrong, Barrow-in-Furness, six from Messrs Cammell Laird, five from Messrs Scotts S & E Co, six from Messrs Vickers Armstrong Ltd, High Walker, and two each from Portsmouth, Devonport and Chatham. The Vickers vessels were to have the Vickers type 8-cylinder supercharged engines and the remainder the Admiralty type 8-cylinder supercharged engines, except for the vessels at Portsmouth and Devonport which were to have Admiralty 6-cylinder supercharged engines.

Vote 8 building cost of a typical submarine was £450,000.

The changes in the war programme at the end of 1944 led first to a proposal for an additional twenty vessels but orders were never placed. Later, as the war progressed, the need for submarines was not so great and thirty of the forty-six vessels ordered were cancelled. Building details of the remaining sixteen are given in the table at the end of this chapter. Of the cancelled vessels only two, *Ace* and *Achates* at Devonport, were well advanced and the hulls of these were used in ship target trials after the war.[12]

The first vessel to completed, *Amphion*, was delivered from Messrs Vickers Armstrong, Barrow, on 27 March 1945. On first of class trials this vessel achieved nearly 18½kts on the surface and almost 8kts submerged, a much quicker diving time than previous classes, and satisfactory performance as regards change of depth, turning and endurance. A deep dive to 600ft, 100ft beyond the designed operational depth, proved entirely satisfactory and except for certain modifi-

cations to the periscope supports to prevent vibration, the class appeared to be acceptable for operational duty. Later experience in *Amphion* and *Affray* indicated the necessity to redispose some of the external oil fuel tanks and fit a bow buoyancy tank to improve seaworthiness. These modifications are described in more detail later.

Prefabrication of the pressure hull of all vessels was carried to a high degree, electric welding being employed, to the complete omission of riveting, throughout the hull, external tanks and casings. The pressure hull was built of S quality plating and was of circular section throughout, fabricated in cylindrical lengths amidships and conical lengths at the ends. The bulkheads at the ends of the pressure hull were specially constructed of dome shape.

As the design progressed and during building of the earlier ships of the class continual revision of the radar requirements was necessary to keep in step with developments in radar. The design originally envisaged a single rotating mast carrying a type 291W array for aircraft warning only. Finally two masts were provided, both rotating, one for aircraft warning and the other for surface warning, the combined equipment being designated type 267MW. The up-to-date version of this equipment, fitted as an A & A in all ships of the class, was known as type 267PW which still entailed two masts but possessed much improved performance and enabled the habitability of the radar office to be improved.

The installation of these two masts and their associated equipment together with improved plotting and fire control arrangements necessitated a rearrangement of the entire control room, the details of which were settled by means of a mock-up. A similar arrangement of control room was followed in T class vessels fitted with this up-to-date equipment.

In the design of the ventilation system a radical departure from previous practice was made by the omission of a separate exhaust system. Except for the radar office and galley, all compartments were ventilated by forced supply and natural exhaust, the supply fans being sited with coolers, compressors and condensers in a special air conditioning compartment directly below the control room. These fans were supplied with air through the hatch to this compartment and delivered it, dried and cooled by the Freon system if necessary, through punkah louvres, via two main supply trunks, one running forward and the other aft. Two Freon units, each of 55,000btu/hr capacity, were fitted for air conditioning and this proved, by sea experience, to be adequate to maintain equable air conditions in vessels of the size of T or

12 *Achates* was lowered to collapse depth after the war. She failed at 877ft compared with a calculated figure of 860ft. See reference in note 1.

[13] Previously the heads
had to be flushed each
time they were used and
the compressed air
needed would make a
visible bubble. It could
also back fire – known as
'getting your own back'.

A class. In the later stages of building of the earlier vessels of A class, and S and T class, provision was made for fitting the newly developed air purification plant consisting of special 'silent running' carbon dioxide absorption units and of generators for burning oxygen candles to maintain an acceptable concentration of oxygen in the air while submerged.

In accommodation arrangements, also, the A class departed from practice in previous vessels. The commanding officer had a cabin which was built as a separate pressure-tight chamber in the bridge structure and reached via the conning tower. All the messing and sleeping quarters for officers and men were grouped forward between the control room and torpedo stowage compartment and the galley and WCs were placed abaft the control room near the engine room. The WCs were gravity drained to a special drain tank which could be blown when a suitable occasion arose without fear of disclosing the position of the submarine to the enemy.[13]

Two major modifications were found to be necessary after trials. The first of these was due to an unacceptable vibration of the periscope at speeds above 2½kts. The method of support had been changed due to the introduction of the CO's cabin and a longer periscope overhang than was usual had been allowed. The vibration was traced to the alternating eddy forces on the periscope tubes and standards and this was aggravated by insufficient rigidity in the support itself and in the connections. The trouble was overcome by increasing the height of the standards to decrease the overhang and by stiffening up the supports. Similar modifications were made to the periscopic radar mast.

The second was made necessary because the rolling motion in certain conditions of swell and sea was found to be very unpleasant. The fundamental causes of this were proved, after lengthy investigations, to be due to a combination of effects arising from the fulfilment of the staff requirements. The requirements for high speed, low silhouette and quick diving acted adversely on seaworthiness, more so than had been appreciated in design. The motion was considerably improved by redisposing some of the external oil fuel tanks in relation to the main tanks to lower the position of the centre of gravity, by fitting a bow buoyancy tank and by subdividing the main tanks into port and starboard tanks by fitting a bulkhead in the ballast keel (formerly the main tanks were continuous from one side to the other and this allowed water to move freely from side to side in a seaway).

Another modification found necessary was the provision of more store space. This was obtained by using one of the forward fresh water tanks as a store. The fresh water capacity was thereby reduced to 63.5 gallons per man and this was accepted in view of the fact that distillers were fitted.

The question of running the diesel engines when submerged was reopened late in 1944, in view of the progress made by the Germans with the 'Schnorkel' apparatus and bearing in mind possible requirements in the Far Eastern theatre. A set of 'Snort' gear based on German design was tried in *Truant* in 1945 with success and arrangements were made to fit all the A class and most of the other submarines with this gear. This programme was slowed down very considerably with the cessation of hostilities.

High Speed Target Submarines

Early in 1944 reports were being received of a new type of German submarine with a 'streamlined' hull form and reported to be capable of 20kts on the surface and 16kts submerged. This high submerged speed was a very considerable increase over the normal 8-9kts of the conventional type and constituted a considerable menace. In order to develop counter measures to such a high speed craft, it was considered essential to carry out exercises with a submarine of comparable speed. (The efficiency of the Asdic equipment against high speed submarines needed to be checked and new attack tactics developed.)

Accordingly DNC looked into the question of converting a British submarine to high speed by 'cleaning up' the hull and casing, blanking torpedo tube apertures, removing the guns etc, fitting a smaller streamlined bridge, removing a periscope and the radar masts, rating up the motors and fitting higher capacity batteries. This was investigated for both U class and S class. In view of the urgency it was decided to convert the S class submarine *Seraph*. Minor modifications to the hydroplane gear were required and T class propellers (which had a bigger pitch) were fitted. The conversion was completed at Devonport within two months, the target date being end August 1944.

The converted *Seraph* carried out First of Class Trials in September 1944. These trials were entirely satisfactory and she achieved a speed at periscope depth of 12.52kts at 411rpm and 1647bhp as compared with 8.82kts at 406rpm and 1460bhp obtained by an unconverted sister ship *Sahib*, on First of Class Trials. On the surface *Seraph* achieved 16.75kts at 460rpm and 92 galls fuel/hour as compared with 14.56kts at 464rpm and 86 galls fuel/hour before conversion. *Seraph* compared very favourably with the normal S class as regards underwater control but, as was expect-

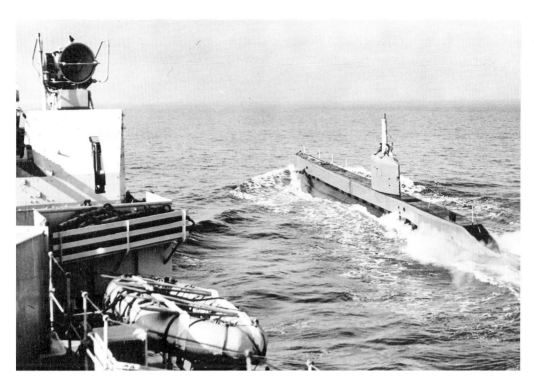

Seraph *showing the basic features of the streamlined high speed targets.*

ed, the diving time was considerably increased due to the deliberate reduction in free flood holes.

The resistance of the converted *Seraph* was estimated to be 55% of that for the unconverted vessel.

Later *Sceptre, Satyr, Statesman, Selene, Solent* and *Sleuth* were also converted to similar high-speed targets.

Improved A Class Submarines

In the latter part of 1944, Admiral (Submarines) and the Technical Departments held discussions on the possible trend of future submarine design, particularly as regards submerged speed, diving depth, duration of submergence and lessons learnt as a result of the war. Admiral (Submarines) then put forward a proposal for three submarines to be built on the lines of the A class incorporating the most up-to-date equipment and improvements arising from war experience. The modifications which were envisaged, such as improved 'Snort' arrangements, increased space in the control room and at the ends of the vessel around the torpedo tubes, and improved surface performance, could only be effected by a redesign.

Whilst this was progressing, information was continually forthcoming regarding German designs for high submerged speeds, and especially information on the hydrogen–peroxide turbine (Walther turbine). In July 1945, Admiral (Submarines) expressed the opinion that the three operational submarines, which had been included in the 1944 programme, should represent a radical change from the A class and should be designed around the Snort at the sacrifice of surface qualities – amounting indeed to surrender of gun power and the acceptance of comparatively moderate surface speed. He also considered that the design should be such as to incorporate, at some future date, a new type of propulsion unit capable of developing the high power necessary to achieve submerged speeds much in excess of that possible by either 'Snort' or batteries. In the light of these views, DNC embarked upon a new sketch design, incorporating novel Snort arrangements and with high battery capacity, in order to obtain a maximum submerged speed well in excess of that of orthodox types of submarine or that possible by Snort, though not comparable with that possible with the hydrogen peroxide turbine.

The design had not been developed very far when views changed once more. The statement of broad staff requirements for these submarines prepared by Admiral (Submarines) called for the definite incorporation of a high power propulsion drive in addition to normal propulsion methods. The design of the high battery power submarine was therefore terminated, as few details of the peroxide turbine were known. Soon after this the three operational submarines were cancelled and replaced, in the 1945 (revised) programme, by an experimental type of submarine using the hydrogen peroxide turbine, with the object of obtaining experience with the turbine and in the control and other problems of high speed submarines.[14]

[14] This requirement led, eventually to the *Explorer* and *Excalibur* known for good reasons as *Exploder* and *Exciter.*

CHAPTER 10
Sloops

[1] See the Annex to: D K Brown, 'Sir Rowland Baker, RCNC', *Warship 1995* (London 1995), which gives Baker's personal views of the problems of these earlier sloops.

[2] A Hague, *Sloops 1926-1946* (Kendal 1993).

[3] See note 1.

Editorial Note

The Flower *class sloops of World War I were designed for a primary role of minesweeping but were found invaluable for many other minor fighting tasks, particularly escort. The vessels described in this chapter are direct descendants of the* Flower *class but note the major change in 1935 when a very much heavier AA armament was fitted. Fire control systems were inadequate for many aircraft to be destroyed but there is some evidence that pilots were deterred from pressing home an attack against such heavily armed vessels making it possible for these ships to operate with confidence in waters, such as the Bay of Biscay,* where there was substantial enemy air capability.

The Modified Black Swan *class will always be remembered for the activities of Captain F J Walker's Second Support Group led by* Starling *which sank twenty-three U boats. This personal achievement makes impossible to distinguish between the merits of different types of A/S vessel by a simple comparison of U boats sunk per operational ship.*

The Black Swan *class also introduced a number of improved design features making them far more seaworthy.*[1] *The background to these ships and their operational history are discussed by Hague.*[2]

With the conclusion of the First World War no further sloops were built until 1927 when *Bridgewater* and *Sandwich*, two sloops to the same design, were included in the new construction programme for that year. These two ships, the first sloops to be designed since the 1914-18 war, embodied improvements resulting from war experience, and successive designs up to *Shoreham* and repeat classes (1929 and 1930 programmes) were very similar and contained no radical changes in design.[3]

The general particulars of the *Bridgewater* were as follows:

Length overall	266ft 4in
Breadth extreme	34ft 1in
Mean draught (deep)	10ft 10in
Displacement (standard)	1045 tons
Shp	2000
Speed (deep)	16¼kts
Endurance at 15kts (trial condition)	4750 miles
Oil fuel capacity	300 tons

All classes up to 1930 programme were fitted for minesweeping and met requirements for service in the tropics.

Shoreham, typical of the early inter-war sloops, seen here on 5 February 1943 with wartime modifications – radar, Oerlikons and zarebas round the guns.

Skipjack *in early 1940. She was a minesweeping sloop of the* Halcyon *class which were frequently employed on escort duties.*

In 1931 it was decided to design and build two classes of sloops - *Halcyon* class and *Grimsby* class.

The *Halcyon* class, a sloop-minesweeper, was designed for simplicity, cheapness and suitability for mass production in war as a minesweeper. In order to improve the minesweeping qualities of this type of ship the displacement and draught were reduced, compared with previous classes.

The general particulars were:

Length overall	245ft 9in
LBP	230ft 0in
Breadth extreme	33ft 6in
Depth (moulded)	16ft 0in
Mean draught (deep)	8ft 8in
Displacement (deep)	1088 tons
Shp	1770
Speed (deep)	16.75kts
Endurance at 15kts	
(trial condition)	4200 miles
Oil fuel capacity	240 tons

These ships were repeated in each building programme up to 1936 and a total of nineteen vessels were built to this design. Two of these vessels were completed as survey ships but were capable of rapid conversion to minesweepers.[4]

The *Grimsby* class was developed as an improved sloop and was fitted out for minesweeping and, unlike *Halcyon* class, for service in the tropics.

Length overall	266ft 3in
LBP	250ft 0in
Breadth extreme	36ft 0in
Depth (moulded)	16ft 6in
Mean draught (deep)	9ft 1in
Displacement (deep)	1330 tons
Shp	2000
Speed (deep)	16.25kts
Endurance at 15kts	
(trial condition)	5350 miles
Oil fuel capacity	300 tons

A total of eight ships were included in the 1931/1934 building programmes.

During the 1939-45 war, and as minesweepers became available from new construction, *Bridgewater*, and classes up to *Shoreham* and *Grimsby* class had their minesweeping winches removed and were fitted out and used as A/S escorts.

In 1933 consideration was given to the development of a sloop to be known as Ocean Convoy. The principal improvements on the *Grimsby* class sloop were increased gun power, both short- and long-range, speed and anti-submarine qualities - minesweeping gear was omitted. These improvements resulted in large increase in displacement over earlier types of sloops. The first of this class was *Enchantress* (changed from *Bittern* during building) and was subsequently used as a yacht for the Board of Admiralty. Particulars of this class were:

Length overall	282ft 0in
LBP	266ft 0in
Breadth extreme	37ft 0in
Depth (moulded)	17ft 6in
Mean draught (deep)	10ft 2in
Displacement (deep)	1520 tons
Shp	3300
Speed (deep)	18.75kts
Endurance at 15kts	
(trial condition)	6400 miles
Oil fuel capacity	388 tons

Concurrently a coastal convoy vessel was being designed for anti-submarine work in coastal waters. The first of this latter class was *Kingfisher*, and the design was very similar to the PC boats built during the First World War. The last three ships of the class were built with a rearrangement of the oil fuel tanks, and were known as the *Guillemot* class.

The general particulars were:

[4] Note that *Seagull*, nominally of this class was the first all-welded ship for the RN. She was built in Devonport Dockyard to a novel, longitudinally framed design by Baker.

Length overall	243ft 3in
LBP	234ft 0in
Breadth extreme	26ft 6in
Depth (moulded)	14ft 0in
Mean draught (deep)	7ft 10in
Displacement (deep)	742 tons
Shp	3600
Speed (deep)	20kts
Endurance at 15kts (trial condition)	4050 miles
Oil fuel capacity	172 tons

Six coastal convoy vessels of the *Kingfisher* class were built between 1934 and 1936 and three *Guillemot* class were included in the 1937 programme, but the design was not repeated during the Second World War.[5] The coastal convoy sloops later became known as patrol vessels and eventually as corvettes.

Included in the 1934 and later programmes were further vessels to the ocean convoy design. They were *Stork* (1934), *Bittern* (1935) and the *Egret* class of three vessels (1936/7), a slightly modified ocean convoy design. A radical change in the armament was made after *Stork* was built; the main armament of four 4.7in guns was replaced by four twin 4in HA mountings and the short-range armament was also improved.

The general particulars of the improved design *Egret* were:

Length overall	292ft 6in
LBP	276ft 0in
Breadth extreme	37ft 9in
Depth (moulded)	17ft 6in
Mean draught (deep)	11ft 0in
Displacement (deep)	1768 tons
Shp	3600
Speed (deep)	18.75kts
Endurance at 15kts (trial condition)	6200 miles
Oil fuel capacity	390 tons

Black Swan Class

The 1937 building programme included two ships of the *Black Swan* design. These ships were slightly larger and faster than the *Egret* class. The main armament was reduced to 3-twin 4in HA mountings, but the close-range armament was increased, and the ships were fitted for minesweeping as well as A/S duties. Two repeat *Black Swan* class were also included in the 1939 programme, but in these the minesweeping gear was omitted.

With the outbreak of the war in 1939 the need for additional sloops with good A/A and A/S armament quickly became apparent and orders for further *Black Swan* class vessels were included in the 1940, 1941 and 1942 building programmes. Before these vessels were laid down it was decided to increase the beam of the design to 38ft 6in as an insurance against added weight and alterations being made whilst the vessels were under construction. Later, in view of the many modifications and alterations made during building the class name was altered to Modified *Black Swan*. The staff requirements for this class altered from time to time during construction but the main requirements were for the ships to be able to operate as A/A and A/S escorts to ocean convoys in any part of the world with endurance of 7500 miles at 12kts and a maximum speed of 19-20kts; one in every six of the class to be capable of minelaying. A secondary requirement was that they should be readily converted for carrying out minesweeping duties.

The principal dimensions of the Modified *Black Swan* class were:

Length overall	299ft 6in
LBP	283ft 0in
Depth to UD (welded)	17ft 6in
Breadth extreme	38ft 6in
Mean draught (deep)	11ft 4in
Displacement (deep)	1960 tons as built
Shp	4300
Speed (deep)	19.25kts
Endurance at 15kts (trial condition)	6100 miles

Legend of weights	
Hull	775 tons
Machinery	200 tons
Equipment	300 tons
Armament	200 tons
Oil fuel	420 tons
RFW	30 tons
Protection	35 tons
Deep displacement	1960 tons

Structural
In order to combine the functions of A/A, A/S and M/S it was accepted that these vessels would not be suitable for mass production. Earlier vessels were all-riveted but as the war progressed and more and more welding was introduced until in the last few of the class as much as 30% of the structure was welded. All vessels were built of mild steel and to the normal building practice. Some ships were fitted with lattice masts.

[5] The draught of these ships was inadequate to use Asdic effectively; a surprising fault since the P and PC classes on which they were based suffered from the same fault.

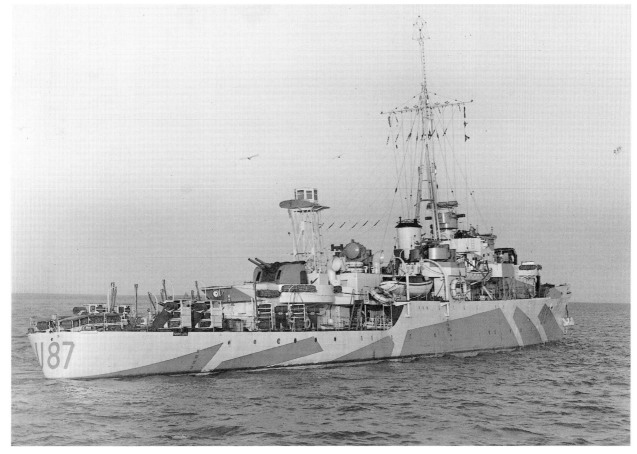

Armament
- 3 twin 4in HA/LA mountings
- 2 twin Bofors
- 2 twin Oerlikons later replaced by 2-single Bofors
- 2 single Oerlikons
- 100 depth charges with 4 throwers and 2 rails
- Some vessels of the class were fitted with a split hedgehog mounting.
- Asdics fitted were types 144 and 147.

Protection
The earlier ships of this class were fitted with a considerable amount of splinter protection but in view of the modifications and additions made to many of the ships during building, it was found necessary to surrender the majority of this protection to preserve the stability of these ships.

Machinery
Ships of this class were fitted with two oil-fired boilers in separate boiler rooms with geared turbines developing 4300shp, ie 2150shp on each of two shafts.

The two propellers were 7ft 6in in diameter, 8ft 6in pitch and 15sq ft developed blade area, running at 300rpm.

On trials a typical ship of the class developed 4300shp at 300rpm and a maximum speed of 19½kts on a displacement of 1790 tons.

Electrical Power was provided by two 70kW steam-driven generators and one 50kW diesel generator. Later, as the power requirements rose due to added electrical equipment, these generators were replaced by others of higher rating. Some ships were eventually fitted with two 100kW steam-driven generators and one 70kW diesel generator.

Radar fitted varied as the war progressed from types 268 to 291 and 293.

Stability
Particulars for a ship of the class were as follows:

	Deep	Light (with water ballast)	Light
Metacentric height	2.7ft	1.89ft	1.48ft
Max GZ	1.82ft	1.09ft	0.80ft
Angle for max GZ	42°	32°	29°
Range	80°	64°	53°
Displacement	1881 tons	1463 tons	1340 tons

Kite, *on 1 March 1943, typical of the early* Modified *Black Swan* class *– tripod mast and a radar tower aft with pom-poms behind the funnel.*

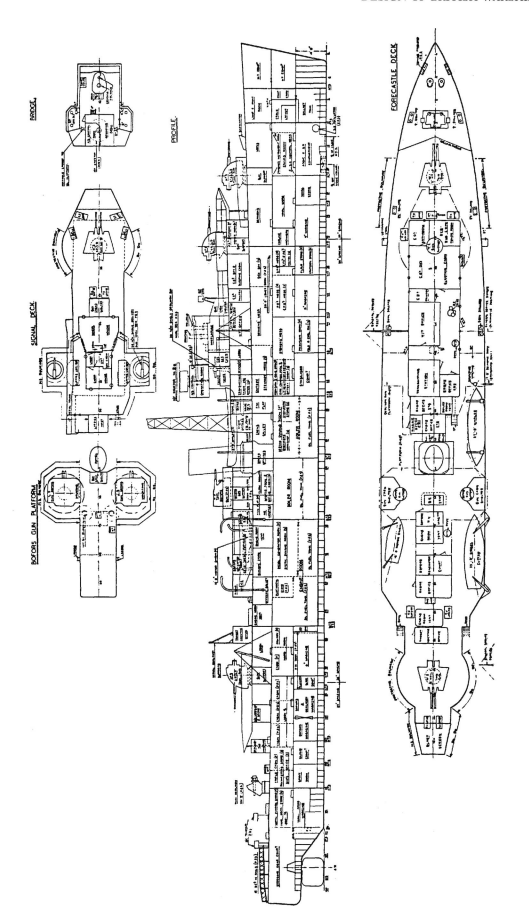

General arrangement of Modified *Black Swan* class of the 1941 programme

No detailed strength calculations were made for the Modified *Black Swan* class – the strength being based on the results of the calculations made for *Black Swan* which gave the following figures:

Max bending	Hogging	Sagging
moment	11,000ton/ft	11,700ton/ft
Stress in forecastle		
deck	5.73ton/in²	5.04ton/in²
Stress in keel	3.72ton/in²	4.32ton/in²

Increase in Displacement
During building and early life of these ships their displacements increased by about 200ton. This was mainly due to improvements in armament etc and growth of electrical equipment. Attempts were made to reduce weight, especially top weight, and the majority of the protection fitted was eventually removed.

Complement
Total varied between 200 and 230, including eight officers.

General
Both the *Black Swan* class and later the Modified *Black Swan* class were fitted with Denny-Brown ship stabilisers.[6] All the earlier vessels were fitted with the single fin type but some of the later ves-

sels were fitted with twin fins. A further departure was made in the last two vessels to complete in that they were fitted with single flap-type fins.

Owing to the shortage of timber, wood deck was not fitted to the weather decks in these ships, and shortage of rubber prevented good substitutes being fitted in lieu. This, together with the congestion caused by heavy increases in complement, resulted in heavy condensation on the mess decks. Where possible lagging was fitted under the weather decks in way of accommodation and ventilation arrangements were considerably improved.

Oiling-at-sea arrangement were fitted in the later vessels to complete.

The vessels were favourably received into the Service and the troubles experienced on service were comparatively few and then only of a minor nature.

A total of twenty-seven vessels of the Modified *Black Swan* class were built; it was intended to build five more but the orders were eventually cancelled. The last three ships of the Modified *Black Swan* programme were to have the beam increased still further to 39ft 6in.

Cost
Vote 8 cost of a modified ship was about £360,000.

Snipe, on 5 September 1946, a later ship of the class, with a lattice mast, Bofors and simple tachymetric directors behind the funnel.

[6] Fin stabilisers were introduced in the *Bittern*, very much due to the personal support of Goodall.

Ship	Firm	Laid Down	Launched	Completed
1927				
Bridgewater	Hawthorn Leslie	6 Feb 1928	14 Sep 1928	14 Mar 1929
Sandwich	Hawthorn Leslie	9 Feb 1928	29 Sep 1928	23 Mar 1929
1928 – Hastings Class				
Folkstone	Swan Hunter	21 May 1929	12 Feb 1930	26 Jun 1930
Scarborough	Swan Hunter	28 May 1929	14 Mar 1930	31 Jul 1930
Hastings	Devonport	29 July 1929	10 Apr 1930	26 Nov 1930
Penzance	Devonport	29 July 1929	10 Apr 1930	15 Jan 1931
1929 - Shoreham Class				
Fowey	Devonport	24 Mar 1930	4 Nov 1930	11 Sep 1931
Shoreham	Chatham	19 Dec 1929	22 Nov 1930	2 Nov 1931
Bideford	Devonport	10 Jun 1930	1 Apr 1931	27 Nov 1931
Rochester	Chatham	24 Nov 1930	16 Jul 1931	31 Mar 1932

Ship	Firm	Laid Down	Launched	Completed
1930 – Repeat *Shoreham* Class				
Falmouth	Devonport	31 Aug 1931	19 Apr 1932	27 Oct 1032
Milford	Devonport	14 Sep 1931	11 Jun 1932	22 Dec 1932
Weston	Devonport	7 Sep 1931	23 Jul 1932	23 Feb 1933
Dundee	Chatham	1 Dec 1931	20 Sep 1932	31 Mar 1933
1931–1936 – *Halcyon* Class				
Halcyon	J Brown	27 Mar 1933	20 Dec 1933	18 Apr 1934
Skipjack	J Brown	4 Apr 1933	18 Jan 1934	3 May 1934
Harrier	Thornycroft	11 Jul 1933	17 Apr 1934	9 Nov 1934
Hussar	Thornycroft	10 Aug 1933	27 Aug 1934	18 Jan 1935
Speedwell	Hamilton	20 Jun 1923	21 Mar 1935	30 Apr 1935
Niger	J S White	1 Apr 1935	24 Jan 1936	4 Jun 1936
Salamander	J S White	18 Apr 1935	24 Mar 1936	18 Jul 1936
Hebe	Devonport	27 Apr 1936	28 Oct 1936	23 Oct 1937
Hazard	Wm Gray & Co	27 May 1936	26 Feb 1937	24 Nov 1937
Sharpshooter	Devonport	8 Jun 1936	10 Dec 1936	16 Dec 1937
Gleaner*	Wm Gray & Co	17 Jun 1936	10 Jun 1936	30 Mar 1938
Gossamer*	Hamilton	2 Nov 1935	5 Oct 1937	31 Mar 1938
Leda	Devonport	16 Nov 1936	8 Jun 1937	19 May 1938
Jason*	Ailsa Shipbuilding Co	12 Dec 1936	6 Oct 1937	9 Jun 1938
Seagull	Devonport	15 Feb 1937	28 Oct 1937	21 Jul 1938
1937 – *Halcyon* Class				
Speedy	Hamilton	1 Dec 1937	24 Nov 1938	7 Apr 1939
Bramble	Devonport	22 Nov 1937	12 Jul 1938	22 Jun 1939
Britomart	Devonport	1 Jan 1938	23 Aug 1938	24 Aug 1939
1931–1934 – *Grimsby* Class				
Grimsby	Devonport	3 Jan 1933	19 Jul 1933	17 May 1934
Leith	Devonport	6 Feb 1933	9 Sep 1933	12 Jul 1934
Lowestoft	Devonport	28 Aug 1933	11 Apr 1934	22 Nov 1934
Wellington	Devonport	25 Sep 1933	29 May 1934	24 Jan 1935
Deptford	Chatham	30 Apr 1934	5 Feb 1935	20 Aug 1935
Londonderry	Devonport	11 Jun 1935	16 Jan 1935	20 Jul 1935
Aberdeen	Devonport	22 Jun 1935	22 Jan 1936	17 Sep 1936
Fleetwood	Devonport	14 Aug 1935	24 Mar 1936	19 Nov 1936
1933–1935 – *Bittern* Class				
Enchantress	J Brown	9 Mar 1934	1 Dec 1934	4 Apr 1935
Stork	Denny Bros	19 Jun 1935	21 Apr 1936	10 Sep 1936
Bittern	J S White	27 Aug 1936	14 Jul 1937	15 Mar 1938
1936–1937 – *Egret* Class				
Egret	J S White	21 Jul 1937	31 May 1938	10 Nov 1938
Auckland	Denny Bros	17 Jun 1937	20 Jun 1938	16 Nov 1938
Pelican	Thornycroft	7 Sep 1937	12 Sep 1938	2 Mar 1939
1933–1936 – *Kingfisher* Class				
Kingfisher	Fairfields	1 Jun 1934	14 Feb 1935	18 Jun 1935
Mallard	Stephen & Sons	12 Jun 1935	26 Mar 1936	15 Jul 1936
Puffin	Stephen & Sons	12 Jun 1935	5 May 1936	26 Aug 1936
Kittiwake	Thornycroft	7 Apr 1936	30 Nov 1936	29 Apr 1937
Sheldrake	Thornycroft	21 Apr 1936	28 Jan 1937	1 Jul 1937
Widgeon	Yarrow	8 Mar 1937	2 Feb 1938	16 Jun 1938
1937 – *Guillemot* Class				
Shearwater	J S White	6 Apr 1938	15 Aug 1938	7 Apr 1939
Guillemot	Denny Bros	6 Apr 1938	22 Aug 1938	28 Oct 1939
Pintail	Denny Bros	6 Apr 1938	23 Aug 1938	28 Nov 1939
1937 and 1939 – *Black Swan* Class				
Flamingo	Yarrow	26 May 1938	18 Apr 1939	3 Nov 1939
Black Swan	Yarrow	20 Jun 1938	7 Jul 1939	27 Jan 1940
Erne	Furness Shipbuilding Co	22 Sep 1939	5 Aug 1940	26 Apr 1941
Ibis	Furness Shipbuilding Co	22 Sep 1939	28 Nov 1940	30 Aug 1941

* Completed as survey ship [*Scott* and *Franklin* have been omitted from the list in the original typescript]

Ship	Firm	Laid Down	Launched	Completed
1940-1942 - Modified *Black Swan* Class				
Cygnet	Cammell Laird	30 Aug 1941	28 Jul 1942	1 Dec 1942
Woodpecker	Denny Bros	23 Feb 1941	29 Jun 1942	14 Dec 1942
Whimbrel	Yarrow	31 Oct 1941	25 Aug 1942	13 Jan 1943
Wren	Deny Bros	27 Feb 1941	11 Aug 1942	4 Feb 1943
Kite	Cammell Laird	25 Sep 1941	13 Oct 1942	1 Mar 1943
Wild Goose	Yarrow	28 Jan 1942	14 Oct 1942	11 Mar 1943
Chanticleer	Denny Bros	6 Jun 1941	24 Sep 1942	29 Mar 1943
Starling	Fairfields	21 Oct 1941	14 Oct 1942	1 Apr 1943
Crane	Denny Bros	13 Jun 1941	9 Nov 1942	10 May 1943
Pheasant	Yarrow	17 Mar 1942	21 Dec 1942	12 May 1943
Woodcock	Fairfields	21 Oct 1941	26 Nov 1942	29 May 1943
Redpole	Yarrow	18 May 1942	25 Feb 1943	24 Jun 1943
Magpie	Thornycroft	30 Dec 1941	24 Mar 1943	30 Aug 1943
Amethyst	Alex Stephen	25 Mar 1942	7 May 1943	2 Nov 1943
Hart	Alex Stephen	27 Mar 1942	7 Jul 1943	12 Dec 1943
Lapwing	Scotts	17 Dec 1941	16 Jul 1943	21 Mar 1944
Lark	Scotts	5 May 1942	28 Aug 1943	10 Apr 1944
Hind	Wm Denny	31 Aug 1942	30 Sep 1943	11 Apr 1944
Peacock	Thornycroft	29 Nov 1942	11 Dec 1943	10 May 1944
Mermaid	Wm Denny	8 Sep 1942	11 Nov 1943	12 May 1944
Alacrity	Wm Denny	4 May 1943	1 Sep 1944	13 Apr 1945
Opossum	Wm Denny	28 Jul 1943	30 Nov 1944	16 Jun 1945
Modeste	Chatham	15 Feb 1943	29 Jan 1944	3 Sep 1945
Nereide	Chatham	15 Feb 1943	29 Jan 1944	6 May 1946
Actaeon	Thornycroft	15 May 1944	25 Jul 1945	24 Jul 1946
Snipe	Wm Denny	21 Sep 1944	20 Dec 1945	9 Sep 1946
Sparrow	Wm Denny	30 Oct 1944	18 Feb 1946	16 Dec 1946

Ex-US Coast Guard Cutters

Ten US Coast Guard cutters were transferred to the RN under Lease-Lend Agreement in the spring of 1941. Surviving ships were returned to the USA under this agreement at the end of the war. They were extensively used as long-range escort vehicles. Five of these vessels were of the *Tahoe* class and five of *Saranac* class. The two classes differed only in respect of some of the internal arrangements and the arrangement of the bridges.

The vessels were designed by the US Coast Guard department, primarily for service on coast guard duties, eg on the Northern Ice Patrol, and therefore for prolonged periods at sea, also for easy conversion for war service.

The vessels were fitted with a single screw and turbo-electric drive. Two Babcock-Wilcox boilers were fitted in one boiler room supplying steam to one large and two small generators supplying current to a single AC synchronous motor coupled to the propeller shaft. The generators, motor, pumps, etc were contained in one engine room.

The WT subdivision of these vessels was poor as no continuous transverse bulkheads were fitted from keel to weather deck; there was very little WT subdivision between the weather deck and the deck below. The engine and boiler room extended from keel to the superstructure, and the wardroom on the berth deck was fitted with an extensive light well in the deck over and a large skylight in the weather deck above that. The weather deck was of composite construction, ie with steel stringers and steel plating in way of the gun mountings, capstans etc, the remainder being of wood planking.

The vessels were beamy and of substantial construction with form tending to merchant ship practice including the rudder and stern frame. The accommodation for both officers and men was exceptionally good for vessels of this size. A suite was provided for the CO, also a sea cabin, and cabins were provided for twenty officers including eight WOs. These WOs were not included in the war complement. A WOs' mess was provided, also pantries and the usual officers' showers and WCs. Sleeping berths, lockers (not seat lockers) etc were provided for the crew and separate enclosed messes for CPOs and POs. A cafeteria system of messing was provided, one portion of the main deck being allocated for this purpose, and fitted with ice cream cabinet and drinking fountain. A general mess, pantry and general mess issuing room was provided. Extensive refrigerator rooms were provided with separate compartments for meat, butter and vegetables. A large combined officers' and crew's galley and bakery was fitted complete with oil-fired galley, steam kettles, electric refrigerator, dough trough, dressers, sinks, etc. The vessel was also fitted with a well-equipped laundry and drying room, sick bay, also crew's reading room complete with writing tables etc. An efficient heating system by steam radiation was fitted.

After being taken over by the RN, As & As were carried out to improve the WT subdivision armament etc, and to equip them as A/S escorts, ie hedgehog, depth charge, armament, also up-to-date radar and W/T was fitted, also arrangements for British-type general messing. These items necessitated removing some of the above amenities, eg reading room was converted to mess deck, laundry to radar office etc.

The stability of the vessels when taken over was found to be below the standard acceptable by the Admiralty and it was necessary to fit 30ton of permanent ballast, impose oil fuel restriction of 50ton and to keep the water ballast tanks under the boilers pressed full.

General particulars of these craft were:

	Tahoe Class	Saranac Class
Length overall	250ft 0in	250ft 0in
Length between perps	236ft 0in	236ft 0in
Beam	42ft 0in	42ft 0in
Moulded depth	27ft 1in	26ft 10in
Deep displacement	2116 tons	2117 tons
Power	3000shp	3220shp
Speed (max)	16kts	16kts
Endurance at 8kts	8000 miles	8000 miles
Oil fuel	314 tons	314 tons

Complement (RN)	10 officers and 150 men
Armament (as RN vessels)	1-4in HA/LA gun
	2-2pdr pom-poms
	1 single Bofors
	7 single Oerlikons
	Hedgehog
	100 depth charges
	and 4 throwers

The corresponding American and British names for these vessels were as follows:

Tahoe Class	Lulworth	ex	Chelan
	Hartland	ex	Pontchartrain
	Fishguard	ex	Tahoe
	Sennen	ex	Champlain
	Culver	ex	Mendota
Saranac Class	Gorleston	ex	Itasca
	Walney	ex	Sebago
	Banff	ex	Saranac
	Landguard	ex	Shoshone
	Totland	ex	Gayuga

These vessels gave valuable service during the late war, serving under C in C Western Approaches, and C in C East Indies Commands as long-range escorts. Towards the end of the war with Germany they were fitted for tropical service for duty in the Far East based on South African ports.

Reports from sea indicated that the ex-US cutters, after modification to meet RN requirements, proved excellent sea boats on service and no complaints were received regarding their stability or sea-keeping qualities.

The Banff, ex-Saranac, one of ten US Coast Guard cutters transferred to the Royal Navy under Lease-Lend. The ship is seen at Portsmouth in December 1945; she was returned to the USA in February 1946. (L&L Van Ginderen)

CHAPTER 11

Corvettes and Frigates

Editorial Note

*All warship design is a compromise but in these
categories the conflict between quality and quality
was extreme. The original* Flower *class ships were
ordered for coastal escort work and seen as superior
to the trawlers previously intended. With the fall of
France there was an urgent need for ocean escorts
and more and more* Flowers *were built and sent into
waters for which they were too short. The* Rivers
*were much superior but their building required much
more effort and resources, in particular they needed
two sets of engines, in short supply, and it is arguable
whether they were twice as effective as a* Flower.

The Lochs *had about the same ship qualities as
the* Rivers *but their far superior Asdic and A/S
weapon (Squid) made them much more effective. In
this context it should be noted that the role of the*

*escort is the safe arrival of merchant ships; sinking
submarines is only a means to that end. The other
great feature of the* Lochs *was the way in which
they were designed for prefabricated construction by
firms outside the shipbuilding industry. This led to
much more rapid construction of the hulls, though at
the expence of greater man-hours, but outfit work
proved a bottleneck.[1]*

*The crews of the smaller escorts suffered badly
from motions and the resulting exhaustion and
sickness. This is discussed in the light of modern
seakeeping theory in footnote 1 but it is fairly
obvious that the* Castle *class were the shortest ships
which would be satisfactory for Atlantic operations.
This approach was used by the editor in the design of
the current* Castle *class OPV.*

Experience in World War I resulted in a progressive increase in the size and speed of the ships
used for anti-submarine work. Prior to 1914 it was
considered that ships of the trawler type could
best carry out anti-submarine work. These ships
were seaworthy, capable of hard work and had a
speed of 11-12kts with an endurance of approximately 3600 miles at 9kts.

In 1939, in view of the increased speed of the
submarine (17-18kts surface speed), there was no
doubt that the trawler-type ships, although suitable for minesweeping work and escorting coastal
traffic, were too slow for anti-submarine work.
Moreover, these ships had neither protection nor
adequate subdivision. Consideration was given to
the conversion for A/S work of ships of the
whale-catcher type, but it was found that, while
these ships were ideal as regards size and dimensions, their watertight subdivision was inadequate, and conversion far more extensive and costly than in the case of trawlers. The possibility of
improving the speed of trawlers was also investigated but found to be impracticable.

As the war progressed patrol and escort vessels
capable of meeting attacks from submarines and
aircraft were needed in increasing numbers. Four
designs were built, namely:

Flower Class Corvettes (originally known as
Patrol Vessels - Whaler type)
River Class Frigates (classification changed
from Twin Screw Corvettes in February 1943)

Castle Class Corvettes (later known as frigates)
Loch Class Frigates
These vessels were ordered mostly from shipbuilders not usually engaged in warship construction. First-class mercantile practice, complying
with the requirements of Lloyd's Register and of
the British Corporation, was adopted as a basis for
the construction. It was never practicable to utilise
the shipbuilding capacity normally engaged in
warship construction, hence the importance of
selecting designs capable of achieving maximum
performance and suitable for rapid production
from the sources available.[2]

To assist in reducing the time for building and
the personnel required for manning, simplicity
and a small complement were requirements at the
outset. These soon became unattainable targets.
War experience quickly showed the imperative
need for adding to and improving the fighting
equipment, and for increasing complements.
Developments in tactics involved the provision of
new weapons and devices, and the result was that
the resources required for the manufacture of
equipment and the time and resources required
for `fitting-out' vessels after launch increased considerably, and became much greater than would be
needed for merchant vessels of comparable size.
The details of the equipment had to be kept constantly under review, to reconcile the conflicting
requirements of operational authorities for
changes improving fighting and sea-going effi-

[1] D K Brown, 'Atlantic
Escorts, 1939-45', *The
Battle of the Atlantic
1939-1945* (London
1994).

[2] P Elliot, *Allied Escort
Ships of World War II*
(London 1977). See also
note 1 for a summary.

Clematis at her builders in Bristol in original Flower *class configuration – no radar and AA guns still to be fitted.*

ciency on the one hand, and of shipbuilders contending for the limitation of changes in the interests of rapid production on the other hand.

Flower **Class Corvettes**

When consideration was being given to the conversion of whale-catchers a number of alternative designs were reviewed. Among the alternatives was a sketch design proposed by Smith's Dock Co Ltd, South Bank, Middlesbrough, based on the whale-catcher *Southern Pride*,[3] designed and built by the firm. This sketch design was adopted as the basis for the *Flower* class, and the detailed design was worked out by the firm in co-operation with the Admiralty Design Departments, the British Corporation and Lloyd's Register. The hull dimensions and layout differed considerably from those of the parent whale-catcher, an increase in length of 30ft, giving better proportions for speed, more space and better watertight subdivision.

The principal dimensions and other particulars were as follows:

Length overall	205ft 0in
Length, between perpendiculars	190ft 0in
Depth moulded to upper deck	17ft 6in
Beam moulded	33ft 0in
Deep displacement	1170 tons
Mean draught in deep condition	13ft 3in
Speed as designed for deep condition	16kts
Endurance at 12kts (clean bottom)	4000 miles

Legend of weights

Hull	491 tons
Machinery	375 tons
Equipment	57 tons
Armament	17 tons
Oil fuel	200 tons
Reserve feed water	30 tons
Deep displacement	1170 tons

Structural

In general the ships were of riveted construction but liberty was given to shipbuilders with welding resources to substitute welded construction for decks, bulkheads, engine seatings, etc. This resulted in a slight saving of weight in these particular ships.

Armament

1-4in BL gun forward on forecastle deck
1-2pdr single-barrel pom-pom
1 Lewis gun
40 depth charges, 2 rails and 2 throwers

The ships were fitted with a type 123 Asdic set.

Machinery etc.

The four cylinder triple expansion engine of the *Southern Pride* was adopted, patterns for this engine being available.[4] To obtain an increase in power the engine speed was increased to 185rpm, estimated to raise the output of the engine to 2750ihp. Steam was supplied by two single-ended

[3] J H Harland, *Catchers and Corvettes.* (Rotherfield 1992).

[4] It is a matter for some surprise that geared turbine plants could be built for a large number of destroyers in the First World War but that a smaller number of turbines could not be made in the Second. The power station builders were not utilised (see also note 3).

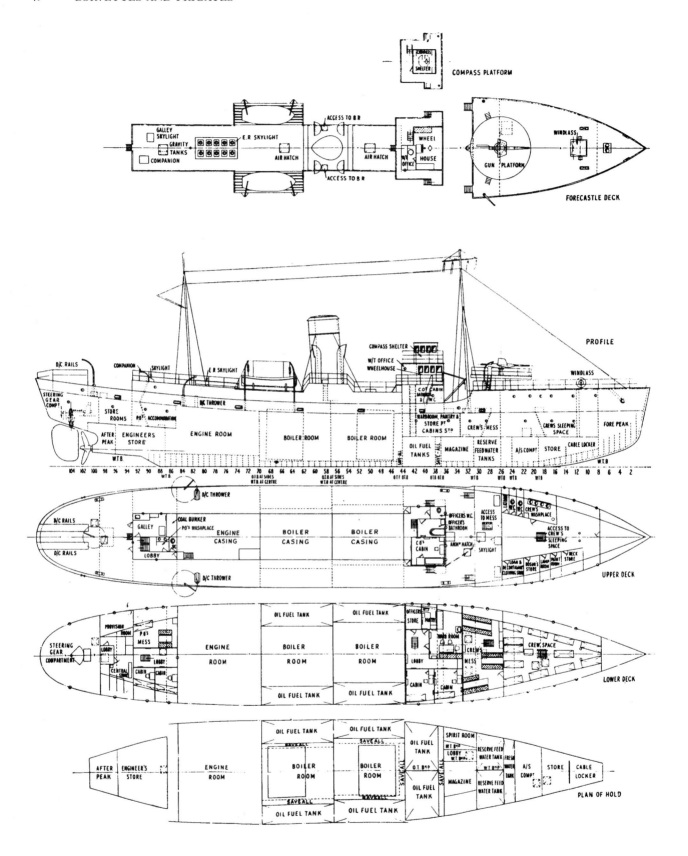

Original short-forecastle *Flower* class corvette general arrangements; note mercantile type bridge

oil-fired Scotch boilers; twenty ships were subsequently fitted with watertube boilers.

Propeller particulars: 3 bladed, diameter 10ft 6in, pitch 10ft 8in.

Electrical Power

The electrical power was supplied by one 15kW steam-driven generator. An additional 15kW generator was subsequently fitted to carry an increased load due to additional wireless, asdic and other services.

Trials

The first ship of the class, *Gladiolus*, commenced her trials in April 1940. Maximum speed obtained on trials was 16.6kts on a displacement of 1118ton, with ihp of 813 at 187rpm; this gave 16.5kts with 2750ihp and 185rpm. Fuel consumption was 11.8ton per 24 hours at 12kts.

The propulsive co-efficient was 0.535.

The steering trials showed that the class had good manoeuvring qualities, obtained with an underhung balanced rudder of area 86sq ft with the deadwood aft well cut away. They had exceptional powers for turning quickly and in a small space. On turns at full speed the measured advance was 2.4 lengths and the tactical diameter 2.1 lengths. The corresponding times to turn through the first 16 and 32 points were 51 and

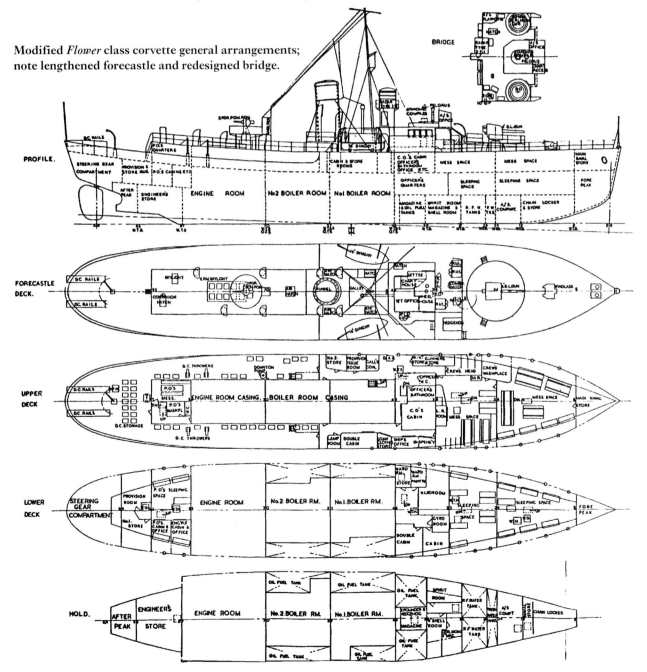

Modified *Flower* class corvette general arrangements; note lengthened forecastle and redesigned bridge.

109½ seconds respectively; the maximum angle of heel during turn was 3°.[5]

It was observed that these ships had a tendency to yaw and the effect of filling in the deadwood at the after cut up was tried in one ship. There appeared to be no particular advantage to be gained by this and it was not carried out in any of the other ships. Excessive rolling was reported from sea and after trials it was decided to fit deeper bilge keels; this effected a considerable improvement.

Lively motion of this class of ship was also reported from sea but this was considered unavoidable in such small vessels, especially when they were on ocean service.[6]

Stability
Particulars for a typical ship of this class were:

	Light condition	Deep condition
GM	1ft	2.1ft
Max value of GZ	0.98ft	1.45ft
Angle of max GZ	48°	47°
Range	84°	over 90°
Displacement	1038 tons	1342 tons

These figures were for a vessel with the lengthened forecastle etc.

Complement
When this design was first produced, accommodation for twenty-nine (including two officers) was provided for. This was increased to fifty, including four officers by the end of 1939.

Cost
Vote 8 cost about £90,000.

General
In 1940 these ships were attached to the Western Approaches Command, for general convoy duties. To improve seaworthiness it was decided that all ships building, and those on order, should have the forecastle lengthened to just abaft the forward boiler room, and in later ships the hull sections were also altered forward above the waterline to give increased sheer and flare.

The anti-aircraft defence was improved by fitting twin Lewis guns on extended bridge wings, but these were soon replaced by single Oerlikons. A hedgehog was fitted on the forecastle abaft the 4in gun and this necessitated a master gyro compass and a LP installation. The depth charge armament was also increased.

The bridge was almost entirely reconstructed as an open type with pelorus and standard compass,

radar type 271, and asdic type 145 in lieu or the type 123 with controls in a new office on the fore end of the bridge.

The increased equipment entailed increasing the complement to seventy-four, including six officers, and in order to relieve congestion the layouts of the cabins and mess spaces were rearranged. In a few of the later ships hammocks were fitted instead of bunks in the crew's quarters.[7]

Twelve ships of this class were fitted for service in the Arctic and seven of the original short forecastle ships were fitted with LL sweeps.

The first twenty-six ships of this class were ordered in 1939, twenty being laid down in that year. Altogether 145 *Flower* class corvettes were built in the United Kingdom. The Canadian Government built twenty-three ships to Admiralty's account, and seventy to their own account.[8]

River **Class Frigates**

The first frigate design was considered towards the end of 1940 when a review was made of the prospects of building vessels for service in the Atlantic more suitable than the 16kt *Flower* class corvettes.

The experience of the corvettes in escorting naval convoys had shown the need for long endurance, good sea-keeping qualities and a speed of 22kts, together with an armament capable of giving a convoy protection against both submarines and long-range aircraft. It was also desirable that the ships should be able to carry out minesweeping duties if required.

To meet these requirements a new design was necessary, and a number of alternatives for obtaining higher speed than that of the existing corvettes were examined. The speed of 22kts required by the staff involved a large increase in power, with displacement limitations necessitating light hull scantlings. This entailed a ship of about 350ft in length with turbine machinery.[9] Many of the corvette builders had no experience of this type of machinery and their berths were not long enough to take the increased length of ship. In order, therefore, to assist production of the new ships under emergency conditions a speed of not less than 20kts and reciprocating engines were accepted.

A new design was prepared and approved by the Board in March 1941. This design embodied experience gained with the *Flower* class as regards sea-keeping qualities, and were built to Merchant Ship Practice and to Classification Societies' rules

[5] In attacking a submarine with depth charges dropped over the stern, turning circle was very important.

[6] The *Flowers* were much the same size and form as the current *Island* class. They are quite safe in any sea but the pitch and heave motions are excessive for human beings to work satisfactorily. In the article quoted in note 1, the editor and Dr A R J M Lloyd used a much simplified version of modern seakeeping theory to estimate the percentage loss of operational time due to motions in bad weather, averaged over the year, for the various classes. The results, below, seem in accordance with the subjective accounts written by those who served in these ships.

Class	% loss of operational time
Flower	28
Castle	21
River, *Loch*	15 – also old destroyers such as the V & W.

For comparison
Leander 9

Both the *Flowers* and the *Islands* had to have their bilge keels increased in size – see K Monk, 'A Warship Roll Criterion', *Transactions of the Royal Institution of Naval Architects* 129 (1987).

[7] Living conditions were appalling and the high incidence of tuberculosis led to some improvement. See note 1.

[8] The text is a record of design history and as such cannot pay tribute to the immense effort put into production by Canada: for this aspect see K Macpherson, and M Milner, *Corvettes of the Royal Canadian Navy* (Ontario 1993).

[9] Note that even at this date the requirement was for 22kts at least.

Wear, *a River* class *frigate, unusual in mounting ten Oerlikons. This appears to have been intended for all ships but was achieved in few.*

and survey. The work of preparing the working drawings was distributed between some of the shipbuilders receiving orders.

The principal dimensions and particulars were:

Length overall	301ft 4in
Length between perpendiculars	283ft 0in
Depth moulded	17ft 6in
Breadth moulded	36ft 6in
Deep displacement	1855 tons
Speed in deep condition	19½kts
Endurance at 15kts (clean bottom)	5000 miles

Legend of weights

Hull	720 tons
Machinery	385 tons
Equipment	140 tons
Armament	70 tons
Oil fuel	440 tons
Diesel oil	30 tons
Reserve feed water	40 tons
Minesweeping gear	30 tons
Deep displacement	1855 tons

Structural

Normal methods of shipbuilding construction were adopted, and as for the *Flower* class corvettes, the partial use of welding saved as much as 30ton in some ships when compared with their riveted counterparts. When the Maritime Commission subsequently undertook the construction of a number of vessels to *River* class design for the US Navy, an all-welded hull was adopted with still greater saving in weight.[10]

[10] R E Johnson, 'The *Tacoma* class frigates of World War 2', *Warship International* 29/2 (1992).

Armament

2-4in HA/LA guns, 1 on superstructure deck forward, 1 on forecastle deck aft
2-2pdr single mountings or twin Oerlikons
2-20mm Oerlikons on bridge wings
2 PAC projectors
100 depth charges, 8 throwers, 2 rails of 15 charges each
Mark 1 Oreposa M/S gear, TWMG, `LL' sweep and SA gear were also fitted.

Machinery

To continue to employ the resources engaged in building corvettes the propelling machinery consisted of two sets of triple expansion reciprocating engines (repeats of those fitted in *Flower* class) developing 5500ihp and driving twin screws at 185rpm. Ample astern power was available with this type of machinery. Turbine machinery with a total shp of 6500 at 300rpm was, however, installed in six ships (three short endurance and three long endurance).

Two watertube oil-fired boilers at 225lb/in^2 were installed each in a separate boiler room.

In ships with reciprocating machinery, two elliptical 3-bladed props were fitted - diameter 9ft 9in, pitch 13ft 5in and developed blade area 30 sq ft. In turbine ships the diameter was 8ft 3in, pitch 9ft 3in and blade area 21ft^2.

Electrical Power

This was supplied by two 60kW reciprocating steam generators and one 60kW diesel generator.

HMS *Rother*, the first ship of the class, was completed in April 1942 and on a trial displacement of 1900ton a speed of 19¾kts was obtained with 5535ihp and 184rpm. This was considered to meet the design requirements and gave a propulsive coefficient of 0.50.

Stability

Particulars for typical ships as built were:

| | Light Condition | | Deep Condition | |
	Rother (short endurance)	Lagan (long endurance)	Rother	Lagan
GM	1.61	1.76	2.5	2.68
Max value of GZ	1.16	1.3	2.37	2.5
Angle of max GZ	44½°	45½°	48½°	50°
Range	75°	78°	90°	90°
Displacement	1383	1321	1962	2100

Strength

	Sagging	Hogging
Maximum bending moment	20,939ton/ft	22,160ton/ft
Maximum stress in UD	5.1ton/in²	6.13ton/in²
Maximum stress in keel	4.4ton/in²	3.88ton/in²

Complement

The complement of this class was 114 including six officers and hammocks were provided for all ratings. Amenities included a canteen, drying room, sick bay and cold and cool rooms. As in minesweepers, alternative mess spaces were arranged on the upper deck abreast of the engine casing, so that men need not be accommodated in the lower mess decks forward when sweeping was in progress.

Cost

Vote 8, about £240,000.

General

Reports from sea stated that these ships were comfortable, very good sea boats and capable of maintaining better speed in bad weather than the ships built on destroyer lines. High freeboard made for a dry ships forward and amidships, but the quarterdeck was wet and some pounding was experienced even at quite low speeds.

In 1942 longer endurance was called for and in twenty-three of the ships laid down that year and eight laid down in 1943, the capacity of the oil fuel tanks aft was increased and additional oil fuel tanks arranged forward to give a total OF capacity of 650 tons. None of these ships was fitted with Oropesa, or 'LL' minesweeping gear and taut wire measuring gear. Anti-submarine protection was increased by the fitting of a hedgehog on the forecastle deck; radar type 271 was installed and in two ships radar type 277 was later installed with a lattice mast for carrying the 277 aerial. The depth charge pattern was reduced to ten, the number of

River class frigate general arrangement

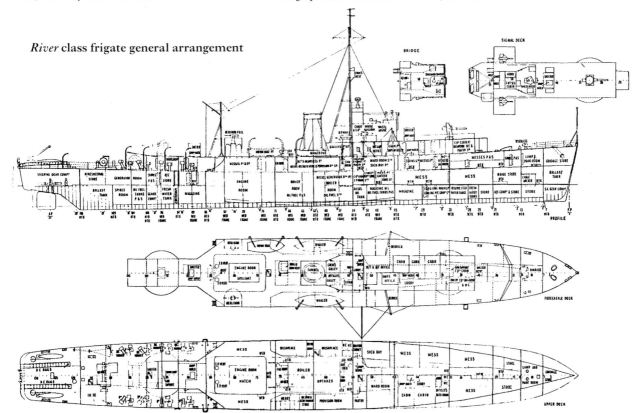

throwers being reduced to four; the complement of depth charges was increased to 150.

The first order for twenty ships was placed in 1941 and these, together with four of the 1941 programme, were built to the original requirements, ie short endurance type, all later ships were of the long endurance type. A total of fifty-seven ships was built in the UK. Canada built ten to Admiralty account (two of which were handed to US) and thirty-nine to her own account; Australia built twenty-two to their own account. All the ships built abroad were of the long endurance type.

Castle Class Corvettes

By 1942 the performance of the *Flower* class had shown that these ships were most satisfactory sea boats and, within the limits of their design, up to the work of ocean convoy. The ships were too small to carry the latest A/S armament with its associated gear, fittings and greater topweight. *River* class frigates, though larger and with greater speed, did not readily lend themselves to the fitting of the latest type of A/S armament and radar. A design for a larger ship, on the lines of the *Flower* class but more suitable for ocean service, was proposed by Messrs Smith's Dock Co as an interim type which could be rapidly produced.

This design was originally turned down in view of its unsuitability for mass production methods, but in view of the urgent requirement for such vessels and in order to maintain the rate of deliveries from the builders a modified form of design was approved by the Board in May 1943.

The principal dimensions and other particulars were as follows:

Length overall	252ft 0in
Length between perpendiculars	225ft 0in
Depth moulded to UD	17ft 6in
Beam moulded	36ft 6in
Deep displacement	1580 tons
Mean draught (deep)	13ft 5in
Speed (deep)	16½kts
Endurance at 15kts (clean bottom)	6200 miles

Legend of weights

Hull	663 tons
Machinery	230 tons
Equipment	111 tons
Armament	56 tons
Oil fuel	480 tons
Reserve feed water	40 tons
Deep displacement	1580 tons

Structure

Normal methods of shipbuilding construction were adopted, welding being introduced wherever possible.

Fabrication of parts of other structure was introduced wherever possible at the shipyards and prefabrication methods were adopted for deck houses such as wireless and radar offices which were delivered complete to the shipyards.

Prefabricated lattice-type masts were also introduced.

Arrangements were made for supply of a large proportion of the fittings by the Admiralty direct to the shipbuilders.

Armament

1-4in mounting on forecastle deck
2 twin Oerlikons amidships

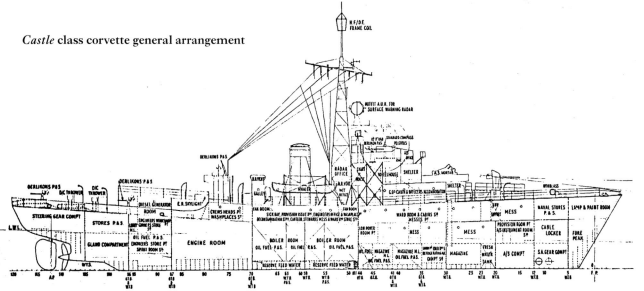

Castle class corvette general arrangement

2 single Oerlikons on bridge wings
1 Squid mounting forward, 81 projectiles
15 depth charges, 1 rail, 2 throwers
Asdic types 145 and 147B

Machinery
The four cylinder triple expansion engine of the *Flower* and *River* classes were repeated in this class, and the two watertube oil-fired boilers, working at 225lb/in^2, were installed in separate boiler rooms.

    Propeller: 1 elliptical three-bladed propeller
                diameter   10ft 3in
                pitch   10ft 8½in

Electrical power in this class was provided by one 30kW and one 60kW steam-driven generator, and one 15kW oil-driven generator.

Trials
The first ship of the class, *Hadleigh Castle*, ran satisfactory trials in September 1943; the results showed that the requirements for a speed of 16½kts in the deep condition with 2750ihp had been met.[11]

Stability
Particulars for *Hadleigh Castle*, a typical ship of the class, were:

	Light Condition	Deep Condition
GM	1.05ft	2.58ft
Max value of GZ	0.75ft	2.24ft
Angle of max GZ	53°	47°
Range	76°	over 90°
Displacement	1013	1586

Complement
One hundred, including five officers. Messes were situated on upper and lower decks forward and hammocks were provided in lieu of bunks. In this design it was found possible to remedy the congestion of living spaces and to improve the amenities in comparison with earlier *Flower* class design.

Cost
Vote 8 – about £190,000.

General
These ships were of the long forecastle type with generous sheer and flare. An open bridge was arranged as in *Flower* class with improvements as regards space and communications.

    Experience with these ships at sea showed that they were exceptionally good and reliable sea boats, even under the worst conditions of weather.[12]

    The first ship was laid down in April 1953 and in all thirty-nine ships were built; some ships were fitted for Arctic service. Five ships of the class were utilised for air/sea rescue.

Loch Class Frigates

The war in the Atlantic made it imperative to have a large number of convoy escorts and, in order to meet this demand, it was decided to use mass production prefabricated methods of building.

    A design for a frigate of special type of construction was prepared. This design was such that a very large portion of the structure could be prefabricated by structural engineering firms before delivery to the shipbuilders for erection. Every

HMCS Kincardine *of the* Castle *class in June 1944, probably the smallest ship which would be effective in Atlantic weather. They were mini-*Lochs, *with a single Squid, which could be built on slips too short for frigates.*

[11] It is interesting that, though bigger than the *Flowers*, they were slightly faster with the same engine due to the improved hull form developed at the Admiralty Experiment Works, Haslar.

[12] Because they were good sea-boats, several were employed as ocean weather ships after the War.

Loch class frigate general arrangement

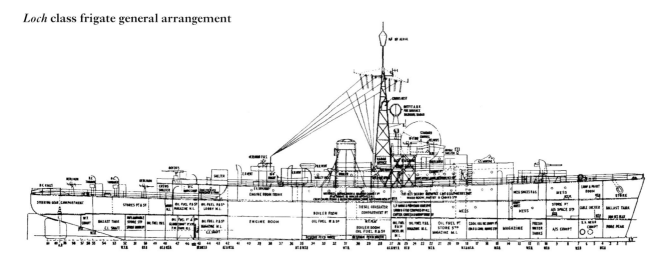

effort as made to standardise equipment and systems such as ventilation, piping, wiring, etc, and a very large proportion of the fittings usually provided by the shipbuilders were supplied by the Admiralty.

The function of these ships was primarily for anti-submarine work, and the armament provided gave the best A/A protection possible without prejudice to the requirements of A/S equipment and good endurance. The ships were required to be capable of operation in any weather in which an A/S escort was required, and of operating Asdics in weather conditions in which a destroyer could so operate.

The design was approved by the Board in May 1943. The general particulars for the class were:

Length overall	307ft 4in
Length between perpendiculars	286ft 0in
Breadth moulded	38ft 6in
Depth moulded to UD	17ft 9in
Mean draught (deep)	12ft 3½in
Displacement (deep)	2260 tons
Speed deep	18½kts
Endurance at 15kts	
(clean bottom)	7000 miles

Legend of weights

Hull	811 tons
Machinery	390 tons
Equipment	170 tons
Armament	100 tons
Oil fuel	724 tons
Diesel oil	30 tons
Reserve feed water	35 tons
Deep displacement	2260 tons

Structure

The structural arrangements, including the prefabrication layout, was worked out in collabora-

tion with the classification societies and a panel of the principal shipbuilders concerned with the construction of the ships.

With this particular class of ship designed for construction by prefabrication procedure, it was essential that the design should be `fixed' in the early stages, and that no major modifications should be accepted to interfere with prefabrication programme. The design was accordingly `sealed' for a period of two years.

To avoid difficulties as regards the final erection of the structural items supplied to shipbuilders by the engineering firms, Messrs John Brown were asked to build a prototype of the class, and during erection to note and report any difficulties encountered, for the information of the other shipbuilders concerned.

The ships were of the long forecastle type and the scantlings conformed to Classification Societies' rules and survey. The ships were longitudinally framed, in association with transverse web frames and deep beams. The structure, as well as being arranged to suit prefabrication methods, allowed for the maximum amount of welding consistent with rapid production.

Armament

1-4in single mounting on the forecastle forward
1-2pdr pom-pom on forecastle aft
2 twin Oerlikons
2 single Oerlikons
2 Squid mountings with 150 projectiles
1 DC rail, 2 DC throwers and 15 depth charges
Asdic types 144 and 147B were fitted.

Machinery

As in *River* class, two sets of triple expansion reciprocating engines were fitted; these developed 5500ihp driving twin screws at 185rpm. Double reduction turbine machinery, 6000shp at 200rpm

Loch Fada *under construction at John Browns. She was the prototype and drawings were prepared from her so that prefabricated hull sections could be made by structural engineers.*

was fitted in two ships of the class. Slight structural modifications were necessary to accommodate these engines.

Two three-drum watertube boilers of Admiralty type at 225lb/in^2 were installed in separate boiler rooms.

In both ships with reciprocating or turbine machinery, three-bladed propellers were fitted:

Diameter	9ft 9in
Pitch	13ft 5in
Developed blade area	30ft^2

Electrical power was provided by two 60kW steam-driven generators and one 60kW oil-driven generator.

Radar type 277 was carried on the lattice mast. The prototype ship *Loch Fada* on trials gave a speed of 19kts at 179rpm and 5335ihp on a displacement of 2180 tons.

Stability (Loch Fada as built)

	Light Condition	Deep Condition
Metacentric height	2.2ft	3.4ft
Max value of GZ	1.7ft	3.25ft
Angle of max GZ	47°	49°
Range	81°	90°
Displacement	1380 tons	2260 tons

Loch Tralaig *on 17 October 1945. The integrated armament of depth finding Asdic and Squid made them formidable ASW ships for at least a decade after the war.*

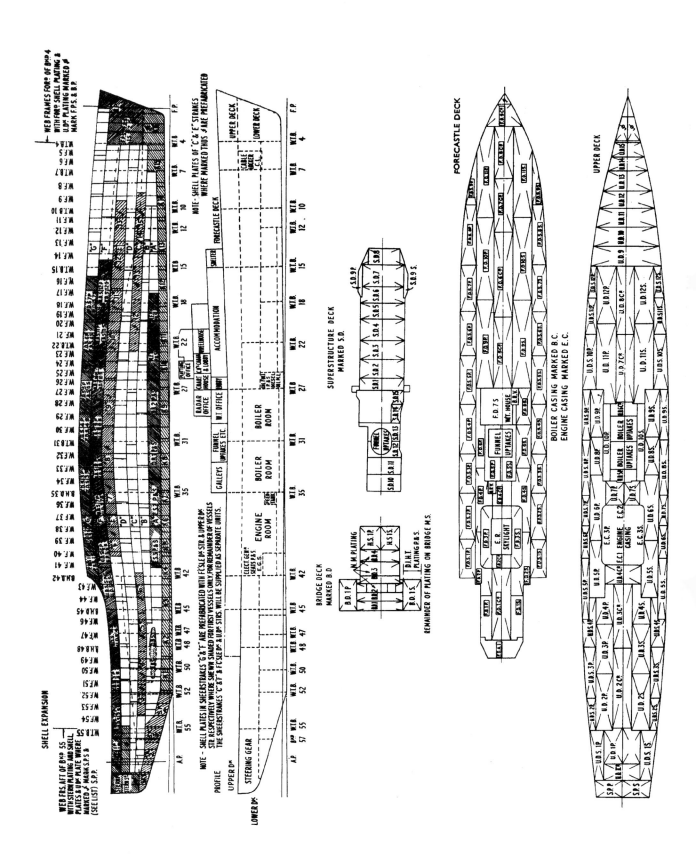

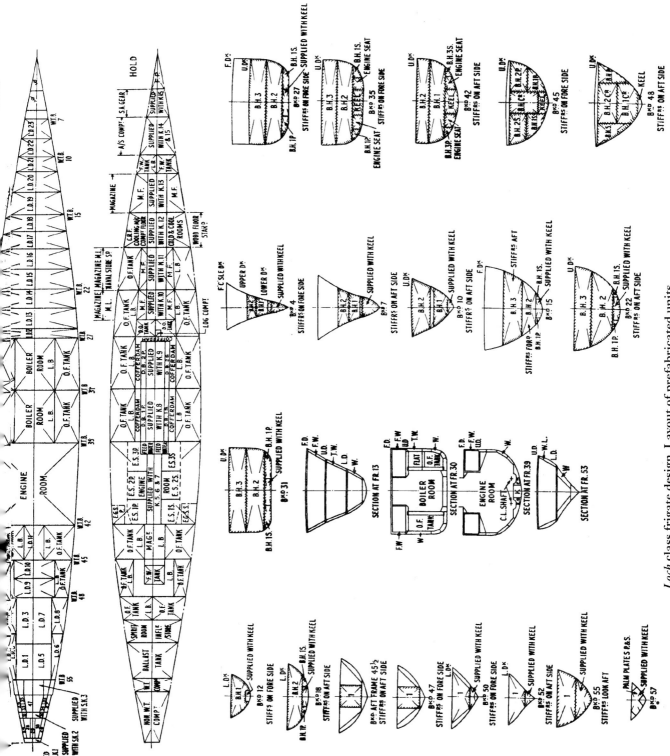

Loch class frigate design. Layout of prefabricated units

Structural arrangements are peculiar to these ships as agreed with Lloyds and BC. Strength figures have never been worked out.

Complement

Total complement was 114 including five officers. The standard of amenities provided was satisfactory for the size of ship and included sick bay, drying room, canteen, cold and cool rooms etc. Endeavours were also made to incorporate latest ideas on ventilation in this class of ship.

A total of twenty-eight vessels was completed. In addition two ships originally building as *Loch* class frigates were completed as coastal forces tenders. They were *Woodbridge Haven* and *Derby Haven*.

Cost

Mean Vote 8 cost was about £300,000.

Bay Class Frigates

Early in 1944 consideration was given to the problem of the war with Japan and approval was given to convert a number of the *Loch* class frigates during construction to AA escorts. These ships were renamed *Bay* class.

Whilst the structural arrangements of the original ships was retained, the armament was entirely revised as follows:

2-4in twin HA/LA mountings, 1 forward and 1 aft
2-40mm twin power worked Bofors
4-40mm single Bofors (or 20mm single Oerlikons)
1-24 charge Hedgehog
2 DC rails; 4 DC throwers
Asdic types 144 and 147B
Radar air warning set type 293 was fitted in place of type 277.

Bay class frigate
general arrangement

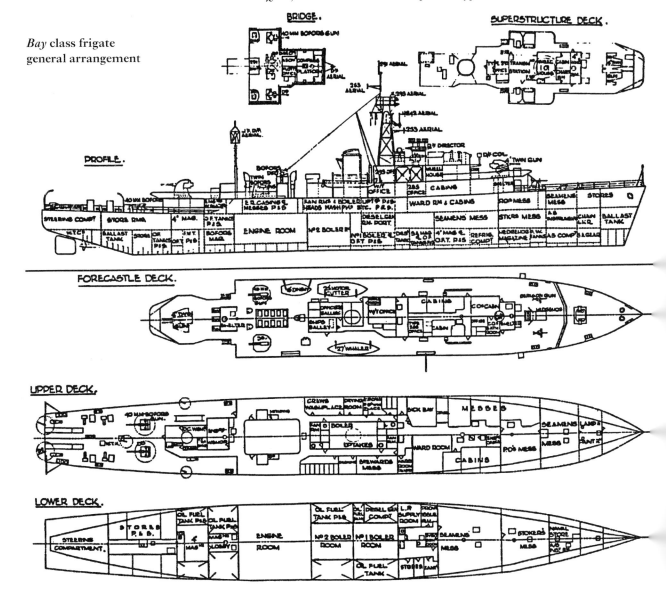

Stability (Type A)

	Light Condition	Deep Condition
GM	0.85ft	2.64t
Max value of GZ	1.04t	2.65ft
Angle of max GZ	45°	47°
Range	–	–
Displacement	1532 tons	2417 tons

A total of 17 vessels was completed.
(Note: ex *Mounts Bay*, *Morecambe Bay*, completed after the war, also *Alert* and *Surprise* completed as despatch vessels and ships completed as survey vessels. Type B conditions are somewhat better than those quoted.)

Complement
The change from A/S to A/A escort necessitated an increase in complement to 160, some congestion in the broadside messes having to be accepted in consequence.

General
Type A ships were fitted with 4in RPC mountings and Mk VI director. Type B ships were fitted with ordinary 4in mountings etc.

Cost
Typical Vote 8 cost was £330,000 per ship.

Captain Class

Seventy-eight of these vessels were built in the United States and delivered to the UK under Lease Lend Agreement. Twenty-four arrived in this country in 1943 and fifty-four in 1944. They were of two classes, Type A and Type B, the leading particulars being:

	Type A (32 in No) Diesel Electric Drive	Type B (46 in No) Turbo Electric Drive
Length (overall)	289ft 5in	306ft
Breadth (extreme)	35ft 0½in	36ft 11½in
Displacement (standard)	1150 tons	1300 tons
Displacement (deep)	1450 tons	1840 tons
Mean draught (deep)	10ft 9in	12ft 6½in
Shp	6000	12,000
Speed (max)	20kts	24kts

The original armament of those vessels consisted of three 3in HA/LA guns, 8-9 Oerlikons. Some were also fitted with twin Bofors. The number of depth charges 100–110 was increased on arrival in UK to 160, all being stowed on the upper deck.

At the end of the war the typical armament for a ship of this class was:

Postwar the Bay *class saw much service overseas: the last of them,* St Brides Bay *shown here, returned home in December 1961 for the first time since sailing for the Far East in 1945.*

[13] Both groups were found to roll very violently. The bilge keels were much increased in depth, top weight increased and weights winged to increase roll period. These changes took them out of service for 3 months but were very successful. In one comparative trial, the ship with original keels rolled 56° (out to out) while the ship with larger keels rolled only 40°. See also N Friedman, *US Destroyers* (Annapolis 1982). It is strange that USN crews do not seem to have complained of their similar (not identical) ships.

3–3in HA/LA guns
15–20m single Oerlikons
Hedgehog
160 depth charges, 2 rails and 4 throwers

During the European war these vessels were employed as convoy escorts, for service Overlord, three type A vessels were fitted out as landing ship headquarters (small) and thirty type B ships were fitted with additional Oerlikons (2) and a 2pdr bow chaser. After the European war some of the B type frigates were taken off convoy escort duties and allocated for service in the tropics, five as fighter direction ships, three as coastal force control ships and five as mobile generating electric supply ships to serve in the Eastern theatre.

Owing to the early collapse of Japan much of this fitting-out work was abandoned and only two of the mobile generating ships were completed, *Hotham* and *Spragge*. Of the seventy-eight ships built and delivered to the UK the following were lost by enemy action: five type A and two type B

sunk, and three type A and seven type B damaged beyond economic repair.

Built in USA during the war, these ships, both A and B types, were of all-welded, prefabricated construction. No serious complaints were received from sea of defects in structure during vessels' service.

Twin rudders were fitted and the steering gear was of the electro-hydraulic type, electrically controlled from the bridge.

Early reports of behaviour at sea showed these ships to be lively and uncomfortable due to excessive rolling and violent lurching, and as gun platforms were only satisfactory under favourable weather conditions.[13] On request records were taken of the actual rolling and pitching at sea and, based on these reports, the class was fitted with larger bilge keels and also ballasted suitably to meet these adverse conditions.

Later reports ascertained that greatly improved conditions resulted consequent on these alterations, and that seaworthiness was satisfactory.

Lawson, a Diesel engined, US built, Captain class. She is seen with later modifications such as extra Oerlikons, a shield to B gun and more numerous depth charges. The extra weight helped to reduce the severity of rolling.

Flower Class Corvette

Ship	Firm	Laid Down	Launched	Completed
1939 Programme				
Gladiolus	Smith's Dock	19 Oct 1939	24 Jan 1940	6 Apr 1940
Gardenia	Wm Simons	20 Sep 1939	10 Apr 1940	24 May 1940
Geranium	Wm Simons	21 Sep 1939	23 Apr 1940	24 Jun 1940
Godetia	Smith's Dock	4 Jan 1940	8 May 1940	15 Jul 1940
Primrose	Wm Simons	22 Sep 1939	8 May 1940	15 Jul 1940

Flower Class Corvette (continued)

Ship	Firm	Laid Down	Launched	Completed
1939 Programme (continued)				
Bluebell	Fleming & Ferguson	25 Oct 1939	24 Apr 1940	19 Jul 1940
Clematis	Chas Hill	11 Oct 1939	24 Apr 1940	27 Jul 1940
Anemone	Blyth Dry Dock	26 Oct 1939	22 Apr 1940	12 Aug 1940
Coreopsis	A & J Inglis	13 Oct 1939	23 May 1940	17 Aug 1940
Primula	Wm Simons	23 Sep 1939	22 Jun 1940	27 Aug 1940
Campanula	Fleming & Ferguson	26 Oct 1939	23 May 1940	6 Sep 1940
Asphodel	G Brown & Co	20 Oct 1939	25 May 1940	11 Sep 1940
Heliotrope	J Crown	23 Oct 1939	5 Jun 1940	12 Sep 1940
Honeysuckle	Ferguson Bros	26 Oct 1939	22 Apr 1940	14 Sep 1940
Salvia	Wm Simons	26 Sep 1939	6 Aug 1940	20 Sep 1940
Cyclamen	J Lewis	30 Nov 1939	20 Jun 1940	30 Sep 1940
Arbutus	Blyth Dry Dock	30 Nov 1939	4 Jun 1940	12 Oct 1940
Candytuft	Grangemouth Dockyard	31 Oct 1939	8 Jul 1940	16 Oct 1940
Crocus	A & J Inglis	26 Oct 1939	26 Jun 1940	20 Oct 1940
Jonquil	Fleming & Ferguson	27 Dec 1939	9 Jul 1940	21 Oct 1940
Snapdragon	Wm Simons	27 Sep 1939	3 Sep 1940	28 Oct 1940
Columbine	Chas Hill	2 Nov 1939	13 Aug 1940	9 Nov 1940
Delphinium	Hy Robb	31 Oct 1939	6 Jun 1940	15 Nov 1940
Tulip	Smith's Dock	30 May 1940	4 Sep 1940	18 Nov 1940
Hollyhock	John Crown	27 Nov 1939	19 Aug 1940	19 Nov 1940
Marguerite	Hall Russell	30 Dec 1939	8 Jul 1940	20 Nov 1940
Verbena	Smith's Dock	29 Jun 1940	1 Oct 1940	19 Dec 1940
Aubretia	G Brown & Co	27 Oct 1939	5 Sep 1940	23 Dec 1940
Hydrangea	Ferguson Bros	22 Nov 1939	4 Sep 1940	3 Jan 1941
Larkspur	Fleming & Ferguson	26 Mar 1940	5 Sep 1940	4 Jan 1941
Daniella	John Lewis	8 Dec 1939	3 Sep 1940	6 Jan 1941
Petunia	Hy Robb	4 Dec 1939	19 Sep 1940	13 Jan 1941
Snowdrop	Smith's Dock	10 Apr 1940	19 Jul 1940	16 Jan 1941
Azalea	Cook, Welton & Gemmell	15 Nov 1939	8 Jul 1940	27 Jan 1941
Sunflower	Smith's Dock	24 May 1940	19 Aug 1940	25 Jan 1941
Veronica	Smith's Dock	9 Jul 1940	17 Oct 1940	18 Feb 1941
Carnation	Grangemouth Dockyard	26 Feb 1940	3 Sep 1940	22 Feb 1941
Nigella	Phillips & Son	28 Nov 1939	21 Sep 1940	25 Feb 1941
Convolvulus	Chas Hill	17 Jan 1940	22 Sep 1940	26 Feb 1941
Marigold	Hall Russell	26 Jan 1940	4 Sep 1940	28 Feb 1941
Begonia	Cook, Welton & Gemmell	13 Apr 1940	18 Sep 1940	3 Mar 1941
Auricula	G Brown	25 Nov 1939	14 Nov 1940	5 Mar 1941
Wallflower	Smith's Dock	23 Jul 1940	14 Nov 1940	7 Mar 1941
Dianthus	Hy Robb	31 Oct 1939	9 Jul 1940	17 Mar 1941
Dahlia	John Lewis	28 Feb 1940	31 Oct 1940	21 Mar 1941
Zinnia	Smith's Dock	20 Aug 1940	28 Nov 1940	30 Mar 1941
Polyanthus	Hy Robb	19 Mar 1940	30 Nov 1940	23 Apr 1941
Celandine	Grangemouth Dockyard	30 Apr 1940	28 Dec 1940	30 Apr 1941
Mignonette	Hall Russell	15 Jul 1940	28 Nov 1940	7 May 1941
Mimosa	Chas Hill	22 Apr 1940	18 Jan 1941	11 May 1941
Lavender	Alex Hall	30 Apr 1940	27 Nov 1940	16 May 1941
Jasmine	Ferguson Bros	23 Dec 1939	14 Jan 1941	16 May 1941
Myositis	John Lewis	24 Jun 1940	28 Jan 1941	30 May 1941
Lobelia	Alex Hall	27 Jun 1940	15 Feb 1941	16 Jul 1941
Narcissus	John Lewis	9 Sep 1940	29 Mar 1941	17 Jul 1941
Pentstemon	Philip & Son	28 Nov 1939	18 Jan 1941	31 Jul 1941
War Emergency Programme				
Arabis	Harland & Wolff	30 Oct 1939	14 Feb 1940	5 Apr 1940
Periwinkle	Harland & Wolff	30 Oct 1939	24 Feb 1940	8 Apr 1940
Clarkia	Harland & Wolff	30 Oct 1939	7 Mar 1940	22 Apr 1940
Calendula	Harland & Wolff	30 Oct 1939	21 Mar 1940	6 May 1940
Hibiscus	Harland & Wolff	14 Nov 1939	6 Apr 1940	21 May 1940
Heartsease	Harland & Wolff	14 Nov 1939	20 Apr 1940	4 Jun 1940
Camellia	Harland & Wolff	14 Nov 1939	4 May 1940	18 Jun 1940
Mallow	Harland & Wolff	14 Nov 1939	22 May 1940	2 Jul 1940

Flower Class Corvette (continued)

Ship	Firm	Laid Down	Launched	Completed
War Emergency Programme (continued)				
Peony	Harland & Wolff	24 Feb 1940	4 Jun 1940	6 Aug 1940
Erica	Harland & Wolff	24 Feb 1940	18 Jun 1940	7 Aug 1940
Gloxinia	Harland & Wolff	21 Mar 1940	2 Jul 1940	22 Aug 1940
Picotee	Harland & Wolff	21 Mar 1940	19 Jul 1940	5 Sep 1940
Gentian	Harland & Wolff	20 Apr 1940	6 Aug 1940	20 Sep 1940
Hyacinth	Harland & Wolff	20 Apr 1940	28 Sep 1940	4 Oct 1940
Rhododendron	Harland & Wolff	22 May 1940	2 Sep 1940	18 Oct 1940
Heather	Harland & Wolff	22 May 1940	17 Sep 1940	1 Nov 1940
Freesia	Harland & Wolff	18 Jun 1940	3 Oct 1940	19 Nov 1940
Orchis	Harland & Wolff	18 Jun 1940	15 Oct 1940	30 Nov 1940
Kingcup	Harland & Wolff	19 Jul 1940	31 Oct 1940	3 Jan 1941
Pimpernel	Harland & Wolff	19 Jul 1940	16 Nov 1940	9 Jan 1941
Violet	Wm Simons	21 Mar 1940	30 Dec 1940	3 Feb 1941
Amaranthus	Fleming & Ferguson	4 May 1940	17 Oct 1940	12 Feb 1941
Spira	A & J Inglis	31 May 1940	31 Oct 1940	27 Feb 1941
Burdock	J Crown	13 Jun 1940	14 Dec 1940	27 Mar 1941
Woodruff	Wm Simons	29 Apr 1940	28 Feb 1941	7 Apr 1941
Starwort	A & J Inglis	11 Jun 1940	12 Feb 1941	26 May 1951
Clover	Fleming & Ferguson	29 Jul 1940	30 Jan 1941	31 May 1941
Alyssum	G Brown	24 Jun 1940	3 Mar 1941	17 Jun 1941
Samphire	Smith's Dock	4 Dec 1940	14 Apr 1941	30 Jun 1941
Campion	John Crown	16 Sep 1940	26 Apr 1941	7 Jul 1941
Aconite	Ailsa	25 Mar 1940	31 Mar 1941	23 Jul 1941
Renoncule	Wm Simons	19 Jul 1940	25 Jun 1941	28 Jul 1941
Stonecrop	Smith's Dock	4 Feb 1941	12 May 1941	30 Jul 1941
Vetch	Smith's Dock	15 Mar 1941	27 May 1941	11 Aug 1941
Coriander	Hall Russell	19 Sep 1940	9 Jun 1941	16 Sep 1941
Roselys (late *Sundew*)	John Lewis	4 Nov 1940	28 May 1941	19 Sep 1941
Coltsfoot	A Hall	4 Sep 1940	12 May 1941	1 Oct 1941
Acanthus	Ailsa	21 Dec 1939	26 May 1941	1 Oct 1941
Rose	Wm Simons	3 Sep 1940	22 Sep 1941	31 Oct 1941
Rockrose	Charles Hill	28 Oct 1940	26 Jul 1941	4 Nov 1941
Loosestrife	Hall Russell	9 Dec 1940	25 Aug 1941	25 Nov 1941
Bellwort	G Brown	17 Sep 1940	11 Aug 1941	26 Nov 1941
Oxlip	A & J Inglis	9 Dec 1940	28 Aug 1941	28 Dec 1941
Saxifrage	Chas Hill	1 Feb 1941	24 Oct 1941	6 Feb 1942
Pennywort	A & J Inglis	11 Mar 1941	18 Oct 1941	5 Mar 1942
Borage	G Brown	27 Nov 1940	22 Nov 1941	29 Apr 1942
Phlox	Hy Robb	26 Mar 1941	16 Jan 1942	9 May 1942
Lotus	Chas Hill	26 May 1941	17 Jan 1942	23 May 1942
Pink	Hy Robb	20 May 1941	16 Feb 1942	2 Jul 1942
Meadowsweet	Chas Hill	12 Aug 1941	28 Mar 1942	8 Jul 1942

Taken over from the French whilst under construction:

La Maloine
La Bastiaise
La Dieppoise
La Pampolaise

Ship	Firm	Laid Down	Launched	Completed
1940 Programme				
Abelia	Harland & Wolff	19 Aug 1940	25 Nov 1940	3 Feb 1941
Alisma	Harland & Wolff	19 Aug 1940	17 Dec 1940	13 Feb 1941
Anchusa	Harland & Wolff	17 Sep 1940	15 Jan 1941	1 Mar 1941
Armeria	Harland & Wolff	17 Sep 1940	16 Jan 1941	28 Mar 1941
Aster	Harland & Wolff	15 Oct 1940	12 Feb 1941	11 Apr 1941
Bergamot	Harland & Wolff	15 Oct 1940	15 Feb 1941	12 May 1941
Vervain	Harland & Wolff	16 Nov 1940	12 Mar 1941	9 Jun 1941
Monkshood	Fleming & Ferguson	1 Oct 1940	17 Apr 1941	31 Jul 1941
Cowslip	Harland & Wolff	16 Jan 1941	28 May 1941	9 Aug 1941
Eglantine	Harland & Wolff	16 Jan 1941	11 Jun 1941	29 Aug 1941
Sweetbriar	Smith's Dock	4 Apr 1941	26 Jun 1941	8 Sep 1941

Flower Class Corvette (continued)

Ship	Firm	Laid Down	Launched	Completed
1940 Programme (continued)				
Montbretia	Fleming & Ferguson	16 Nov 1940	27 May 1941	29 Sep 1941
Thyme	Smith's Dock	30 Apr 1941	25 Jul 1941	23 Oct 1941
Fritillary	Harland & Wolff	15 Feb 1941	2 Jul 1941	1 Nov 1941
Snowflake (late *Zenobia*)	Smith's Dock	19 May 1941	22 Aug 1941	2 Nov 1941
Genista	Harland & Wolff	15 Feb 1941	24 Jul 1941	19 Dec 1941
Tamarisk	Fleming & Ferguson	10 Feb 1941	28 Jul 1941	26 Dec 1941
Chrysanthemum	Harland & Wolff	17 Dec 1940	11 Apr 1941	26 Jan 1942
Pontentilla	Wm Simons	28 Feb 1941	18 Dec 1941	5 Feb 1942
Nettle	Alex Hall	24 Dec 1940	23 Sep 1941	23 Feb 1942
Godetia	John Crown	15 Jan 1941	24 Sep 1941	23 Feb 1942
Buttercup	Harland & Wolff	17 Dec 1940	10 Apr 1941	24 Apr 1942
Poppy	Alex Hall	6 Mar 1941	20 Nov 1941	12 May 1942
Bryony	Harland & Wolff	16 Nov 1940	15 Mar 1941	16 Jun 1942
Balsam	G Brown	16 Apr 1941	30 May 1942	28 Nov 1942
1941 Programme				
Betony	Alex Hall	26 Sep 1942	22 Apr 1943	31 Aug 1943
Burnet	Ferguson Bros	2 Nov 1942	31 May 1943	23 Sep 1943
Buddleia	Alex Hall	30 Nov 1942	19 Jun 1943	7 Nov 1943
Bugloss	J Crown	26 Nov 1942	21 Jun 1943	8 Nov 1943
Ceanothus	Ferguson Bros	5 Feb 1943	30 Aug 1943	10 Dec 1943
Bulrush	J Crown	22 Feb 1943	11 Oct 1943	15 Feb 1944
1942 Programme				
Candytuft	A & J Inglis	27 Feb 1943	28 Sep 1943	15 Jan 1944
Charlock	Ferguson Bros	6 Apr 1943	16 Nov 1943	10 Mar 1944
Arabis	G Brown	26 Feb 1943	28 Oct 1943	16 Mar 1044
Arbutus	G Brown	1 May 1943	26 Jan 1944	5 Jul 1944

River Class

Ship	Firm	Laid Down	Launched	Completed
1940 Programme				
Rother	Smith's Dock	26 Jun 1941	20 Nov 1941	3 Apr 1942
Spey	Smith's Dock	18 Jul 1941	18 Dec 1941	19 May 1942
Swale	Smith's Dock	19 Aug 1941	16 Jan 1942	24 Jun 1942
Tay	Smith's Dock	10 Sep 1941	18 Mar 1942	5 Aug 1942
Exe	Fleming & Ferguson	16 May 1941	19 Mar 1942	6 Aug 1942
Waveney	Smith's Dock	8 Oct 1041	30 Apr 1942	16 Sep 1942
Test	Hall Russell	15 Aug 1941	30 May 1942	12 Oct 1942
Wear	Smith's Dock	16 Oct 1941	1 Jun 1942	24 Oct 1942
Jed	Chas Hill	27 Sep 1941	30 Jul 1942	30 Nov 1942
Lagan	Smith's Dock	7 Jan 1942	28 Jul 1942	2 Dec 1942
Kale	A & J Inglis	22 Sep 1941	24 Jun 1942	4 Dec 1942
Ness	Hy Robb	3 Sep 1941	30 Jul 1942	22 Dec 1942
Itchen	Fleming & Ferguson	14 Jul 1941	29 Jul 1942	28 Dec 1942
Moyola	Smith's Dock	9 Feb 1942	27 Aug 1942	15 Jan 1942
Teviot	Hall Russell	4 Oct 1942	12 Oct 1942	30 Jan 1942
Nith	Hy Robb	5 Sep 1941	25 Sep 1942	16 Feb 1943
Trent	Chas Hill	31 Jan 1942	10 Oct 1942	27 Feb 1943
Tweed	A & J Inglis	31 Dec 1941	24 Nov 1942	28 Apr 1943
Mourne	Smith's Dock	21 Mar 1942	24 Sep 1942	30 Apr 1943
Bann	Chas Hill	18 Jun 1942	29 Dec 1942	7 May 1943
Dart	Blyth Dry Docks	8 Sep 1941	10 Oct 1942	13 May 1943
Derg	Hy Robb	16 Apr 1942	7 Jan 1943	10 Jun 1943
Ribble	Wm Simons	31 Dec 1941	23 Apr 1943	25 Jun 1943
Ettrick	J Crown	31 Dec 1941	5 Feb 1943	11 Jul 1943
Strule (ex *Glenarm*)	Hy Robb	15 Jul 1942	8 Mar 1943	30 Jul 1943
Ballinderry	Blyth Dry Docks	6 Nov 1941	7 Dec 1942	2 Sep 1943
Chelmer	G Brown & Co	29 Dec 1941	27 Mar 1943	29 Sep 1943

River Class (continued)

Ship	Firm	Laid Down	Launched	Completed
1941 Programme				
Deveron	Smith's Dock	16 Apr 1942	12 Oct 1942	2 Mar 1943
Nene	Smith's Dock	20 Jun 1942	9 Dec 1942	8 Apr 1943
Plum	Smith's Dock	1 Aug 1942	4 Feb 1943	16 May 1943
Towy	Smith's Dock	3 Sep 1942	4 Mar 1943	10 Jun 1943
Helford	Hall Russell	27 Jun 1942	6 Feb 1943	26 Jun 1943
Fal	Smith's Dock	20 May 1942	9 Nov 1942	2 Jul 1943
Tavy	Chas Hill	17 Oct 1942	3 Apr 1943	3 Jul 1943
Usk	Smith's Dock	6 Oct 1942	3 Apr 1943	14 Jul 1943
Aire	Fleming & Ferguson	12 Jun 1942	22 Apr 1943	28 Jul 1943
Tees	Hall Russell	21 Oct 1942	20 May 1943	28 Aug 1943
Helmsdale	A & J Inglis	13 Aug 1942	5 Jun 1943	15 Oct 1943
Windrush	Hy Robb	18 Nov 1942	18 Jun 1943	3 Nov 1943
Meon	A & J Inglis	31 Dec 1942	4 Aug 1943	31 Dec 1943
Braid	Wm Simons	1 Dec 1942	30 Nov 1943	21 Jan 1944
Cam	G Brown & Co	30 Jun 1942	31 Jul 1943	31 Jan 1944
Wye	Hy Robb	18 Nov 1942	16 Aug 1943	9 Feb 1944
Dovey	Fleming & Ferguson	23 Mar 1943	14 Oct 1943	25 Feb 1944
Frome	Blyth Dry Docks	30 May 1942	11 Jun 1943	3 Mar 1944
Torridge	Blyth Dry Docks	17 Oct 1942	16 Aug 1943	6 Apr 1944
1942 Programme				
Odzani	Smith's Dock	18 Nov 1942	19 May 1943	2 Sep 1943
Avon	Chas Hill	8 Jan 1943	19 Jun 1943	18 Sep 1943
Taff	Chas Hill	14 Apr 1943	11 Sep 1943	7 Jan 1944
Nadder	Smith's Dock	11 Mar 1943	15 Sep 1943	20 Jan 1944
Lochy	Hall Russell	23 Feb 1943	30 Oct 1043	8 Feb 1944
Monnow	Chas Hill	28 Jun 1943	4 Dec 1943	11 Mar 1944
Teme	Smith's Dock	25 May 1943	11 Nov 1943	16 Mar 1944
Awe	Fleming & Ferguson	27 May 1943	28 Dec 1943	21 Apr 1944
Halladale	A & J Inglis	25 Jun 1943	28 Jan 1944	11 May 1944
Annan	Hall Russell	10 Jun 1943	29 Dec 1943	29 Jun 1944
Ribble	Blyth Dry Docks	31 Dec 1942	10 Nov 1943	4 Aug 1944

Castle Class

Ship	Firm	Laid Down	Launched	Completed
1942 Programme				
Hadleigh Castle	Smith's Dock	4 Aug 1943	21 Jun 1943	18 Sep 1943
Kenilworth Castle	Smith's Dock	7 May 1943	17 Aug 1943	22 Nov 1943
Bamborough Castle	John Lewis	1 Jul 1943	11 Jan 1944	30 May 1944
Allington Castle	Fleming & Ferguson	22 Jul 1943	29 Feb 1944	19 Jun 1944
Pembroke Castle	Fleming & Ferguson	3 Jun 1943	12 Feb 1944	17 Jul 1944
Lancaster Castle	Fleming & Ferguson	10 Sep 1943	14 Apr 1944	15 Sep 1944
Norham Castle	A & J Inglis	27 Aug 1943	12 Apr 1944	20 Sep 1944
Caistor Castle	John Lewis	26 Aug 1943	22 May 1944	29 Sep 1944
Oakham Castle	A & J Inglis	30 Nov 1943	20 Jul 1944	10 Dec 1944
Denbigh Castle	John Lewis	30 Sep 1943	5 Aug 1944	30 Dec 1944
Farnham Castle	John Crown	25 Jun 1943	25 Apr 1944	31 Jan 1945
Hedingham Castle (ex *Gorey Castle*)	John Crown	2 Nov 1943	30 Oct 1944	12 May 1945
1943 Programme				
Portchester Castle	Swan Hunter	17 Mar 1943	21 Jun 1943	8 Nov 1943
Carisbrooke Castle	Caledon S B Co	12 Mar 1943	31 Jul 1943	17 Nov 1943
Berkeley Castle	Barclay Curle	23 Apr 1943	19 Aug 1943	18 Nov 1943
Flint Castle	Henry Robb	20 Apr 1943	1 Sep 1943	31 Dec 1943
Leeds Castle	Wm Pickersgill	22 Apr 1943	12 Oct 1943	15 Feb 1944
Rushen Castle	Swan Hunter	8 Apr 1943	16 Jul 1943	24 Feb 1944
Dumbarton Castle	Caledon S B Co	6 May 1943	28 Sep 1943	25 Feb 1944
Oxford Castle	Harland & Wolff	21 Jun 1943	11 Dec 1943	10 Mar 1944
Guildford Castle	Henry Robb	25 May 1943	13 Nov 1943	11 Mar 1944
Knaresborough Castle	Blyth Dry Dock	22 Apr 1943	28 Sep 1943	5 Apr 1944
Tintagel Castle	Ailsa S B Co	29 Apr 1943	13 Dec 1943	7 Apr 1944

Castle Class (continued)

Ship	Firm	Laid Down	Launched	Completed
1943 Programme (continued)				
Shrewsbury Castle (later *Tunsberg Castle*)	Swan Hunter	6 Feb 1943	16 Aug 1943	29 Apr 1944
Changeville (later *Hedingham Castle*)	Henry Robb	23 Jul 1943	26 Jan 1944	10 May 1944
Sandgate Castle	Smith's Dock	23 Jun 1943	28 Dec 1943	18 May 1944
Hurst Castle	Caledon S B Co	6 Feb 1943	23 Feb 1944	9 Jun 1944
Pevensey Castle	Harland & Wolff	21 Jun 1943	11 Jan 1944	10 Jun 1944
Wolesey Castle	Ailsa S B Co	1 Jun 1943	24 Feb 1944	15 Jun 1944
Launceston Castle	Blyth Dry Dock	27 May 1943	27 Nov 1943	20 Jun 1944
Rising Castle	Harland & Wolff	21 Jun 1943	8 Feb 1944	26 Jun 1944
Tamworth Castle	Smith's Dock	25 Aug 1943	26 Jan 1944	3 Jul 1944
Morpeth Castle	Wm Pickersgill	23 Jun 1943	26 Nov 1943	13 Jul 1944
Sherbourne Castle	Harland & Wolff	21 Jun 1943	24 Feb 1944	14 Jul 1944
Hever Castle	Blyth Dry Dock	29 Jun 1943	24 Feb 1944	15 Aug 1944
Walmer Castle	Smith's Dock	23 Sep 1943	10 Mar 1944	5 Sep 1944
Nunney Castle	Wm Pickersgill	12 Aug 1943	26 Jan 1944	8 Oct 1944
Alnwick Castle	G Brown	12 Jun 1943	23 May 1944	11 Nov 1944
Amberley Castle	S P Austin	31 May 1943	27 Nov 1943	24 Nov 1944

Loch Class

Ship	Firm	Laid Down	Launched	Completed
1942 Programme				
Loch Fada	J Brown	8 Jun 1943	14 Dec 1943	10 Apr 1944
Loch Achanalt	Hy Robb	13 Sep 1943	23 Mar 1944	11 Aug 1944
Loch Eck	Smith's Dock	25 Oct 1943	25 Apr 1944	7 Nov 1944
Loch Boisdale	Blyth Dry Dock	8 Nov 1943	5 Jul 1944	1 Dec 1944
1943 Programme				
Loch Killin	Burntisland S B Co	22 Jun 1943	29 Nov 1943	12 Apr 1944
Loch Dunvegan	Chas Hill	29 Sep 1943	25 Mar 1944	30 Jun 1944
Loch Morlich	Swan Hunter	15 Jul 1943	25 Jan 1944	2 Aug 1944
Loch Alvie	Barclay Curle	31 Aug 1943	14 Apr 1944	21 Aug 1944
Lock Ruthven	Chas Hill	4 Jan 1944	3 Jun 1944	6 Oct 1944
Loch Shin	Swan Hunter	6 Sep 1943	23 Feb 1944	10 Oct 1944
Loch Insh	Hy Robb	17 Nov 1943	10 May 1944	20 Oct 1944
Loch Craggie	Harland & Wolff	28 Dec 1943	23 May 1944	23 Oct 1944
Loch Fyne	Burntisland S B Co	8 Dec 1943	24 May 1944	9 Nov 1944
Loch Lomond	Caledon S B Co	7 Dec 1943	19 Jun 1944	16 nov 1944
Loch Gorm	Harland & Wolff	28 Dec 1943	8 Jun 1944	18 Dec 1944
Loch Scavaig	Chas Hill	31 Mar 1944	9 Sep 1944	22 Dec 1944
Loch Katrine	Hy Robb	31 Dec 1943	21 Aug 1944	29 Dec 1944
Loch Quoich	Blyth Dry Dock	3 Dec 1943	2 Sep 1944	11 Jan 1945
Lock Achray	Smiths's Dock	13 Dec 1943	7 Jul 1944	1 Feb 1945
Loch Tarbert	Ailsa S B Co	30 Nov 1943	19 Oct 1944	22 Feb 1945
Lock Glendhu	Burntisland S B Co	29 May 1944	18 Oct 1944	23 Feb 1945
Loch More	Caledon S B Co	16 Mar 1944	3 Oct 1944	24 Feb 1945
Loch Cree	Swan Hunter	18 Oct 1943	19 Jun 1944	8 Mar 1945
Loch Ard	Harland & Wolff	20 Jan 1944	2 Aug 1944	21 May 1945
Loch Tralaig	Caledon S B Co	26 Jun 1944	12 Feb 1945	4 Jul 1945
Loch Killisport	Harland & Wolff	28 Dec 1943	6 Jul 1944	9 Jul 1945
Loch Arkaig	Caledon S B Co	1 Nov 1944	7 Jun 1945	17 Nov 1945
Lock Veyatie	Ailsa S B Co	30 Mar 1944	8 Oct 1945	13 Jul 1946

Bay Class

Ship	Firm	Laid Down	Launched	Completed
1943 Programme				
Widemouth Bay	Harland & Wolff	24 Apr 1944	19 Oct 1944	13 Apr 1945
Veryan Bay	Chas Hill	8 Jun 1944	11 Nov 1944	13 May 1945
St Austell Bay	Harland & Wolff	30 May 1944	18 Nov 1944	29 May 1945
St Brides Bay	Harland & Wolff	30 May 1944	16 Jan 1945	15 Jun 1945
Cardigan Bay	Hy Robb	14 Apr 1944	28 Dec 1944	25 Jun 1945
Bigbury Bay	Hall Russell	30 May 1944	16 Nov 1944	10 Jul 1945

Bay Class (continued)

Ship	Firm	Laid Down	Launched	Completed
1943 Programme (continued)				
Whitesand Bay	Harland & Wolff	8 Aug 1944	16 Dec 1944	30 Jul 1945
Start Bay	Harland & Wolff	31 Aug 1944	15 Feb 1945	6 Sep 1945
Burghead Bay	Chas Hill	21 Sep 1944	3 Mar 1945	20 Sep 1945
Carnarvon Bay	Hy Robb	8 Jun 1944	15 Mar 1945	20 Sep 1945
Tremadoc Bay	Harland & Wolff	31 Aug 1944	29 Mar 1945	11 Oct 1945
Cawsand Bay	Blyth Dry Docks	24 Apr 1944	26 Feb 1945	13 Nov 1945
Enard Bay	Smith's Dock	27 May 1944	31 Oct 1944	4 Jan 1946
Wigtown Bay	Harland & Wolff	24 Oct 1944	26 Apr 1945	19 Jan 1946
Largo Bay	Wm Pickersgill	8 Feb 1944	3 Oct 1944	26 Jan 1946
Porlock Bay	Chas Hill	22 Nov 1944	14 Jun 1945	8 Mar 1946
Padstow Bay	Hy Robb	25 Sep 1944	24 Aug 1945	11 Mar 1946
Completed as Despatch Vessels				
Gerrans Bay	Smith's Dock	21 Apr 1944	14 Mar 1945	9 Sep 1946
Dundrum Bay	Blyth Dry Dock	28 Jul 1944	10 Jul 1945	24 Oct 1946
Completed as A/A Frigates				
Morecambe Bay	Wm Pickersgill	30 Apr 1944	1 Nov 1944	11 Mar 1944
Mounts Bay	Wm Pickersgill	23 Oct 1944	8 Jun 1945	11 Apr 1949
Completed as Survey Ships				
Herne Bay	Smith's Dock	7 Aug 1944	15 May 1945	14 Jun 1948
Luce Bay	Wm Pickersgill	29 Apr 1944	12 Apr 1945	10 Feb 1949
Thurso Bay	Hall Russell	30 Sep 1944	19 Oct 1945	23 Sep 1949
Pegwell Bay	Wm Pickersgill	30 Nov 1944	24 Sep 1945	20 Jul 1950

CHAPTER 12

Fleet Minesweepers

Editorial Note

All the earlier sloops were designed to sweep moored mines and the Halcyon *class sloops were specifically intended as minesweepers. (Chapter 10). It was realised that a very large number of cheaper ships would be required and the* Bangor *was designed by R Baker[1] as the smallest possible ship for wire sweeping. The additional and later requirements for magnetic and acoustic sweeps, radar and more AA guns made them very cramped and the virtue of the original design has been obscured. It seems that the original intention was for all diesel engined ships but the industry could not produce them in quantity.*

The Algerines *were bigger, more capable and much more demanding in resources. Both classes were designed with bow trim to ensure that if they hit a contact mine it would be well forward.*

On the outbreak of war in 1939, classes of vessels capable of performing the duties of a fleet minesweeper, as then prescribed, were confined to the few remaining coal-fired twin-screw mine-sweepers (known as Smokey Joes) and sloops of the *Bridgewater, Shoreham, Grimsby, Halcyon, Bittern* and *Black Swan* classes, designed and built during the intervening period between the two great wars. Vessels of *Halcyon* class were primarily designed as sloop-minesweepers with a view to rapid production in war, but their general characteristics and dimensions were affected by their dual purpose duties. Although the *Halcyon* class were fitted out with Mk I Oropesa equipment, minesweeping was nevertheless regarded as a subsidiary feature, and there is no record of them being employed on active minesweeping operations.[2] Their wide use as escort vessels led to their minesweeping equipment being removed as other minesweepers became available from new construction.

Bangor Class

In 1938, DNC was instructed to investigate the design of a fleet minesweeper, smaller, simpler, and cheaper than those of *Halcyon* class, but designed solely for minesweeping duties.[3]

The main requirements were for the ship to be fitted for minesweeping duties only and capable of carrying out and searching or clearing sweepings either in the vicinity of fleet bases or elsewhere, home and abroad. The simplest possible design was required so that the vessels would be suitable for rapid production in large numbers in an emergency, cheap to build and economical to man. The complement was to be the lowest necessary for minesweeping, running and maintenance.

The endurance required was to permit of passage to the Far East, ie 3000 miles at 14kts, and the main armament to be a single 4in QF gun with simplest possible control arrangements for defence against a submarine operating on the surface.

[1] (Sir) Rowland Baker's own account of this design, of which he was very proud, is given in D K Brown, *A Century of Naval Construction* (London 1983). See also Brown's article on Baker in *Warship 1995*.

[2] Though the *Halcyon*s were often used for escort work, particularly on the Murmansk run, they also were frequently used as sweepers. See the series of articles by R A Ruegg in *Warships*, World Ship Society (Kendal 1994-95).

[3] It is interesting to note that the diesel vessels came out much smaller with fewer crew.

Blackpool, *a diesel engined Bangor, in June 1942. This was the original design which had to be modified to take various steam plants when it was realised that sufficient diesels could not be made. The Bangors were intended to be the smallest possible wire sweepers and became very crowded when other sweeps, radar and more AA guns were added.*

The designs produced were known as the *Bangor* class minesweepers, and there were two types – I with turbine-driven machinery, and II with diesel-driven machinery. The designs were approved in May 1939 and orders were immediately placed for ten ships. With the outbreak of war it was decided to build more ships of this class and further orders were placed with small shipbuilding firms.

To make full use of the capacities of these small firms and to assist in the rapid production of these ships, further types of machinery were introduced; this necessitated slight modifications to dimensions, lines and internal layouts to suit the particular type to be installed.

The general particulars of each type of vessel are shown in the table below.

Structure

With a view to facilitating construction it was decided, with certain specified reservations, to adopt mercantile practice in regard to details of hull and machinery. The details were drawn up in conjunction with Lloyds Register, under whose oversight the vessels were built in the UK.

Armament of this class was to consist of:

    1-4in QF gun
    1-0.5in multiple machine gun
    4 depth charges in 2 chutes

Early in the war, however, it was decided to increase this armament and the majority of the ships of this class were eventually fitted with:

    1-4in HA
    1-2pdr pom-pom
    2-0.5in twin machine gun and in some cases
        Oerlikons
    40 depth charges with 4 double chutes and 2
        throwers

Machinery

Four types of machinery were fitted in this class of ship, and each type was designed to have maximum efficiency when towing a single Mk I Oropesa sweep and the sweeping speed of 12kts.

(i) *Diesel Machinery* – two diesel engines developing 1000shp on each of two shafts at 360rpm, for towing – 320rpm.

Propeller particulars		
diameter	6ft 7in
pitch	5ft 1in
developed blade area	12.5sq ft

(ii) *Steam turbines* – two oil-fired boilers with turbines developing 1000shp on each of two shafts at rpm360 (320rpm for towing)

Propeller particulars		
diameter	6ft 9in
pitch	5ft 7in
developed blade area	12.5sq ft

	Diesel driven	Steam turbine	Steam fast reciprocating	Steam slow reciprocating
Length Overall	162ft 0in	174ft 0in	174ft 0in	180ft 0in
LBP	153ft 6in	165ft 6in	165ft 6in	171ft 6in
Extreme Breadth	28ft 0in	28ft 6in	28ft 6in	28ft 6in
Depth (moulded) to OD at side	15ft 6in	15ft 6in	15ft 6in	15ft 6in
Mean Draught (deep)	8ft 2in	8ft 9in	8ft 10in	8ft 10½in
Displacements (deep)	578 tons	687 tons	699 tons	725 tons
Speed (deep)	16½kts	16½kts	16½kts	16½kts
Endurance at 10kts (clean bottom & trial conditions)	5900 miles	4000 miles	4000 miles	4000 miles
HP of engines	2000shp	2000shp	2400ihp	2400ihp
Legend of Weights				
Hull	277.5	295	294	300
Machinery	136	144	156	175
Equipment	82	76	77	77
Armament	13	13	13	13
Oil Fuel	62	154	154	154
RF	7.5	5	5	6
Total (Deep)	578 tons	687 tons	699 tons	725 tons

Rhyl, *on 17 May 1942, fitted with slow speed, steam reciprocating engines.*

(iii) *Fast Reciprocating Engines* – two boilers and fast-running reciprocating engines developing 1000shp on each of two shafts at 320rpm (300rpm for towing)

Propeller particulars		
	diameter	6ft 9in
	pitch	5ft 7in
	developed blade area	12.5sq ft

(iv) *Slow Reciprocating Engines* – two slow-running reciprocating engines developing 2400ihp, i.e. 1200 on each shaft at 210rpm (180rpm when towing)

Propeller particulars		
	diameter	8ft 8in
	pitch	9ft 5in
	developed blade area	22sq ft

Electric Generators fitted were:

    2-30kW steam-driven generators
    1-5kW diesel generator

except in the diesel-driven type, which was fitted with:

        2-75kW diesel generators
        1-5kW diesel generator

Stability Particulars (as built):

	Light Condition	Deep Condition
(i) *Diesel-driven type*		
GM	1.39ft	1.38ft (fl)
Max GZ	0.86ft	1.15ft
Angle of Max GZ	40°	42°

(ii) *Turbine type*

GM	1.42ft	1.55ft (fl)
Max GZ	0.65ft	1.0ft
Angle of Max GZ	35°	45°
Range	65°	78°
Displacement	567 tons	758 tons

(iii) *Fast Reciprocating Types*

GM	1.31ft	1.47ft
Max GZ	0.85ft	1.20ft
Angle of Max GZ	38°	46°
Range	71°	83°
Displacement	625 tons	825 tons

(iv) *Slow Reciprocating Types*

GM	1.37ft	1.46ft (fl)
Max GZ	0.8ft	1.1ft
Angle of Max GZ	37°	42°
Range	70°	81°
Displacement	628 tons	827 tons

Strength

Based on detailed calculations of other ships, the longitudinal strengths for diesel type and turbine type were as given below:

	Hogging	Sagging
Diesel type		
Maximum Bending Moment	4280ton ft	3420ton ft
Stress in UD	3.40ton/in	2.33ton/in
Stress in keel	2.01ton/in	1.88ton/in

Turbine type
Maximum Bending

Moment	4200ton ft	4550ton ft
Stress in UD	3.15ton/in	2.90ton/in
Stress in keel	2.00ton/in	2.50ton/in

Increase in Weight

Complement

For diesel-driven type was forty-seven, for the other types of the class fifty-four officers and men.

General

Early war experience and the necessity for making use of as many vessels as possible for escort duties showed that the minimum dimensions imposed in the design of *Bangor*s were a serious detriment to re-introducing features which had been purposely omitted in the interests of simplicity and cheap-ness. The urgent requirement for escort vessels led to the introduction of Asdics, increased DC armament, improved A/A armament, gyro compass and radar equipment, accompanied by large increases in complements; this resulted in congestion and a further reduction in stability. This class, however, successfully operated as escort vessels in all the theatres of war. As Oropesa minesweepers they had a good record, but limitations of space prohibited the introduction of modern minesweeping equipment to deal with the new mining devices employed by the enemy.

A total of forty-five ships of this class were built in this country; others of the class were built in Canada (twelve to UK account) and India. Four were under construction in Hong Kong until seized by the Japanese. In all 109 ships were built to this design. In all cases detailed drawings and specifications were supplied by the Admiralty.

Bangor Class

Ship	Type	Firm	Laid Down	Launched	Completed
1939 Programme					
Bridlington	D	Denny Bros	11 Sep 1939	29 Feb 1940	5 Oct 1940
Bangor	D	Harland Wolff	19 Sep 1939	23 May 1940	4 Nov 1940
Rhyl	SR	Lobnitz	23 Nov 1939	21 Jun 1940	9 Nov 1940
Bridport	D	Denny Bros	11 Sep 1939	29 Feb 1940	28 Nov 1940
Romney	SR	Lobnitz	27 Feb 1940	3 Aug 1940	12 Dec 1940
Blackpool	D	Harland & Wolff	19 Sep 1939	4 Jul 1940	7 Feb 1941
Bude	SR	Lobnitz	2 Apr 1940	4 Sep 1940	12 Feb 1941
Cromer	SR	Lobnitz	16 May 1940	7 Oct 1940	4 Apr 1941
Polruan	T	Ailsa Shipbuilding Co	6 Nov 1939	18 Jul 1940	9 May 1941
Eastbourne	SR	Lobnitz	29 Jun 1940	2 Dec 1940	26 May 1941
Blyth	FR	Blyth Dry Dock Co	11 Jan 1940	2 Sep 1940	17 Jun 1941
Rothesay	T	Hamilton & Co	29 Sep 1939	18 Mar 1941	3 Jul 1941
Felixstowe	SR	Lobnitz	8 Aug 1940	15 Jan 1941	11 Jul 1941
Sidmouth	SR	Henry Robb	11 Jun 1940	15 Mar 1941	4 Aug 1941
Ilfracombe	T	Hamilton & Co	11 Oct 1939	29 Jan 1941	20 Aug 1941
Beaumaris	T	Ailsa Shipbuilding Co	21 Dec 1939	31 Oct 1940	28 Aug 1941
Peterhead	FR	Blyth Dry Dock Co	15 Feb 1940	31 Oct 1940	11 Sep 1941
Fraserburgh	SR	Lobnitz	9 Sep 1940	12 May 1941	23 Sep 1941
Poole	T	Stephen & Son	25 Jul 1940	25 Jun 1941	8 Oct 1941
Whitehaven	T	Philip & Son	24 Jul 1940	29 May 1941	14 Nov 1941
Stornoway	SR	Henry Robb	17 Jul 1940	10 Jun 1941	17 Nov 1941
Rye	T	Ailsa Shipbuilding Co	27 Nov 1939	19 Aug 1940	20 Nov 1941
Tenby	T	Hamilton & Co	29 Sep 1939	10 Sep 1941	8 Dec 1941
Cromarty	T	Blyth Dry Docks	12 Jun 1949	24 Feb 1941	13 Dec 1941
Seaham	SR	Lobnitz	15 Oct 1940	18 Jun 1941	19 Dec 1941
Boston	T	Ailsa Shipbuilding Co	27 Nov 1939	30 Dec 1940	26 Jan 1942
Hythe	T	Ailsa Shipbuilding Co	20 Jul 1940	4 Sep 1941	5 Mar 1942
Dunbar	T	Blyth Dry Dock Co	21 Jun 1940	5 Jun 1941	3 Mar 1942
Worthing	T	Philip & Son	15 Nov 1940	22 Aug 1941	20 Mar 1942
Llandudno	T	William Hamilton	20 Oct 1939	20 Oct 1939	29 Mar 1942
Bootle	T	Ailsa Shipbuilding Co	31 Aug 1940	31 Aug 1940	23 Apr 1942
Ardrosson	T	Blyth Dry Dock Co	6 Sep 1940	6 Sep 1940	21 May 1942
Clacton	T	Ailsa Shipbuilding Co	12 Nov 1940	12 Nov 1940	4 Jun 1942
Lyme Regis	T	Stephen & Son	9 Sep 1941	9 Sep 1941	5 Jun 1942
Dornoch	T	Ailsa Shipbuilding Co	13 Jan 1941	13 Jan 1941	22 Jul 1942
Brixham	T	Blyth Dry Docks	6 Nov 1940	6 Nov 1940	19 Aug 1942

Bangor Class built for RIN

Ship	Type	Firm	Laid Down	Launched	Completed
Orissa	SR	Lobnitz	15 May 1941	20 Nov 1941	14 Mar 1942
Rajputana	SR	Lobnitz	21 Jun 1941	31 Dec 1941	30 Apr 1942
Ronkan	SR	Lobnitz	15 Aug 1941	18 Feb 1942	12 Jun 1942
Khyber	T	William Hamilton	10 Dec 1940	17 Feb 1942	12 Aug 1942
Carnatic	T	William Hamilton	28 Mar 1941	29 Jul 1942	27 Oct 1942
Baluchistan	T	Blyth Dry Dock Co	28 Jul 1941	11 May 1942	28 Oct 1942
Kumaon	T	William Hamilton	12 Dec 1940	2 May 1942	30 Nov 1942
Kathiawar	T	Blyth Dry Dock Co	28 Oct 1941	14 Jul 1942	23 Dec 1942
Rohilkhand	T	William Hamilton	29 Aug 1941	29 Oct 1942	5 Feb 1943

Bangor Class Vessels built in Canada to UK Account

Ship	Type	Firm	Laid Down	Launched	Completed
Mayfield	SR	North Van Ship Repairs	30 Dec 1940	26 May 1941	16 Feb 1942
Fort York	SR	Dufferin SB Co	26 Feb 1941	28 Jun 1941	27 Feb 1942
Canso	SR	North Van Ship Repairs	30 Dec 1940	9 Jun 1941	5 Mar 1942
Tadoussac	SR	Toronto SB Co	16 Apr 1941	2 Aug 1941	18 Mar 1942
Caraquet	SR	North Van Ship Repairs	31 Jan 1941	2 Jun 1941	31 Mar 1942
Wedge Port	SR	Toronto SB Co	26 Apr 1941	18 Aug 1941	21 Apr 1942
Guysborough	SR	North Van Ship Repairs	28 May 1941	21 Jul 1941	22 Apr 1942
Ingonish	SR	North Van Ship Repairs	6 Jun 1941	30 Jul 1941	9 May 1942
Qualicum	SR	Toronto SB Co	7 Apr 1941	3 Sep 1941	13 May 1942
Parrsboro	SR	Dufferin SB Co	19 Mar 1941	12 Jul 1941	27 May 1942
Locke Port	SR	North Van Ship Repairs	17 Jun 1941	22 Aug 1941	27 May 1942
Shippigan	SR	Toronto SB Co	18 Apr 1941	27 Sep 1941	17 Jun 1942

Algerine Class

As a result of the limitations in the general minesweeping capabilities of *Bangor* class, imposed by the minimum dimensions of these vessels, it was decided in September 1940 to build larger minesweepers with better sea-keeping qualities. The general requirements were for a ship capable of being used for sweeping moored, magnetic and acoustic mines, and for general A/S duties, both home and abroad. In particular it was a requirement for the design to have good sea-keeping and manoeuvring qualities and to be capable of sweeping in seas up to Force 5.

A design was rapidly prepared embodying all known minesweeping requirements, and also capable of service as an Escort Vessel if and when required; the name given to ships of this design was *Algerine* class.

A second type of *Algerine* was included in the 1941 programme. The principal dimensions of this type were the same as those of the original design, but the general arrangements and lines were modified slightly to suit reciprocating machinery instead of turbines.

Later a fast reciprocating type of engine was introduced into the vessels built by Lobnitz, Renfrew; they were highly successful.

General Particulars

Length overall	225ft 0in
Length between perps	212ft 6in
Breadth extreme	35ft 6in
Depth moulded (to UD at side)	16ft 0in
Displacement (deep)	1122 tons
	1162 tons (reciprocating type)
Speed (deep)	16½kts
Power	2000shp (2400)ihp reciprocating type)
Endurance at 12kts (clean condition)	6000 miles

Legend of Weights

	Turbine Driven	Reciprocating Type
Hull	532	532
Machinery	154	194
Equipment	129	129
Armament	44	44
Oil Fuel	255	255
RFW	8	8
Total (deep)	1122 tons	1162 tons

Structure

Ship was of mild steel and the structure was kept as simple as possible to facilitate rapid production.

Armament

> 1–4in HA/LA QF gun
> 4–20mm Oerlikons
> 2 Lewis guns
> 80 depth charges, 4 throwers and 2 rails

Minesweeping equipment consisted of Mk I Oropesa sweet outfit, triple-barrelled minesweeping winch and LL sweep equipment with B3 impulse generator set. Ships were also fitted for laying and weighing of dans.

Type 128 Asdics were fitted.

Protection

The only protection provided in this class was in the form of 20lb protective plating fitting around the bridge and wheelhouse – total weight about 8 tons.

Machinery

The first design, the 1940 *Algerine*, was fitted with two oil-fired boilers with turbine engines developing 2000shp, ie 1000shp on each of two shafts, at 275rpm. Sweeping speed was 11½kts at 245rpm.

Propeller particulars	two 3-bladed propellers	
	Diameter	7ft 6in
	Pitch	7ft 0in
	Developed blade area	15.75ft²

The 1941 *Algerines* were fitted with two oil-fired boilers with reciprocating engines developing 1200ihp on each of two shafts at 210rpm.

Sweeping speed was 11½kts at 180rpm.

Propeller particulars	two 3-bladed propellers	
	Diameter	8ft 3in
	Pitch	9ft 6in
	Developed blade area	22ft²

Propeller particulars for the fast reciprocating type, built later, were:

	two 3-bladed propellers	
	Diameter	6ft 9in
	Pitch	6ft 0in
	Developed blade area	12.5ft²

Stability

The stability particulars for typical ships of the class as built were as follows:

	Light Condition	Deep Condition
Turbine Type		
GM	1.78ft	2.45ft (fl)
Max GZ	1.17ft	2.19ft
Angle of Max GZ	42°	48°
Range	74°	90°
Displacement	891 tons	1225 tons
Reciprocating Type (FR & SR)		
GM	2.39ft	2.79ft (fl)
Max GZ	1.47ft	2.44ft
Angle of Max GZ	47°	49°
Range	79.5°	90°
Displacement	901 tons	1235 tons

Flying Fish, *an Algerine class sweeper, built in Canada with reciprocating engines. Much bigger and more capable than the Bangors –* but more demanding on scarce resources.

Mutine, *a turbine engined Algerine.*

Strength

Based on detailed calculations for similar ships the longitudinal strengths for the 1940 design were estimated as being:

	Hogging	Sagging
Maximum Bending Moment	9540ton ft	9880ton ft
Maximum stress in UD	2.98ton/in²	2.71ton/in²
Maximum stress in keel	2.41ton/in²	2.84ton/in²

Cost: Typical Vote 8 cost was £210,000.

General

Vessels of the *Algerine* class operated in all theatres of war as fleet minesweepers and as escort vessels with great success. They were designed with good initial stability and it was found practicable to embody all the up-to-date requirements for this class of vessel as the war progressed. All ships of the class were fitted for service in tropical waters and twelve were specially fitted out for service in Arctic conditions.

A total of 107 *Algerines* were ordered, fifty-one in the UK and fifty-six in Canada; nine others were subsequently cancelled, twelve vessels of this design were also built for the Royal Canadian Navy.

Algerine Class

Ship	Type	Firm	Laid Down	Launched	Completed
1940 Programme					
Algerine	T	Harland & Wolff	15 Mar 1941	22 Dec 1941	23 Mar 1942
Alarm	T	Harland & Wolff	15 Mar 1941	5 Feb 1942	16 May 1942
Albacore	T	Harland & Wolff	24 Jul 1941	2 Apr 1942	16 Jun 1942
Acute	T	Harland & Wolff	24 Jul 1941	14 Apr 1942	30 Jul 1942
Cadmus	T	Harland & Wolff	21 Jul 1941	27 May 1942	9 Sep 1942
Circe	T	Harland & Wolff	21 Jul 1941	27 Jun 1942	16 Oct 1942
Espiegle	T	Harland & Wolff	5 Feb 1942	12 Aug 1942	1 Dec 1942
Fantome	T	Harland & Wolff	5 Feb 1942	22 Sep 1942	22 Jan 1943
Mutine	T	Harland & Wolff	24 Nov 1941	10 Oct 1942	26 Feb 1943
Onyx	T	Harland & Wolff	24 Nov 1941	27 Oct 1942	26 Mar 1943
Loyalty	T	Harland & Wolff	14 Apr 1942	9 Dec 1942	22 Apr 1943
Ready	T	Harland & Wolff	14 Apr 1942	11 Jan 1943	21 May 1943
Rinaldo	T	Harland & Wolff	22 Sep 1942	20 Mar 1943	18 Jun 1943
Rosario	T	Harland & Wolff	22 Sep 1942	3 Apr 1943	9 Jul 1943
Spanker	T	Harland & Wolff	22 Sep 1942	20 Apr 1943	20 Aug 1943
Vestal	T	Harland & Wolff	11 Jan 1943	19 Jun 1943	10 Sep 1943

Ship	Type	Firm	Laid Down	Launched	Completed
1940 Supplementary Programme					
Cockatrice	SR	Fleming & Ferguson	29 Dec 1941	27 Oct 1942	10 Apr 1943
Rattlesnake	FR	Lobnitz	5 Jun 1942	23 Feb 1943	23 Jun 1943
Waterwitch	FR	Lobnitz	15 Aug 1942	22 Apr 1943	6 Aug 1943
1941 Programme					
Fly	SR	Lobnitz	6 Oct 1941	1 Jun 1942	20 Oct 1942
Hound	SR	Lobnitz	2 Dec 1941	29 Jul 1942	11 Dec 1942
Hydra	SR	Lobnitz	31 Jan 1942	29 Sep 1942	12 Feb 1943
Orestes	SR	Lobnitz	27 Mar 1942	25 Nov 1942	10 Apr 1943
Aries	SR	Toronto SB Co	23 Mar 1942	19 Sep 1942	17 Jul 1943
Brave	T	Blyth Dry Docks	23 Apr 1942	4 Feb 1943	2 Aug 1943
Antares	SR	Toronto SB Co	26 Jan 1942	15 Aug 1942	23 Aug 1943
Clinton	SR	Toronto SB Co	7 Apr 1942	5 Oct 1942	25 Aug 1943
Friendship	SR	Toronto SB Co	22 Apr 1942	24 Oct 1942	15 Sep 1943
Gozo	SR	Redfern Constn Co	5 Aug 1942	27 Jan 1943	2 Oct 1943
Pelorus	FR	Lobnitz	8 Oct 1942	18 Jun 1943	7 Oct 1943
Pickle	T	Harland & Wolff	11 Jan 1943	3 Aug 1943	15 Oct 1943
Lightfoot	SR	Redfern Constn Co	18 Aug 1942	14 Nov 1942	10 Oct 1943
Acturus	SR	Redfern Constn Co	21 Feb 1942	31 Aug 1942	23 Oct 1943
Pincher	T	Harland & Wolff	11 Jan 1943	19 Aug 1942	12 Nov 1943
Persian	SR	Redfern Constn Co	8 Oct 1942	22 Feb 1943	12 Nov 1943
Fancy	T	Blyth Dry Docks	22 Jul 1942	5 Apr 1943	21 Nov 1943
Larne	FR	Lobnitz	25 Jan 1943	2 Sep 1943	22 Nov 1943
Postillion	SR	Redfern Constn Co	17 Nov 1942	18 Mar 1943	25 Nov 1943
Plucky	T	Harland & Wolff	20 Apr 1943	29 Sep 1943	10 Dec 1943
Helita	SR	Redfern Constn Co	2 Sep 1942	8 Dec 1942	20 Dec 1943
Recruit	T	Harland & Wolff	20 Apr 1943	26 Oct 1943	14 Jan 1944
Lennox	FR	Lobnitz	3 Mar 1943	15 Oct 1943	18 Jan 1944
Rifleman	T	Harland & Wolff	20 Apr 1943	25 Nov 1943	11 Feb 1944
Octavia	SR	Redfern Constn Co	22 Sep 1942	31 Dec 1943	24 Feb 1944
Truelove	SR	Redfern Constn Co	7 Jan 1943	8 Jul 1943	3 Apr 1944
Welfare	SR	Redfern Constn Co	8 Feb 1943	15 Jul 1943	4 Apr 1944
Mary Rise	SR	Redfern Constn Co	25 Feb 1943	5 Aug 1943	24 Apr 1944
Skipjack	SR	Redfern Constn Co	19 Nov 1942	7 Apr 1943	29 Apr 1944
Providence	SR	Redfern Constn Co	17 Apr 1943	27 Oct 1943	15 May 1944
Regulus	SR	Redfern Constn Co	15 Apr 1943	18 Sep 1943	20 May 1944
Thisbe	SR	Redfern Constn Co	14 Dec 1942	12 Apr 1943	8 Jun 1944
Seabear	SR	Redfern Constn Co	12 Jul 1943	6 Nov 1943	22 Jun 1944
Moon	SR	Redfern Constn Co	23 Mar 1943	2 Sep 1943	7 Jul 1944
Coquette	SR	Redfern Constn Co	9 Aug 1943	24 Nov 1943	13 Jul 1944
Felicity	SR	Redfern Constn Co	22 Sep 1943	19 Jan 1944	10 Aug 1944
Golden Fleece	SR	Redfern Constn Co	25 Oct 1943	29 Feb 1944	29 Aug 1944
Courier	SR	Redfern Constn Co	7 Sep 1943	22 Dec 1943	31 Aug 1944
Serene	SR	Redfern Constn Co	19 Jul 1943	18 Oct 1943	14 Sep 1944
Prompt	SR	Redfern Constn Co	25 Nov 1943	30 Mar 1944	27 Sep 1944
Flying Fish	SR	Redfern Constn Co	30 Oct 1943	16 Feb 1944	14 Oct 1944
Lysander	SR	Port Arthur SB Co	3 Jun 1943	11 Nov 1943	21 Nov 1944
Lioness	SR	Redfern Constn Co	10 Nov 1943	15 Mar 1944	11 Dec 1944
Mariner	SR	Port Arthur SB Co	26 Aug 1943	9 May 1944	23 May 1945
Marmion	SR	Port Arthur SB Co	30 Aug 1943	15 Jun 1944	29 Jun 1945
1942 Programme					
Storm Cloud	FR	Lobnitz	4 May 1943	28 Dec 1943	28 Mar 1944
Sylvia	FR	Lobnitz	5 Jul 1943	28 Feb 1944	17 May 1944
Tanganyika	FR	Lobnitz	20 Sep 1943	12 Apr 1944	7 Jul 1944
Squirrel	T	Harland & Wolff	29 Aug 1943	20 Apr 1944	16 Aug 1944
Rowena	FR	Lobnitz	29 Oct 1943	5 Jun 1944	6 Sep 1944
Chameleon	T	Harland & Wolff	20 Aug 1943	6 May 1944	14 Sep 1944
Cheerful	T	Harland & Wolff	20 Aug 1943	22 May 1944	13 Oct 1944
Hare	T	Harland & Wolff	27 Nov 1943	20 Jun 1944	10 Nov 1944
Wave	FR	Lobnitz	17 Mar 1944	18 Aug 1944	14 Nov 1944
Jewel	T	Harland & Wolff	27 Nov 1943	20 Jul 1944	9 Dec 1944
Liberty	T	Harland & Wolff	27 Nov 1943	22 Aug 1944	18 Jan 1945
Welcome	FR	Lobnitz	3 May 1944	14 Nov 1944	18 Jan 1945

Ship	Type	Firm	Laid Down	Launched	Completed
1943 Programme					
Jaseur	SR	Redfern Constn Co	27 Dec 1943	19 Apr 1944	27 Oct 1944
Maenad	SR	Redfern Constn Co	1 Mar 1944	8 Jun 1944	16 Nov 1944
Laertes	SR	Redfern Constn Co	20 Jan 1944	25 Mar 1944	2 Mar 1945
Mameluke	SR	Redfern Constn Co	16 Mar 1944	19 Jul 1944	19 Mar 1945
Mandate	SR	Redfern Constn Co	1 Apr 1944	9 Aug 1944	23 Mar 1945
Marvel	SR	Redfern Constn Co	19 Apr 1944	30 Aug 1944	2 Apr 1945
Romola	SR	Collingwood Shipyard	16 Mar 1944	21 Nov 1944	3 May 1945
Magicienne	SR	Redfern Constn Co	19 Feb 1944	24 Jun 1944	11 May 1945
Michael	SR	Redfern Constn Co	25 May 1944	20 Sep 1944	21 May 1945
Minstrel	SR	Redfern Constn Co	27 Jun 1944	5 Oct 1944	9 Jun 1945
Bramble	FR	Lobnitz	30 Jun 1944	26 Jan 1945	28 Jun 1945
Myrmidon	SR	Redfern Constn Co	19 Jul 1944	21 Oct 1944	9 Jul 1945
Rosamund	SR	Collingwood Shipyard	26 Apr 1944	20 Dec 1944	16 Jul 1945
Mystic	SR	Redfern Constn Co	9 Aug 1944	11 Nov 1944	2 Aug 1945
Orcadia	SR	Port Arthur SB Co	18 Nov 1943	8 Aug 1944	11 Aug 1945
Nerissa	SR	Redfern Constn Co	30 Aug 1944	25 Nov 1944	28 Aug 1945
Niger	FR	Lobnitz	5 Nov 1944	1 May 1945	21 Sep 2945
Ossary	SR	Port Arthur SB Co	20 Nov 1943	3 Oct 1944	27 Sep 1945
Pluto	SR	Port Arthur SB Co	20 Nov 1943	3 Oct 1944	27 Sep 1945
Polaris	SR	Port Arthur SB Co	15 May 1944	13 Dec 1944	29 Oct 1945
Pyrrhus	SR	Port Arthur SB Co	22 Jun 1944	19 May 1945	31 Oct 1945
Fierce	FR	Lobnitz	26 Nov 1944	11 Sep 1945	28 Nov 1945

CHAPTER 13

Motor Launches, Motor Torpedo Boats, Motor Gun Boats

Editorial Note

The Admiralty has often been criticised for its apparent lack of interest in fast craft but this chapter shows that very large numbers were built to the more successful designs and, also, that many experimental craft were built or purchased to try new ideas, including several before the war – and were almost always unsuccessful. The main successes were the 'B' type ML, the Vosper MTBs, British Power Boat MGBs and the 'D' type MGB/MTB. It should be noted that even the successful designs had many teething troubles, mainly due to the very high loads on small craft moving fast in heavy seas and the lack of suitable engines.

The DNC officer responsible for all these craft was W J (Bill) Holt, a wildly enthusiastic yachtsman, who devoted a rare wartime Christmas leave to a voyage to Iceland in one of his MLs. He was directly responsible for the overall design of the 'B' type and for the HDMLs, the latter being his favourite, and for the hull forms of the 'D's and the big Camper & Nicholson craft. He influenced many of the other designs, particularly the strength of the 71ft6in MGBs.

A surprising number of these craft survive, mainly as houseboats[1] including at least one World War I motor launch and a pair of CMBs. The most extensive account of these craft is in Lambert's two-volume history.[2]

In the early war years there were no suitable engines and, even later, the petrol dependent Packard was far from ideal for such craft. Weapons, too, presented early problems but by the end of the war most operational craft packed a truly impressive punch. The limits lay in the men; however dedicated, the combination of motions – pitch and heave – vibration, noise and exposure would exhaust the toughest and could lead to wrong decision making.[3]

Motor Launches

In the early stages of World War I (1914-18), 600 motor launches were built in America for use in the United Kingdom as anti-submarine launches. They were 80ft in length and similar in form to the sheltered water type of motor cruiser popular in America. A more detailed description is given in *Records of Naval Construction* for 1914-18. They were not well suited to the open water conditions around the coasts of Britain, being very wet in a seaway and were of limited operational value.

For their own services, the Americans developed a more seaworthy type, 110ft in length, known as the sub-chaser, some of which made the passage of the Atlantic on their own keels.

During the period 1918-1938 stray proposals were received from time to time from outside designers for motor launches but no money was applied to building craft of this type.

Experimental Motor Launch *Tarret*
In 1938 Mr Gordon Pratt linked up with Swan Hunters of Wallsend-on-Tyne in the production of a hundred-foot steel all-welded high-speed motor launch named *Tarret*. The launch was entirely experimental, length 110ft, beam 15ft, depth 9ft, with an all-welded hull of 5lb plating. The deck was wood on steel beams.

The form included a flat bottom, an arrangement of two chines and a concave portion of bottom between the chines. One chine was above water and the other below.

The engines were lightweight diesels, Davey Paxman, each 1000bhp. Two engines were fitted and each engine shaft had a hydraulically operated two-speed gear box. The engines were a newly developed design.

Trials carried out during 1940 revealed that the engines needed redesign in some respects. The speed realised was 23½kts instead of the designer's predicted 30kts on 80 tons displacement. The propellers did not give full revolutions, but whether the trouble was due to excessive resistance, overlarge propellers, or lack of power in the engine was never established.

Tarret never became an operational unit and was scrapped soon after being taken over by the Admiralty.

[1] T G Holtham, World Ship Society, *Small Craft Group Journal* (from 1993).

[2] J Lambert and A Ross, *Allied Coastal Forces of World War II*, (Vol I London 1990, Vol II 1993).

[3] D K Brown, 'Fast Warships and their Crews'. *Small Craft Supplement No 6, The Naval Architect* (1984).

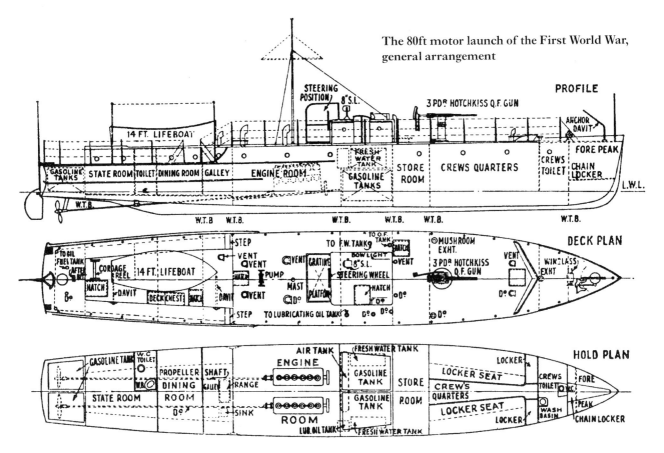

The 80ft motor launch of the First World War,
general arrangement

The Type 'A' Fairmile ML was converted for minelaying duties in 1942 and ML 106 *is seen here carrying six ground mines amidships*

Fairmile 'A' type motor launch

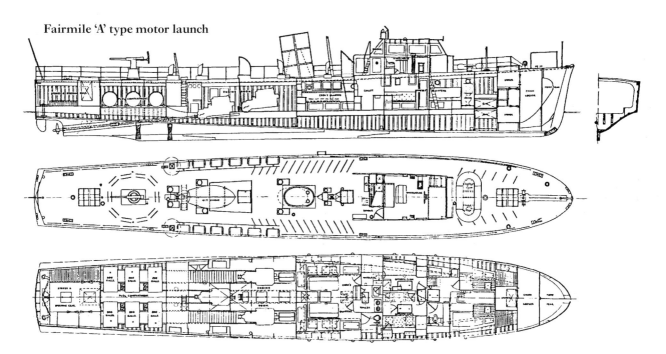

'A' Type Motor Launches (Fairmile)

At the outbreak of war no motor launches were on service but a start had been made on the building of the first 'A' type Fairmile motor launch.

The Fairmile Marine Company played a prominent part in the production of the 'A' and 'B' type motor launches, 'C' type motor gun boats and 'D' type motor torpedo boats and motor gun boats. The shadow organisation[4] which they had built up approached the Admiralty some months before war broke out with a scheme for the mass production of a large motor launch. No armament was indicated. The scheme put forward was that the framing, keels, stem etc, should be prefabricated by sawmills and furniture makers in London and, after prefabrication sent out to selected yacht builders, for assembly of the hulls on the building stocks.

The scheme of prefabrication involved the use of widely spaced transverse frames, sawn to the transverse sectional shape of the motor launch out of large sheets of waterproof bonded plywood. The plywood transverse frames were notched at intervals round their peripheries to receive longitudinal stringers. The keel pieces, stem pieces, stern pieces, deadwoods, bulkheads (sawn from plywood sheets) and transom were all shaped, scarphed etc by the London prefabricators ready for assembly by the yacht yards. At the yacht yards the sections of the keels were brought together on the building blocks and the bulkheads, transverse frames, stem pieces, etc assembled on the keel in their proper relative positions. The longitudinal stringers were then fitted in the notchings of the transverse frames and secured to the frames. This gave a rigid skeleton of the motor launch ready to receive the planking. The timber for planking was sawn to size and planed by the prefabrication firms and delivered to the yacht yards ready for fitting.

After discussion between representatives of Admiralty departments and the Fairmile Marine Co, the Board of Admiralty approved the placing of an order for a motor launch with Fairmile and detailed the armament to be fitted. The Fairmile Marine Co agreed to strengthen the deck of their design and to use double skin planking instead of the single skin planking they had put forward. The first motor launch was laid down at Woodnutts Yard, Bembridge, Isle of Wight and was styled the 'A' type Fairmile motor launch.

General particulars of the 'A' type Fairmile motor launch were as follows (see also Appendix I):

Length overall	110ft
Beam	17ft 5in over rubbers
Draught forward	4ft 6in
Draught aft	6ft 0in

This boat was of hard chine form, with hull planking of African mahogany and ring frames of 1in birch plywood, spaced approximately 4ft 6in apart with four intermediate bent timbers.

As originally designed the craft was engined with three Hall Scott Defender engines, each giving an approximate bhp of 600.

The armament was one 3pdr gun aft, two Lewis guns and twelve depth charges; Asdic gear type 134 was fitted and fuel stowage below deck had been arranged for 1200 galls.

4 See reference in note 2.

Accommodation was provided for two officers, two petty officers and twelve ratings.

On trial the speed was approximately 25kts maximum, and 22kts continuous speed, on a displacement of 50ton.

In all twelve 'A' type motor launches were built and later boats of the type were fitted with two engines only.

The motor launches were converted to minelayers early in their service.

'B' Type Fairmile Motor Launches

In late 1939 it was clear that there was an urgent requirement for a great number of motor launch type of craft. The production of the 'A' type motor launch had served to show that the scheme of prefabrication was sound. On the other hand, the 'A' type fell short of requirements in important particulars - the fuel tank capacity was about half that required, due to the hard chine form the boat was very resistful at cruising speeds, the bow was inclined to throw up light spray and to pound in a seaway and the accommodation was awkward.

A round bilge form which had been designed by DNC and tested at Haslar was known to be better, both in resistance and seakeeping ability. An outline general arrangement had also been drawn out by DNC to meet the known requirements for a motor launch. It was approved to put this design, the 'B' motor launch, into rapid production and entrust the building to the Fairmile organisation.[5] The lines drawing and general arrangement drawing were turned over to Fairmiles and the company arranged the scheme of framing to suit their system of prefabrication.

The original design for a round bilge motor launch had provided for three Hall Scott Defender engines but the limited rate of supply of engines from America made it necessary to fit two engines only and accept the loss of speed involved. The use of two engines instead of three for each boat resulted in 50 per cent increase of the number of boats produced.

To ensure that production was kept going at full strength, the Admiralty instructed the Fairmile Marine Company to name an adequate number of yacht building firms who were willing to associate themselves with the Fairmile scheme for the production of the 'B' motor launches. The Admiralty made arrangements to refrain from placing orders for other types of Admiralty boats with these particular firms. Altogether thirty-eight firms undertook this type of construction during the war.

The assembly of prefabricated hulls is not well suited to the organisation of most well-equipped yacht building firms. These builders are usually equipped with sawmills, joiners' shop, smithery etc, as required for the complete building of high-class wooden craft. If an outside firm undertakes the prefabrication and the yacht yard the assembly, a good proportion of the plant and labour of the yacht yard will be left idle. Full use was made of the building capacity of yacht yards outside the orbit of Fairmiles by placing orders for harbour defence motor launches with them.

[5] Holt's description of the approval process is quoted in D K Brown, *A Century of Naval Construction.* (London 1983). The First Sea Lord concluded a tough inquisition by saying 'I like it, go away and build 200.'

ML 145, *one of the numerous multi-purpose 'B' type motor launches.*

General particulars of the 'B' motor launches are given in Appendix I.

In the early stages of the war there was a great shortage of coastal force craft and the 'B' motor launches were the one type of craft available in any numbers; at the same time the operational position was critical. To make the most of the craft available it was arranged that the 'B' motor launches could be convertible at short notice to one or other of the services of minelayer, motor torpedo boat, anti-submarine boat, anti-invasion boat, anti-E-boat or air sea rescue at 48 hours' notice.

The transformation of the 'B' motor launch to a motor torpedo boat was arranged as follows: the torpedo tubes removed from ex-American *Town* class destroyers were split up into single tube units. This source of supply furnished torpedoes and torpedo tubes sufficient to equip any fifty 'B' motor launches. Suitable stools were designed under the torpedo tubes to attach on the deck of any motor launch fitted with suitable tapping strips. The quick changes of armament were fitted with tap holes to suit the base holding down arrangements of various types of armament, such as depth charges chutes, torpedo tube supports, gun supports, mine rails and so on. The armament was secured to these steel 'tapping strips' by means of tap bolts. To effect the change of armament it was necessary only to take out the tap bolts securing the existing armament, lift out the armament, place the required new type of armament on board and secure to another set of tapping strips.

Particulars of the alternative armaments fitted for the various duties thus made possible are given in Appendix II.

In preparation for carrying out landing operations in conjunction with landing craft, a number of these craft was fitted with additional navigational appliances, namely echo-sounding gear, bottom log and a radar set either 291 or 970. For the radar set a trellis work mast 19ft high was needed.

At the end of 1944 thirteen 'B' motor launches building in the United Kingdom were offered to the War Office for service as hospital carriers. The conversion consisted primarily in altering the after accommodation to a hospital ward and adding a deck house for an additional hospital ward to accommodate twenty stretcher cases.

During 1944, twenty-six 'B' type motor launches were modified for service as motor launches/gunboats in the Far East. These craft were selected for this duty in view of the reduced amount of maintenance required for them, compared with the larger four-engined motor torpedo boats and motor gun boats known as the 'D' type

motor torpedo boats. For this service the depth charge equipment was removed and the armament was arranged as follows:

1-6pdr Mk VI gun forward
1 Oerlikon Mk XIA gun amidships
1-2pdr Mk VIII gun aft
Radar type 268

An internal hydrophone type 615A was fitted. Twenty-two further craft were to be similarly fitted at Alexandria and South Africa.

The 'B' type motor launch was found to be very seaworthy and when fitted with deck tanks, which increased fuel capacity from 2300 gallons to 5000 gallons, it was capable of long ocean passages.

In motor launches and coastal force craft generally a GM of not less than 2ft with a range of stability of 90° or more was aimed at. The increase of armament in the 'B' motor launches reduced the GM to about 1.7ft but the range was not appreciably below 90°. A good range of stability is very necessary in a small boat designed to undertake ocean passages.

In general, the boats were found to be habitable on service, both in the United Kingdom and on tropical stations. For the service in home waters, the boats were fitted with Courtier type stoves for crew space heating and with a coal-fire lagged cooker in the galley.

For tropical service, pressure paraffin cookers were fitted initially; these were found to be unsatisfactory for Naval service. Later the oil cookers were replaced by coal-fired cookers, except in boats manned by the Royal Indian Navy. Small paraffin heaters were fitted for crew space heating when required. A set of awnings was supplied. It was not possible to fit any adequate system of artificial ventilation due to the lack of electric power on board. A paraffin operated Electrolux-type refrigerator was fitted. Boats intended for foreign service were fitted with copper sheathing.

The use of petrol was a source of great danger in these craft, several boats being lost by explosions of petrol vapour; fatal accidents occurred due to the presence of toxic gases from the use of methyl bromide fire extinguisher systems (Essex type). This extinguisher was favoured as it was the one type found to be capable of extinguishing small petrol fires on a low weight of extinguisher. There were some cases of carbon monoxide poisoning due to leakage of exhaust fumes.

In all, 388 'B' motor launches were built at Home and 264 in the Dominions, of which 156 were to Dominion account.

Harbour Defence Motor Launches
A design of small motor launch, for protection of

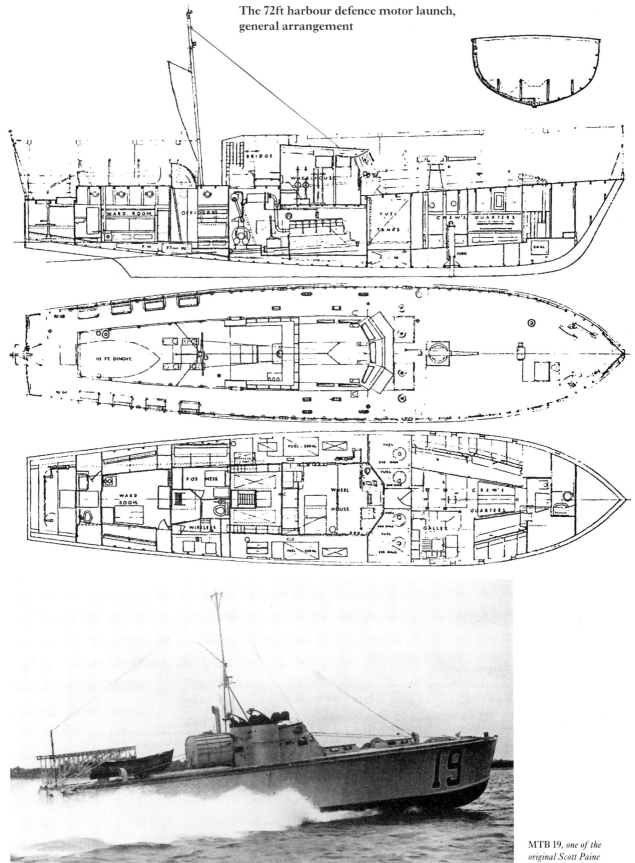

The 72ft harbour defence motor launch, general arrangement

MTB 19, *one of the original Scott Paine designed 60-footers.*

harbours and estuaries against submarines, was prepared by DNC in late 1939. The staff requirements were for a craft not exceeding 72ft in length and capable of being shipped abroad on the deck of a ship.

The harbour defence motor launch was of round bilge form and was provided with two large rudders to ensure adequate turning during an anti-submarine attack.

The hull was of double diagonal planking with bent timber construction over stringers, with reinforcing bent timbers inside the stringers at intervals. Early boats were planked with mahogany. When mahogany became scarce it was necessary to use larch for planking and in some cases this led to leaky boats due to larch being used in partly seasoned condition and the unsuitability of soft timber for double skin work. The use of larch was discontinued immediately the supply position for mahogany improved.

The power units were two diesel engines, manufactured either by Henty and Gardner (150hp each), Glennifer (160hp each) or Thornycroft (130hp each). These engines gave the boats speeds between 11 and 12kts on 54ton displacement.

Initially the craft were armed with one 3pdr gun forward, two Lewis guns on pedestals, eight depth charges and A/S gear type 134. Later a single Oerlikon was fitted on the coach roof aft.

Fuel tanks were provided for 1250 gallons in the main tanks and 300 gallons additional in tanks in the engine room, giving an endurance of about 2000 miles at 10kts.

Accommodation was provided for two officers, two petty officers and eight ratings. The wheelhouse in early boats was fitted with protective plating but in later boats the bridge was armoured instead of the wheelhouse.

Orders for these craft were placed with yacht builders who were in possession of well-equipped yards since, with the exception of fittings such as steering gear, shaft brackets and rudders, the boat builders was required to provide the whole of hull fittings and material. The builders thus equipped were not attracted by the Fairmile Marine Company's scheme. Fittings such as steering gear, shaft brackets and rudders were provided by the Admiralty to each of the builders concerned. Large numbers were built abroad.

The harbour defence motor launches saw service in nearly all operational zones.

The early vessels were shipped to their destinations abroad, but subsequently arrangements were made for the vessels to proceed on their own bottoms, as shipping capacity was no longer available. For service in the Mediterranean and tropical stations all boats were completely sheathed with copper sheathing as protection against the ravages of the teredo worm.

Four boats were fitted for service in Iceland and were provided with additional heating and insulation, and these proceeded to Iceland on their own bottoms. Eight vessels were required for service in the West Indies and to ensure that they could make the long passage from the Cape Verde Islands to Brazil, they were fitted with an outfit of sails.

Later boats were fitted so that they could tow one leg of an Oropesa Mark V equipment for minesweeping in sheltered waters; numbers of the boats were fitted out as navigational leaders for assisting landing craft and were equipped with radar sets, type 291; eighteen boats were fitted with radio counter measures gear, this necessitating the fitting of a generator in the after accommodation.

The harbour defence motor launches were very seaworthy, their engines were most reliable. Their actual service was far beyond anything visualised when the staff requirements were outlined. In a seaway they seemed to possess an unusual harmony of weight, form, buoyancy and shape forward, in relation to pitching and speed, which enabled them to move in rhythm with the seas to make the best of prevailing conditions.[6]

The systems of framing of the hull proved itself resilient and strong.

They had a great record of operational service in Crete, Normandy, Sicily and as convoy escorts off the north and west coasts of Africa.

Total numbers built were 300 at Home, 56 in the Dominions, and 74 under lease-lend.

Motor Torpedo Boats

At the end of the 1914-18 war the British Navy was in possession of three types of motor torpedo craft, styled at that time coastal motor boats. The first type was the 40ft coastal motor boat carrying a single 18in torpedo in a trough aft and fitted with a single aero engine 250hp, giving a speed of 33kts on a displacement of 4¼ tons. The second type was the 55ft coastal motor boat carrying two 18in torpedoes, in trough aft, two engines each 375hp, speed 35-40kts on a displacement of 12 tons. The third type was a 70ft coastal motor boat designed to carry four moored mines,[7] four engines on two shafts, total hp 1300, speed 40kts, displacement 20 tons. These coastal motor boats were all of the single step type; the designs were due to Thornycrofts and were based on the racing motor boat *Miranda IV* which had been successful in fast motor-boat racing during the early 1900s.

[6] This passage well conveys Holt's delight in his success.

[7] Though the 70ft boats could carry moored mines, it is generally believed that their main role was with the magnetic mine, the 'M' Sinker of World War I.

At the end of the war most of the coastal motor boat bases closed down, but the base at Haslar was maintained for a few years. No new boats were added to those left over from the war period.

In the 1920s a number of model experiments on various shapes of planing forms was carried out at Haslar tank. A high speed target on the hydrofoil principle was built in 1924 but no motor torpedo boats of any sort were built for the British Navy until 1935.[8]

In the 1920s and 1930s, Thornycrofts built a large number of coastal motor boats for foreign navies. These coastal motor boats were substantially of similar design to those built during the 1914/18 war, but the boats were given more engine power.

60ft British Power Boat Coastal Motor Boats

In the early 1930s a number of hard chine, fast, semi-planing boats were built by the British Power Boat Co, Vospers, Thornycrofts and J S Whites for the Royal Navy to serve as ships' boats. The idea of fast skimming boats to be carried by was very popular at the time and the tendency was to replace the existing types of round bilge boats carried by ships, with fast motor boats. In 1935, developing the idea of the hard chine fast motor boat, Mr Scott Paine of the British Power Boat Co put forward a design for a small hard chine motor torpedo boat, 60ft in length, and powered with three Napier Lion petrol engines, each having an emergency rating of 600bhp.

Two 18in torpedoes were carried in the engine room on overhead runways and were launched through ports in the transom. Two lattice-work girders, normally carried hinged down on deck, could be hinged about their after ends on the transom to form an extension of the torpedo runways in the engine room. The method of launching the torpedoes was to hinge the lattice girders to their abaft stern position, take the checks off the torpedoes and suddenly accelerate the boat. Due to gravity and inertia effects, this caused the torpedo to run aft along the rails and overboard.

The gun armament consisted of two groups of four .303 machine guns, one group mounted on a slip ring on a hatch at the extreme fore end of the boat and the other mounted on a hatch at the extreme after end of the boat.

The boat was of wood construction, the bottom planking being mahogany worked on the double diagonal system and the side planking single thickness mahogany worked on long diagonals on the seam strip system, the seam strips being fir battens. The transverse frames were mahogany sawn frames with Canada rock elm capping on the inboard edge; the frame spacing was 1ft 6in in early boats, but in later boats the spacing forward was reduced to about 12in to strengthen the hull against pounding action. Inside the double diagonal bottom planking small fore and aft stringer battens were worked spaced about 6in apart and notched into the sawn frames.

The top speed on a service displacement of 20-22 tons was 33kts, although speeds between 35 and 37kts had been attained on a trial displacement of 18 tons.

Originally six of these boats were ordered, the first being delivered in March 1937. Subsequently the total order was increased to nineteen, these comprising three flotillas, which were the only motor torpedo boats in commission at the outbreak of war.

[8] D K Brown, 'Historic hydrofoils of the RN', *Warship* 14 (1980).

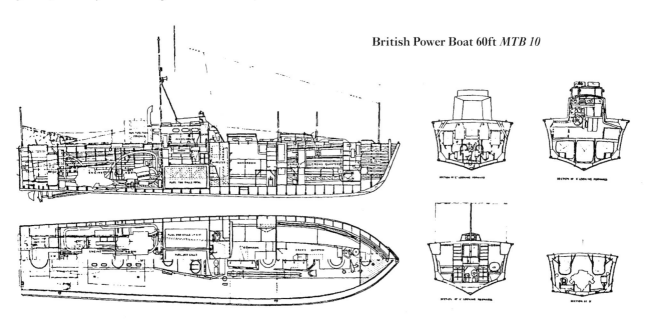

British Power Boat 60ft *MTB 10*

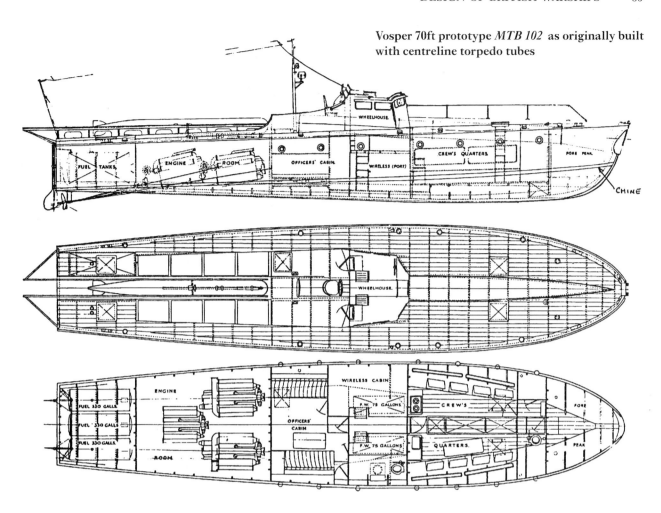

Vosper 70ft prototype _MTB 102_ as originally built with centreline torpedo tubes

The 60ft motor torpedo boats were very good sea boats for their size but, in common with all hard chine boats, it was found that when they were driven into a head sea they pounded very heavily and were liable to suffer frame damage. On fleet manoeuvres in the Mediterraneanwhen there was any weight in the weather it was found that the boats did not make good to windward at sufficient speed to take up position to attack the fleet. Experience with these boats proved that the gunnery arrangements with the slip rings at the forward and after ends of the boats were unacceptable and dangerous to personnel. In later boats the guns were mounted on tubular supports abreast the bridge. The Scott-Paine idea for torpedo launching arrangements was very unsatisfactory. The Birmabright deck plating gave trouble due to corrosion and in some boats was replaced by double diagonal mahogany deck planking. The single thickness side planking was not satisfactory as it was found that the fastenings worked loose.

70ft Vosper Prototype Boat – _MTB 102_
In 1935/6, Vospers, who were among the leading builders of hard chine fast motor boats, embarked on the construction of a motor torpedo boat to their own design, 68ft in length, 32ton load displacement and powered with three Isotta Franschini engines, each having an emergency rating of 1150bhp. The boat also had two Ford V8 engines for silent approach at low speed.

Initially the boat was fitted with a single torpedo tube on the middle line arranged on a declivity firing through the stem of the boat, and the design provided for a second torpedo tube mounted on deck on the middle line firing aft with torpedo head forward. The torpedo arrangements were soon seen to be unsatisfactory and _Vernon_ designed two lightweight loose fit tubes to be fitted on deck, one each side of the bridge, torpedoes being fired forward. The torpedo tubes were inclined to the middle line in plan about 10°. Cordite firing was used. This arrangement of torpedo tubes was the pattern for all subsequent motor torpedo boats.

Oerlikon guns were carried mounted on ring supports, sided and near the middle of length of the boat.

Main details of structure were as follows: bottom planking – three thicknesses of mahogany having a total thickness of 1in; side planking - two thicknesses mahogany worked diagonally, total thickness ¾in; framing - sawn frames of mahogany 2ft 4in spacing with two intermediate bent timbers; deck - double diagonal mahogany.

The Vosper boat was subjected to rough weather trials in competition with the 60ft power boat motor torpedo boat. These and earlier trials proved the necessity for more substantial framing and the number of sawn mahogany transverse frames was doubled. As modified this boat formed the basis of all Vosper design motor torpedo boats put into service during the war.

Soon after commissioning this motor torpedo boat was damaged due to the side planking tearing away from the gunwale when the boat was driven at speed through sharp seas in the Needles Channel. This accident gave clear indication of the very severe stresses which come on the side, deck and gunwale structure when hard chine type boats are driven at speed into head seas.

As initially fitted the boat carried only 1000 gallons of petrol, and accommodation was provided for two officers and eight men.

On trial a maximum speed of 43.7kts was attained, with a continuous rating speed of 35.5kts, displacement 31 tons.

The boat was finally put into service as *Motor Torpedo Boat 102.*[9]

The British Power Boat Co's Private Venture Boat

Early in 1938, Mr Scott-Paine of the British Power Boat Co invited Admiralty Officers to attend the trials of a 70ft motor torpedo boat which had been built by his firm, later named the private venture boat.

The power units were three Rolls Royce Merlin engines which had been marinised - a new departure for the Rolls Royce Company. Each engine gave an output of 1000bhp at 3000rpm emergency rating.

The intention was to carry four 18in torpedoes in swivelling-type light loose-fit torpedo tubes designed by the British Power Boat Co.

The displacement of the boat was kept secret but was known to be about 30 tons in the load condition. In the trial load condition the speed was 44.4kts maximum, with continuous rating speed of 40.5kts.

Comparative moderate weather trials of the PV boat and of one of the 1938 programme Vosper motor torpedo boats were carried out on the same day, in a sea of 4, off St Catherine's Point. During these trials the boats maintained a speed of about 25kts with the sea 4, and about 6 points off the bow. It was found that the Scott-Paine boat was much drier than the Vosper boat but, on the other hand, the Vosper boat appeared to have a more

[9] *MTB 102* is preserved in seagoing condition.

British Power Boat's PV boat

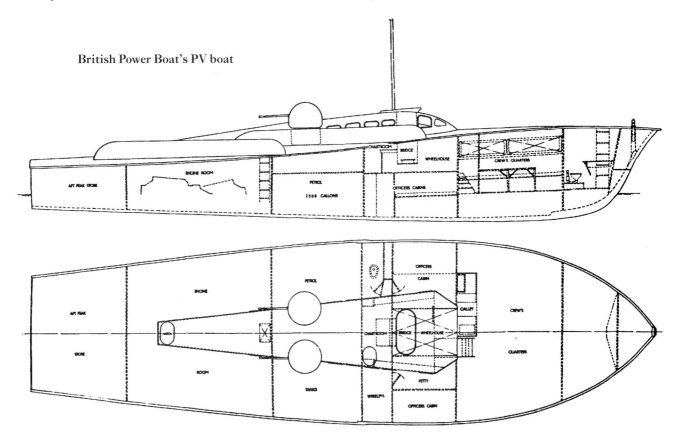

MTB 34 seen on 6 January 1943, was an early Vosper boat of the 1939 programme.

rigid and stronger bottom better able to withstand pounding.

The form of the boat was conventional hard chine but with the maximum beam carried well forward, giving the boat a bulbous bow. The deck had a 'hollow back' profile.

As regards structure, the bottom, sides and deck were of double diagonal planking, the bottom being about ¾in total thickness. Small longitudinal stringer battens were fitted fore and aft inside and adjacent to bottom, sides and deck, secured to main planking and notched into the transverse frames. The frames were of sawn African mahogany spaced about 10in apart in the forward part of the boat, the spacing being increased in engine room. At the keel, chines and gunwale, the sections of frame were connected by waterproof plywood brackets, worked double. The inboard edge of all frames was fitted with Canada Rock Elm tension strips.

On service it was found that the hulls of these boats were not strong and were very liable to damage when driven into head seas at speed. Principal damage was the cracking of the side planking near the middle of length and the tendency of the gunwale to work loose from the frames, deck beams, and side and deck planking, and to develop a pumping action fore and aft.

Similar boats, powered with three Napier Lion 500hp engines, came into service as 70ft motor anti-submarine boats.

The PV boat form was retained in all motor torpedo boats, motor gun boats and motor anti-submarine boats built by the British Power Boat Company during the war, except that in the 71ft 6in motor gun boats (to be described later) the hull structure was greatly strengthened.

70ft Motor Torpedo Boats – 1938 Programme

Under this programme six motor torpedo boats were ordered - four from Vospers and two from Thornycrofts - based generally on the Vosper Prototype *Motor Torpedo Boat 102*, but with considerably increased strength and Thornycrofts were allowed to use their own hull form.

The gun armament consisted of quadruple Vickers .303 guns mounted on scarph rings, the rings being sided en echelon on towers abaft the bridge. Wheelhouses were armoured with ¼in protective plating, and the fuel capacity was 1500 gallons

At full load displacement of 36ton, the boats had a top speed of 42kts emergency rating and a continuous rating speed of 40kts.

1939 Programme

During the early days of the war orders for motor torpedo boats were placed with Vospers, Thornycrofts and Whites, but the E-boats had not begun their activities in the Channel and motor gun boats were not in production. The British Power Boat Company was occupied with motor anti-submarine boats, air-sea rescue boats and motor torpedo boats for foreign navies.

The motor torpedo boats in production were very similar to the Vosper Prototype *Motor Torpedo Boat 102*, and the form did not change much during the war, although the structure was gradually improved.

Development was chequered during this period due to lack of, or shortage of, armament and power units. The supply of torpedo tubes and torpedoes just about met the slow production of motor torpedo boats with little margin.

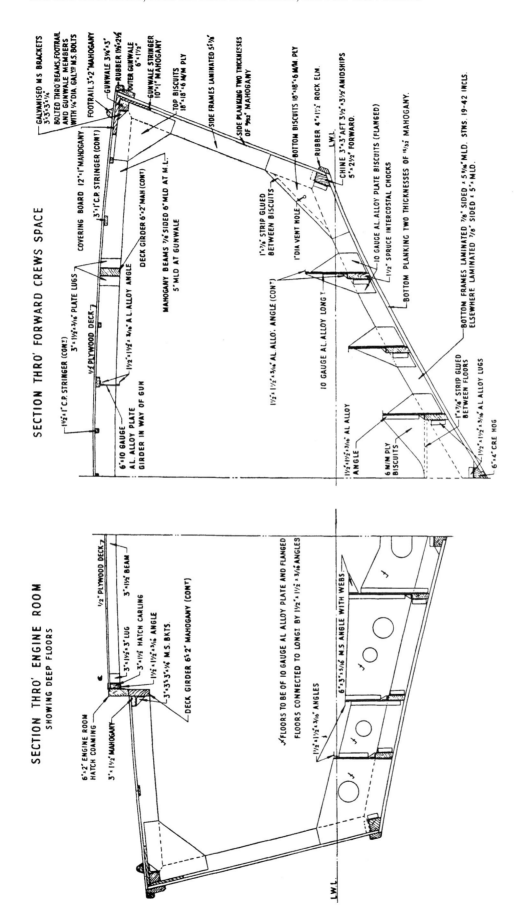

Construction sections of the standard 70ft MTB

No suitable guns were available, consequently the boats were inadequately and unsuitably armed. In the 1939 programme the Vickers .303 guns on scarph rings were replaced by a twin 0.5in Vickers gun on a special hydraulic mounting arranged on the middle line.

When Italy entered the War in 1940, the supply of Isotta Fraschini engines dried up and the Admiralty were faced with the position that no engine really suitable for powering motor torpedo boats was available. It was necessary to accept an engine installation of three Hall Scott Sea Invader engines, each giving a nominal output of about 850bhp. The reduced horsepower available had a disastrous effect on the speed of later boats, which showed a maximum emergency speed of about 29kts and a maximum continuous speed of about 25kts.

Motor torpedo boats *49* to *56*, built by Thornycrofts, were powered with four Thornycroft RY 12 engines, two engines being geared to one shaft. The RY 12 engine had an output of about 550bhp. The gear box fitted in these boats was of the two-speed type and was arranged also to take the input of the Ford V8 auxiliary engines. The gearboxes were to have been of a type produced in Switzerland. Due to entry of Italy into the war and the collapse of France, only one set of gearboxes reached this country and this set was brought over in small pieces by air transport. Arrangements had to be made for the manufacture of gearboxes in England and, in consequence, the Thornycroft motor torpedo boats did not come into service until the middle of 1941.

The Thornycroft boats were heavy and when carrying 2000 gallons of fuel the displacement was about 50 tons. The maximum emergency speed

was about 29kts, the maximum continuous speed about 25½kts. They gave trouble on service due to the frames immediately forward of the tank compartment persistently breaking. It was thought that the breakage of frames was primarily due to the joggling of one of the engine girders in the vicinity of this particular transverse frame.

In the repeat 1939 programme Packard engines became available and saved the situation. Auxiliary engines for slow speed approach were not fitted in this or later classes. The beam of the vessels was increased to give a better engine layout and to accommodate extra fuel, bringing the capacity up to 2600 gallons.

1940-1941 Programme

To obtain uniformity in shaping of docking chocks and thus simplify slipping and docking of motor torpedo boats, it was decided that all motor torpedo boats of the 1940 programme should be of one standard hull form. Arbitrarily it was decided that the Vosper form should be used.

To increase the rate of output of motor torpedo boats it was decided that Vospers should subcontract orders for motor torpedo boats to Harland & Wolff of Belfast, McGruers of Clynder, Macleans of Renfrew and Morgan Giles of Teignmouth. After this programme, however, subcontracting of motor torpedo boats was discontinued, as Vospers was not suitably organised for this arrangement.

The boats had similar hull form to 1939 programme but the fuel capacity was increased to 2700 gallons. Fuel tanks were arranged in two sets of compartments, one set of tanks before the engine room and the other set abaft. The power units were three Packard W8 engines fitted with 1½ - 1 reduction gear.

MTB 238 was a later Vosper boat of the 1941 programme. Note the radar and Oerlikon on the forecastle.

**70ft Vosper *MTB 73* prototype
of the 1940 programme boats**

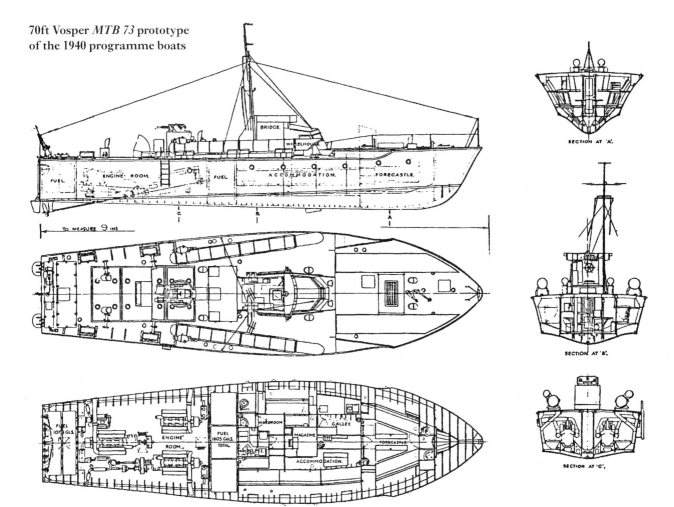

In this programme of building a good deal of trouble was experienced in matching propellers to the engines and the hull. These troubles were due, in the main, to three factors:

(a) attempts to extract the absolute maximum allowable horsepower out of the engines at top speed;

(b) due to changes of ideas during building the design displacement was exceeded;

(c) the torque characteristic of the highly supercharged Packard engines with increasing revolutions had an extremely steep gradient.

The propeller troubles brought to light some interesting facts:

(i) The propeller manufacturer had been allowed wide tolerances. The finish of the blades was comparatively rough and it was quite common to find as much as an inch difference in pitch between individual blades of the same propeller. Often the edges of the propellers were blunt. This attitude towards propeller manufacture resulted in wide differences in the torque characteristics of propellers of nominally similar dimensions. To cure this trouble, it was necessary to insist on much reduced tolerances in manufacture, much higher standard of finish and great insistence was laid on having sharp edges to the blades, to reduce as far as possible the onset of cavitation.

(ii) Another lack of concord between engine and propeller occurred at low revolutions, when the torque output of the engine was insufficient to drive the propellers in a heavily loaded boat. The consequence of the low torque was that the engine was liable to detonate at speeds where there was a hump in the hull resistance characteristic. This detonation on more than one occasion wrecked the engine.[10]

When suitable propellers had been found for the 1940-41 programme boats, the speeds obtained were 38.9kts maximum and 35.2kts maximum continuous rating on full load displacement. The trouble attending the use of highly supercharged engines in motor torpedo boats added strength to the arguments in favour of developing variable

[10] A propeller converts the torque developed by the engines into forward thrust. At low rpm a highly tuned engine cannot produce enough torque to overcome the resistance of the hull. This is a particular problem at the two 'humps' in the resistance curve at $V/\sqrt{L} = 1$ and $V/\sqrt{L} - 1.3$, where V is craft speed in knots and L is length in feet. The cavitation tunnel opened at Haslar in 1941 helped considerably in solving the problem.

MTB 252, a J S White designed boat.

pitch propellers for association with these engines. It was approved to develop variable pitch propellers and the development was entrusted to Messrs Rotol.

There was a good deal of structural trouble in the 1940 motor torpedo boats, partly due to faulty design and partly due to insufficiently careful workmanship. It was found that the deck planking had a tendency to work loose from the gunwale as also did the sheer plank. The scarph of the gunwale was badly placed in some boats and was subject to crepitation. The defects were got over by fitting two continuous pieces of planking about 12in deep by 1¼in thick along the deck edge as a stringer and over the sheer plank to act as an additional sheer plank. In later craft, the thickened planks in the way of the gunwale were arranged inside the ship and were incorporated with the gunwale structure.

Steering

All Vosper motor torpedo boats of earlier programmes and including *Motor Torpedo Boat 73* had been fitted with the hydraulic steering gear supplied by Automotive Products Ltd, and styled the Lockhead Mark VI gear. It was found on service that the hydraulic pipelines were subject to leakage, and furthermore the slightest touch of a bullet resulted in spilt liquid and the steering going out of action. As a secondary steering system a tiller was shipped through the deck on to the top of the rudder stock and steering was then by hand with a rating perched on deck just forward of the transom. This arrangement was not very satisfactory. In the 1940-1941 programme boats a

modified type of power steering styled the Lockhead Mark VI was fitted. In this gear there was a positive mechanical connection between the wheel and the rudder and the hydraulic power was arranged to act as a booster to the manual effort applied by the man at the wheel. This revised steering system had the advantage over the Mark V that, in the event of a breakdown of the hydraulic system, the man at the wheel had full control of the boat but had to exert rather more effort than usual to turn the wheel. The disadvantage of the Mark VI gear was that it was extremely heavy and involved the same excessive maintenance which had been a feature of the Mark V gear.

Protection

Boats of the 1939 and earlier programmes had been fitted with protective plating over the wheelhouse but none around the bridge. Steering wheels had been arranged in the wheelhouse and on the bridge. In the 1940-1941 programme boats the protective plating was fitted around the bridge and not over the wheelhouse, as it had been found on service that the main operational position in motor torpedo boats was the open bridge.

Use of Sterling Admiral Engines

About this time, there was a shortage of Packard engines and in the White built boats it was necessary to accept Sterling Admiral engines. The output of these engines was 1100bhp and they were heavier than the Packard engines, resulting in 2 tons added weight near the stern of the boat. In later boats built by Whites (motor torpedo boats

252 to *257*) the firm were allowed to use a modified form to make the best use of the Sterling Admiral engine. With a reduced fuel allowance of 2300 gallons and modified form, the boats attained speeds of 40.2kts maximum and 33.5kts maximum continuous rating on a displacement of 44 tons. In these boats, Whites were given permission to use slightly reduced planking thickness and slightly reduced framing in comparison with the Vosper boats. These reduced scantlings did not result in trouble in these particular boats, but with similar scantlings used in a later series of boats, building by Whites for the Poles, and with an altered distribution of armament, all boats suffered serious frame breakage on service.

1942 Programme

These boats were generally similar in form and arrangement to the 1940 programme boats but the Packard engines were not fitted with reduction gear.

Initially, the gun armament was one .5in Mark V power turret abaft the bridge. Later on the .5in turret was replaced by an Oerlikon Mark IX twin mounting and, in addition, a single Oerlikon Mark VIIA mounting was fitted on the deck forward of the bridge.

Radar type 286 was fitted but was subsequently replaced by radar type 291 which resulted in a requirement for an additional generator in the engine room.

1943 Programme

These boats were about 1ft longer than the 1942 programme boats, the additional length being added at the after end, to accommodate rudders hung through the bottom instead of being attached to the back of the transom, as in earlier classes of motor torpedo boats. Another alteration in this type of boat was that the weather deck was made continuous from stem to stern and there was no forecastle breakdown such as had been fitted in earlier Vosper boats.

Hand steering only was fitted, power steering being done away with altogether. This saved a good deal of weight, was found entirely satisfactory on service and resulted in reduced maintenance effort.

Originally the armament of these boats was four 18in torpedoes in deck tubes with an Oerlikon Mark IX gun on the middle line forward of the wheelhouse.

When the boats came into service, the idea was raised of sending them to the Far East although they were not eventually sent. They were fitted with paraffin cookers, opening sidelights, paraffin refrigerators, wind sails, awnings and special freshwater tank. These 'tropical' fittings increased the displacement by 2 tons.

1944 Programme

These boats were of similar construction to the 1943 motor torpedo boats, but were fitted with

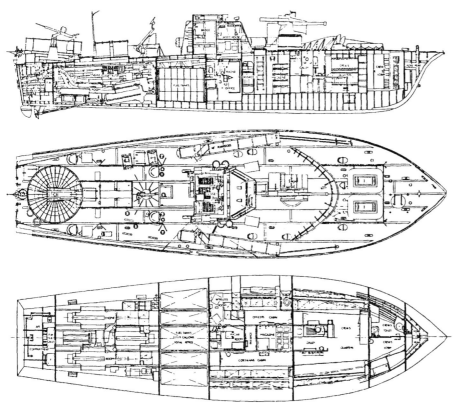

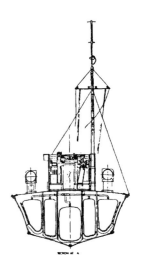

A late-war 71ft 6in British Power Boat MTB with automatic 6pdr forward

11 As 6.

two 18in deck tubes, a 6pdr automatic gun forward of the wheelhouse, an Oerlikon twin Mark IXA on the middle line aft, and radar type 268.

Motor Torpedo Boat 537 was constructed as an experiment in the use of plywood for framing and hull planking to test how far scantlings and weight of hull could be reduced. Considerable use was made of glueing and the lamination of structural units.

Small 45ft Motor Torpedo Boats
An operational service visualised for the 40ft coastal motor boat developed during the 1914–18 war was that the boat should be carried in a cruiser's davits and dropped from davits to make torpedo attacks on enemy shipping at a suitable opportunity.

The idea of small, very high speed motor torpedo boats carried in ships' davits and launched on the high seas to make torpedo attacks has been put forward in one form or another from time to time.

Early in 1939, the Naval Staff stated the requirement for a motor torpedo boat of very high speed, capable of being lifted by a cruiser's aircraft crane and capable of being launched to make torpedo attacks. Tenders were invited from leading British motor torpedo boat builders for a motor torpedo boat meeting the statement of requirements as follows: speed fully loaded, 50kts; displacement in the full load condition to be not in excess of 8 tons, the full load, displacement to include 2 tons of armament weight; length 40–45ft; endurance 100 miles at 2/3 full power.

It was stated that a Rolls Merlin Engine of 1000hp would be supplied by the Admiralty. Crew to be four men, no wireless to be fitted, no guns and no auxiliary engines. Armament to consist of two 18in torpedoes in sided deck loose fit tubes. Admiralty guaranteed the weight of torpedoes and tubes not to exceed 2 tons.

Several promising designs were received from the builders but clear decision on the relative merits of the designs was never obtained as Messrs Thornycrofts, who had developed this type of craft during the last war, informed the Admiralty that they were already building a boat to meet their own ideas, which approximated to the statement of requirements put forward by the Admiralty.

The boat built by Thornycrofts was a single step form; the torpedo was arranged in a swivelling deck tube on the middle line aft with a machine gun superimposed on the tube.

In some respects the design was good. The turning circle was an outstanding improvement on the large diameter turning circle which was a regrettable feature of the old 1914–18 coastal motor boat. The small turning circle was achieved by fitting a rudder forward of the step in addition to the normal rudder at the stern. The forward rudder was linked up with the after rudder and was angled and acted in the reverse direction.

The torpedo arrangements and gun arrangements were a complete failure. The light deck was in no way fitted to withstand the swaying inertia effects of the swivelling deck tube and it was necessary to bowse the tube down with securing wires and bottle screws to keep it quiet when the boat was in motion.

An auxiliary engine Ford V8 with reverse gear furnished the drive at low speed, but this appeared to be unnecessary.

The hull was not well designed and was subject to structural trouble. The boat was purchased by the Admiralty and became motor torpedo boat *105*.

Other hulls building by Thornycroft were also fitted up as small motor torpedo boats and became motor torpedo boats *104*, *106*, *107* and *346*.

The small motor torpedo boats achieved little on operations, however.

Special Experimental Craft

1. Hydrofoils
As an introduction to the small amount of experimental work done on hydrofoil boats in Britain just previous to and during the 1939–45 war, it is appropriate to include a short history of hydrofoil investigations in which the British Navy have been involved up-to-date.

A craft built on the hydrofoil principle, invented by Dr Graham Bell of telephone fame, was brought to the notice of the British Admiralty in 1919; Admiralty Officers visited Canada and witnessed trials of the boat.[11] The main hull was 60ft long and the maximum speed attained was about 55kts with a load of five men, power units being two Liberty engines each of 320bhp, and each driving a four-bladed air propeller. The hydrofoil was of outrigger type, with four sets of foils, one pair amidships, port and starboard under each outrigger; one set on the middle line forward; and one set on the middle line right aft.

In 1921 a tender from Canada for a 67ft hydrofoil boat with a guaranteed speed of 40kts was declined.

In the same year Yarrows, in conjunction with Handley Page, approached the Admiralty with the proposal for a hydrofoil craft, but the proposal was not developed.

The Admiralty embarked on the design of a hydrofoil towed target in 1922–24. This target was not a success. It was found that with a long span of heavy towing wire, at high speed (30kts), in a seaway the target was subject to alternate jumping clean out of the water and then plunging down right under the surface with a periodic motion of about four seconds. The target weighed 5 tons and a towing wire of 40 tons breaking strength was parted at 30kts due to the periodic jumping.

II. White Hydrofoil Boat – Motor Torpedo Boat 101

Early in 1936, Commander Hampden RN, teamed up with Whites of Cowes and in conjunction with them interested the Admiralty in a small 18ft runabout boat which had been fitted with a set of hydrofoils.

The boat was an 18ft dinghy with a flared bow fitted with an improvised step and powered by a single engine of 150bhp. There were three hydrofoils, one fitted each side forward, about one third of the boat's length from the bow, and one set fitted on the middle line aft attached to the back of the transom. The forward sided foils extended well beyond the maximum beam of the wood hull and had a certain amount of dihedral angle. The foils were in the form of ladders supported on single struts at their mid length, five foils to each ladder, gap between foils 3in, upper span 24in, lower span 18in, and chord 4in. The angle of incidence varied from 8° for the top foils to 1° for the bottom foils.

A trial of the 18ft hydrofoil dinghy was carried out at Cowes in May 1936. The boat was driven by Commander Hampden. As far as could be judged from the trial, speed was about 33kts on 130bhp in calm water, at a displacement of 1.34 tons. Whites stated that the boat had attained a speed of 36kts on 145bhp. The boat rose with the hull a clear 6in above the water at full speed. The trials did not serve to demonstrate the ability of the runabout boat in a seaway, but Whites stated that it had been tested in roughish water off Cowes and considered that, making allowance for the size of the boat, behaviour was satisfactory. The forward foils showed a tendency to throw spray over the boat. The turning circle was about 100yds.

At the time a comparison was made between the hydrofoil dinghy and typical fast motor boats. The comparison was as follows:

	Length	Displacement	Speed	HP
Hydrofoil dinghy	18ft	1.34 tons	33kts	130bhp
Fast dinghy	16ft	1.12 tons	24kts	50bhp
Fast motor boat	24½ft	1.78 tons	24kts	100bhp

As a sequel to the trials of the small dinghy, the firm stated that with a 60ft hydrofoil boat powered with a 2500hp engine, it was anticipated that a speed of 70-80kts would be realised.

The firm put forward a design for an aluminium stepped hull 60ft long with hydrofoils, powered with 3000hp, displacement about 20 tons. It appeared that with the hp available and on a 20 tons displacement, a Thornycroft coastal motor boat would have attained a speed of about 60kts.

Later Whites put forward a proposal for one 67ft boat fitted with two power units totalling 3000hp, the total cost being £34,000, and Admiralty made overtures towards placing an order for a boat to the design as an experiment.

Particulars of the design were as follows:

The hull was based on coastal motor boat stepped form, but was built of aluminium alloy. The engine units were to be three Isotta Fraschini engines each of 1000hp.

Ladders of foils were used as in the 18ft boat, but the designers considered it necessary to introduce struts into the ladders of foils for strength purposes with the result that in end-on view the foils resembled an egg crate.

Preliminary trials with the hydrofoil boat showed very unsatisfactory speed results. Later on the propellers were changed and new sets of foils were designed to have sharper leading edge. The number of struts was not reduced. At this stage Commander Hampden parted company with Whites.

Final trials were carried out in May 1940. Particulars of the trial result were as follows:

Displacement	22.8 tons
Max speed	41.35kts

The rise of the boat at full speed was about 16in.

On displacement of 28 tons the maximum speed was 34.23kts with a lift of 7in.

The trials demonstrated that with the increase of speed, severe cavitation set in over the surface of the foils and that after the boat had risen so far on the foils increase of input horsepower or revolutions, did not result in the boat rising any further.

This hydrofoil boat was considered to be unsatisfactory and was not accepted into service.

III. Denny's Semi-Hydrofoil Boat – Motor Torpedo Boat 109

In late 1939 Denny of Dumbarton became interested in a proposal for a semi-hydrofoil boat of very high speed. The design showed an ordinary coastal motor boat type hull fitted with a foil at the after end, so that at high speed the boat would be riding on the forward step, which was part of the planing hull, the after end of the boat being right out of water and supported on the foil.

After some tests on a model of the boat carried out in the Denny experimental tank, a 20ft experimental hydrofoil boat was built by McGruer, Clynder, to Denny's design. The form of the boat was hybrid. The engine was situated at the extreme aft end of the boat and was fitted with a V-drive, the V-drive gearbox being situated in the extreme forward part of the boat. The foil aft was fitted immediately abaft the propeller and a deep dagger-shaped rudder was hung on the transom. Demonstration runs were carried out in the Gareloch, when the boat rose well on the after foil and at full horsepower the measured speed was 23.7kts on a displacement of 19cwt (including two men). The stability at full speed was not satisfactory as the boat was inclined to loll from side to side. It was thought that the lolling might be due to excessive dihedral angle of the after foil (15°).

As a result of the tests on the 20ft boat, Sir Maurice Denny put forward a proposal for a high-speed motor torpedo boat comparable to the stepped *Motor Torpedo Boat 105* (45ft – 50kts Thornycroft design) having an armament of two 18in torpedo tubes, and powered by a Rolls Merlin engine. It was anticipated that the speed would be 55-60kts at full power in calm water with the boat fully loaded. The proposal was approved although some doubt was expressed as to its service value.[12]

Results of trials carried out in September 1944 were:

At 2000rpm maximum continuous rating 32.6kts.
At 2500rpm maximum continuous rating 45.9kts.

The boat was taken to Portland for torpedo firing trials and it was found that satisfactory firing could be obtained at speeds below 25kts, but not above.

The stability of this boat on the turn was found to be unsatisfactory at high speeds and it was necessary to reduce speed before attempting to turn the boat. The trouble was lack of lateral stability.

The end of the war in Europe was in sight before the boat was through her torpedo trials. The lack of lateral stability was considered to render the boat unsafe and non-operational.

IV. Vosper Design Stepped Motor Torpedo Boat 103
In January 1938 Vospers put forward a proposal for a stepped motor torpedo boat. The semi-planing form of *Motor Torpedo Boat 102* had shown good speed but it was thought that with the use of a stepped type of hull it would be possible to achieve a speed about 5kts greater than *Motor Torpedo Boat 102* when carrying the same load,

and using the same horsepower. Vospers claimed that a stepped form would not be 'hard riding'.

Later in the year Vospers constructed a model boat on the stepped principle. The model was fitted with twin engines, was 24ft 6in long and the total displacement was 4038lb. The boat was fitted with two rudders aft and with a single rudder on the middle line forward of the step, the forward rudder acting in the reverse direction to the after rudders.

On 3200rpm the boat attained a speed of 33.6kts. The designers stated that on 162bhp at 3500rpm the speed reached was 36kts. The turning ability of the boat was very good. There was no chance to assess the tendency of the boat to bump in a seaway.

The Admiralty wished the boat to be designed to carry similar armament load to the 1938 motor torpedo boats so Vospers submitted a proposal for a boat 70ft in length and with anticipated full speed between 50 and 52kts in the deep load condition.

To get over the difficulty of the high resistance of the stepped form of hull at low speeds, the designers put forward the idea of the stepped fairing, which they stated would improve the efficiency of the form at low speeds to such an extent as to be comparable with a hard chine boat. They stated that a practical solution of the stepped fairing had been worked out.

Vospers visualised a hull of steel construction. Some details of a composite design were worked out but it was never sufficiently developed to receive consideration.

The original idea had been to fit Rolls Merlin engines, but these were unobtainable and Vospers then came forward with the proposal to use two supercharged 1500hp Isotta Fraschini engines, the superchargers being driven by separate auxiliary engines.

With the advent of Italy into the war the 1500hp Isotta Fraschini engines were not forthcoming and it was found necessary to fit two Packard engines each of 1100hp instead. The lower power available killed all prospect of exceptional speed in this design.

Motor Torpedo Boat 103 was never used on operational service.

V. Fairmile Motor Torpedo Boat 2001
In 1942 the Fairmile Company put forward a proposal for an experimental motor torpedo boat in which the machinery was to consist of four 1500shp Bristol Hercules Mark XVII engines, the form and construction of the boat being similar to the standard 'D' Fairmile. The engines were of the air-cooled variety and the proposal showed an

12 The DNC, Goodall, seems to have taken a special interest in this craft based on the number of entries in his diary.

arrangement of a separate air conduit to each of the engines, the conduit containing an air impeller driven off the main engines shaft. Gearing was arranged between the engines and the propeller, the propeller revolutions being .444 times the engine shaft speed. The propellers were of the Rotol variable pitch type electrically controlled.

It was approved to build one boat of the type as an experiment. An order was placed with Kris Cruisers in October 1942.

A series of unofficial trials was attempted to get over the teething troubles with the new design. Apart from numerous mechanical difficulties, which were rectified one by one, it appeared that the fan impellers on the air intakes absorbed an inordinate proportion of the total bhp developed by the engines.

The Fairmile Company had estimated that the top speed would be of the order of 37kts. Isolated unofficial trials on a displacement of 102 tons gave the following results:

rpm	Mean Speed in Knots	
2000	26.87	
2200	27.95	with boosting
2400	28.60	

Apart from the fact that the boat furnished some information on the novel scheme of using air-cooling instead of the orthodox water cooling of the main engines in a motor torpedo boat, this experiment must be considered to have been a failure.

Motor Gun Boats

In the years before the war, there were no boats of the motor gun boat type in the Royal Navy.

In 1940 German E-boats and R-boats based on Channel ports began their raids on our Channel convoys and commenced minelaying in British coastal waters. These enemy craft were almost immune from attack by torpedo and the provision of very fast small craft armed with light automatic guns became a matter of grave urgency.

The first gun boats were scratched up from all quarters:

1. Ex-70ft motor torpedo boats of the PV boat type intended for the French, which became *Motor Gun Boats 50-67*. Engines three Rolls Royce Merlins, direct drive.

2. Ex-63ft motor torpedo boats intended for Sweden. Engines two Rolls Royce Merlins, each 1000bhp.

3. Later on ex-70ft motor anti-submarine boats re-engined with three Packards (*Motor Gun Boats 6-21*).

The guns fitted were equally miscellaneous and generally not very suitable. Some of the earlier boats were fitted with a Boulton & Paul electrically operated turret taken from aircraft. These were soon rendered useless by damage due to salt water. Others were fitted with a hand-operated 2pdr Mk XIV Rolls gun, which was liable to throw the gunner off his balance in a seaway. Later and luckier boats were fitted with two 0.5in Mark V twin

MGB 8 was a British Power Boat 70ft boat. Note the Rolls gun aft.

power turrets abreast the bridge. Later still the Rolls gun aft was replaced by an Oerlikon Mark IV mounting. Torpedo tubes were not fitted.

The heavy load of guns and ammunition in these improvised motor gun boats caused overloading of the highly supercharged Rolls Merlin engines and there were many cases of serious damage to the engines due to detonation.

The lightly built hulls were not suitable to carry the heavy loads without damage when operating at speed in a seaway. The damage which occurred to this type of hull has been described on pages 85-88.

71ft 6in Motor Gun Boats

All the improvised motor gun boats which have been described showed structural weakness of the hull and the armament was not satisfactory. Apart from the makeshift guns, the boats were lacking in ahead fire. It was decided to build a properly designed motor gun boat. The design was prepared by the British Power Boat Company in conjunction with DNC and the boats were very much stronger structurally than the private venture Scott-Paine boat. The hull from was almost exactly similar to the Scott-Paine private venture boat but the hollow back profile of the deck was eliminated and the deck given a hogged sheer from stem to stern.

Originally the boats were armed with a 2pdr automatic gun, on the middle line forward of the wheelhouse, and a twin Oerlikon gun, power operated, on the middle line aft.

Earlier boats of the class were fitted with streamlined wheelhouse, bridge, chart room and wireless office, on deck, more or less similar to the

MGB 64, *in 1942, was a later 70ft Power Boat craft.*

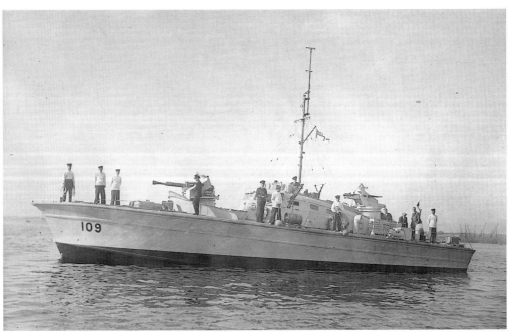

MGB 109 *was a 71ft 6in British Power Boat craft with a much stronger structure developed by Holt.*

old PV boat, but in later boats this streamline deckhouse design was replaced by a bridge somewhat similar to the arrangement in the Vosper type motor torpedo boats.

Later boats were fitted with radar type 286 which was subsequently replaced by radar type 291.

Steering Troubles

In order to improve the silencing of the main engines without fitting heavy silencers, the British Power Boat Company proposed that the engine exhausts should be led out through the boat's bottom immediately in front of the rudders. This arrangement of exhaust was found to give satisfactory silencing and reduction of the running trim with slight increase of the maximum speed. The main drawback to this system of exhaust was that in certain circumstances it was found that putting the wheel hard-over did not effect an alteration of course. After extensive steering trials and experiments, positive action of the rudder was obtained by fitting small cavitation plates acting as a roof over the rudder blade; but a tendency to overbalance, which resulted in great difficulty in bringing the wheel back to amidships from hard-over, remained.

Later in the war it was decided to convert the 71ft 6in motor gun boats into combined motor torpedo boats and motor gun boats, two 18in torpedo tubes being fitted abreast the bridge in addition to the existing gun armament, more or less on the lines of the arrangements in the latest 70ft motor torpedo boats.

Large Type Motor Gun Boats

'C' Fairmiles

When the need for motor gun boats became urgent in 1940, the complete building jigs for the 'A' type Fairmile boats were available and not in use. As an interim measure, to provide gun boats quickly pending the design and production of a true motor gun boat, it was decided to build a number of 'A' type Fairmile boats, exactly similar as regards construction and accommodation to the original 'A' type Fairmile motor launches, but fitted with three supercharged Hall Scott engines each of 900hp to give extra speed. The bridge arrangement was brought into line with motor torpedo boat practice.

The guns fitted were a 2pdr power-operated gun forward, a 2pdr Mark XIV Rolls hand-operated gun aft and two 0.5in Mark V twin power turrets sided and arranged immediately abaft the bridge. Four depth charges were carried.

The fuel capacity was 1800 gallons, giving an endurance of about 500 miles at 10kts. On a displacement of 75 tons, the speed was 26½kts maximum.

These boats put in some good service. One defect, however, was the unduly large turning circle caused by the large deadwood aft, which was a feature of the 'A' type Fairmile design.

From time to time the armament was changed and the final armament was a 2pdr power-operated gun forward, a 2pdr hand-operated pom-pom aft and three twin hand-operated Oerlikons amidships.[13]

[13] No evidence has been found that this armament was actually fitted.

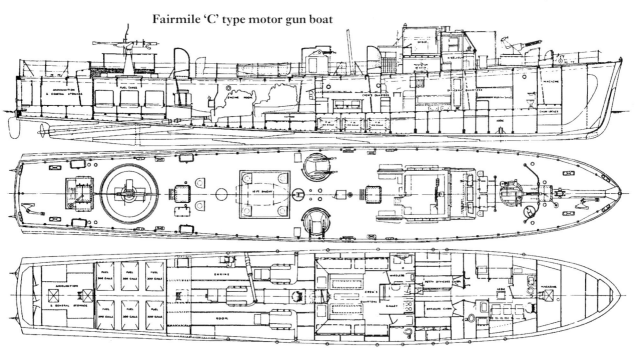

Fairmile 'C' type motor gun boat

14 H A K Lay and L Baker, 'Steam Gunboat Machinery – A Lightweight Steam Plant', *Transactions of the Institution of Naval Architects* 91 (1969).

Steam Gun Boats

In the search for an effective counter to the E-boat in 1940 and in the absence of any suitable light-weight high-power diesel machinery in Great Britain, consideration was given to the production of high-speed gun boats using high-power light-weight steam turbine machinery. The Engineer-in-Chief had stated that steam machinery could be produced developing about 8000hp on an all-in machinery weight of about 50 tons.[14]

The limitations of steam machinery, its excessive weight, high fuel consumption and vulnerability were recognised, but it was imperative to produce boats having highest possible sea-keeping ability in combination with heavy gun armament and high speed to effectively deal with the E-boat and approval was given to build nine boats. Orders were placed, two with Messrs Yarrows of Scotstoun, two with Dennys of Dumbarton, two with Hawthorn Leslie of Hebburn and one with Whites of Cowes. Two placed with Thornycrofts were not started due to enemy action.

The design of this craft was commenced in October 1940 and the first boat commenced trials in November 1941.

The lines drawing and general arrangement drawing were produced by DNC. The lines were for a round bilge boat somewhat similar in form to the round bilge wood motor torpedo boats. The details of the design of structure were the joint effort of DNC and building firms. The weight of hull structure was very light in relation to the overall dimensions of the boat.

The vessel was 135ft in length on the waterline, and load displacement as designed was 165 tons.

The hull was of mild steel, the outer bottom plating varying from 7lb keel and sheer strake to 5lb elsewhere. The deck varied from 7lb at the stringers amidships to 4lb elsewhere. An open bridge was fitted amidships with a chart house on its forward side. Chart house was constructed of wood but the bridge was built up of 30lb non-magnetic protective plating.

The arrangement of machinery was twin screw driven by two steam turbines through reduction gear. The power unit was a single boiler either La Mont or Foster Wheeler designed to give 8000shp to the propellers.

The total fuel stowage was 50 tons of diesel oil, but on ordinary operations 30 tons only were carried.

Accommodation was provided initially for three officers and twenty-four men, but later rose to forty-four as a result of increases in armament.

Armament

The armament carried originally was a 2pdr power-operated gun forward, two twin .5in power-operated turrets abreast the bridge, a 2pdr hand-operated gun aft and arrangements were made for two 21in lightweight torpedo tubes. The latest boat of the series to go on service, built by J S White, carried the following armament:

1 single Oerlikon right forward
1-2pdr automatic on forecastle forward of charthouse
2 single Oerlikons abreast the bridge
2 twin Vickers GO guns on top of torpedo tubes
1-2pdr power-operated gun on engine casing
1-3in QF gun on after deck
1-2pdr hand-operated gun right aft
2-21in torpedo tubes

Grey Fox. The armament of these steam gunboats was frequently changed. In this photo, taken in December 1942, she seems to have a pom-pom in the bows with another forward of the bridge. Twin 0.5in machine guns abreast the bridge, torpedo tubes, Oerlikons behind the funnel and aft with a 3in on the quarterdeck.

Steam gunboat, general arrangement

15 It does not seem that this armament was fitted. By late 1944 several of the SGBs were used in experiments on pressure minesweeping. A number of boats in line abreast would steam fast towards the suspect mine(s), turning off at the last moment. The wave formation which they had generated would continue on the original track, it being hoped that this would activate the pressure firing mechanism. They seem to have had a light magnetic sweep to deal with combination mines.

16 P Scott, *The Battle of the Narrow Seas* (London 1945).

Trials

The first boat to go on trials was *Steam Gun Boat 3*, built by Yarrows and fitted with the La Mont boiler. As a result of several trials, it was found that the La Mont boiler was capable of delivering 7000shp only to the propeller shafts, instead of 8000 provided for in the design. The earliest set of trials also revealed considerable propeller cavitation. By improvements in propeller design and using a Foster Wheeler boiler, which was capable of delivering 8000hp to the propeller shafts, a speed of 35.7kts was attained on a displacement of 170 tons using a shaft horsepower of 8200.

The fuel consumption of these boats was very high, about 3½ton of fuel per hour being used at full speed, also the boilers used half a ton of fuel per hour even when the boat was not running. This high fuel consumption gave the boats very low endurance.

On service it was found that the boiler and its associated pumps, steam pipes, etc, were too vulnerable to machine-gun fire. Actions with E-boats were often fought at almost point-blank range and the steam gun boat was easily stopped by a puncture of any one of the numerous steam pipes, boiler trunks, water tubes, pumps, etc. The vulnerability of the power unit showed signs of exercising a bad effect on the morale of the crews. After a small amount of operational service the drastic step was taken of fitting ¾in thick protective plat-

ing over the whole of the boiler and engine installation. This great weight of armour, together with additions to the armament and complement, resulted in the load displacement of the steam gun boats increasing to 260 tons.

Considerable additions to armament were made during the life of the steam gun boats and the armament finally approved was as follows:

1-6pdr power-operated gun forward
1-6pdr power-operated gun amidships
1-3in hand-operated gun aft
2 twin Oerlikon hand-operated mountings abreast the bridge
2-21in torpedo tubes[15]

Radar type 286 (later replaced by radar 291), echo sounding gear and a pitometer log were also fitted.

The hulls of these vessels proved themselves to be very strong on service and suffered very little structural damage, due to stress of weather or high-speed driving. In action, the steam gun boats were successful against the E-boats and it has since become known that the E-boat commanders had a particular dislike for actions with them.[16]

D Type Fairmile MGBs

The lines of the 'D' type Fairmile boat were developed by DNC late in 1939. The form was developed by grafting a destroyer-type bow on to a fast motor boat type stern in an attempt to

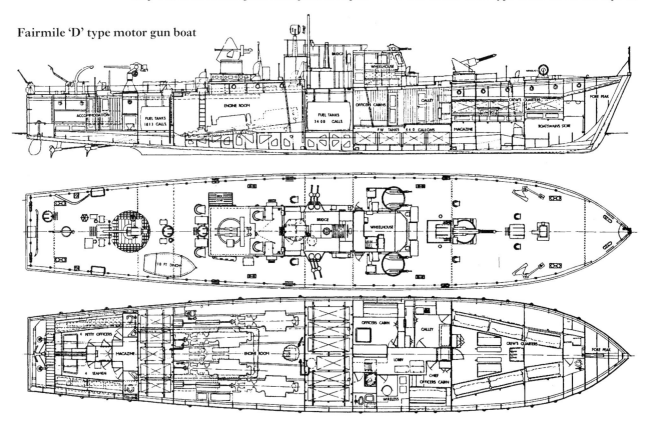

Fairmile 'D' type motor gun boat

obtain less pounding when driven at high speed into head sea and also to produce a dry boat forward by ploughing over the bow wave. In late 1939 this form had been tested at Haslar tank in comparison with a round bilge form, also developed by DNC. It was decided to use the hard chine form for the 'D' Fairmiles as it was intended to fit four engines and propellers in these craft. The rather wide flat transom of the 'D' form lent itself well to the arrangement of four propellers. The design of the 'D' Fairmile was commenced in March 1941 and the first boat ran trials in February 1942.

These craft were powered with four Packard engines, on four separate shafts, giving a total of 5000bhp.

The design provided for a combination of motor torpedo boat and motor gun boat but to limit displacement the torpedo tubes were not fitted in some of the earlier boats and these particular boats were styled motor gun boats.

The motor gun boats carried a 2pdr power-operated gun forward, a twin Oerlikon power-operated gun aft and two twin .5in power-operated turrets abreast the bridge. In addition, twin Vickers GO guns were fitted on the wings of the bridge and a Holman projector was fitted on the coach roof over the engine room.

The fuel tanks had a total capacity of 5000 gallons. The propellers were designed for a load condition with 3000 gallons of petrol on board. The first boats, not fitted with reduction gear, attained a maximum speed of 30kts on a displacement of 91 tons.

With reduction gear fitted the speed was about 32½kts on a load displacement about 98 tons.

As the war progressed there was a requirement for increased gun armament in the 'D's and there came about a succession of rearmaments:

(a) The twin Oerlikon power-operated mounting aft was moved to a position on the coach roof over the engine, and a 6pdr Mark VI hand-operated mounting was fitted aft.

(b) Combined motor torpedo boats/motor gun boats. The armament of the combined boats was as follows:
    1–6pdr power-operated gun forward
    2–.5in power-operated turrets abreast bridge
    4–18in lightweight torpedo tubes
    1 twin Oerlikon hand-operated mounting on the coach roof
    1–6pdr power-operated gun aft

This latest armament brought the displacement of the 'D' Fairmile up to 120 tons and the speed was 29kts when fitted with reduction gear.

The majority of 'D' Fairmiles had type 291 radar but a few of the later boats had type 268.

Structural Defects
The 'D' type Fairmile boats brought to light some of the limitations of the Fairmile method of construction applied to boats over 100ft in length driven at high speeds into ahead seas. It was found that the boats were prone to break their plywood frames in the forward part of the boat, also the keel scarphs were liable to pull and work and the scarphs of the gunwales and the deck stringers in the way of the engine room were liable to crepitation. The main frames were originally 4ft 7in apart with one intermediate frame between each

MGB 502, *an early Fairmile 'D' type. The hull form was one of two developed by Holt, the other being used for the Camper & Nicholson craft.*

pair of main frames. It was found necessary to double the number of plywood frames forward and to fit steel angle bars along the inboard edges of the plywood frames to act as tension strips to prevent fracture. Steel 'fish' plates about 10ft long were fitted over the keel scarphs, which were found subject to movement, to act as a reinforcement. In some boats, margin plates were fitted along the deck, adjacent to the engine casing coaming, to strengthen the deck and compensate for the weakness due to the large deck opening. The strengthened boats were found to be just about adequately strong and kept clear of serious structural troubles.

The collapsible cradles provided around the coast for docking coastal force class boats imposed very severe structural strains on the 'D' type Fairmiles. During the operation of slipping, the forefoot at one stage bears on the foremost transverse member of the cradle with the rest of the boat afloat. In these circumstances, an upward force of about 20ton vertical thrust comes on a small section of the wooden keel of the 'D' type Fairmile. The collapsible slips were not very suitable for docking this class of motor torpedo boats but had to be accepted owing to lack of other more suitable slips.

The 'D' type Fairmiles saw more real service than any other class of motor torpedo boat/motor gun boat and, being available in large numbers, they were of great value to coastal forces. They were mass production vessels using the Fairmile method of production. The need for quick production ruled out the use of the composite system of construction which would have been specified in normal circumstances for a high-speed craft over 100ft in length. The need for quick production also resulted in the use of clumsy and excessively heavy accommodation and fittings generally. This led to excessive displacement.

A total of 288 was built, the time to build being 11 months each.

Motor Gun Boat 501

In late 1939, an outline design and set of lines for a large combined motor torpedo boats and anti-submarine boat was prepared by DNC. The form of the boat was to be round bilge and a model to the lines put forward had already been sent to Haslar for test and was known to be very efficient at speeds of 30-35kts. Board approval was obtained to build a boat to this design and the order was placed with Messrs Camper & Nicholson.

The vessel was 110ft in length, design displacement 95ton with 5000 gallons of fuel, and the power units were three Packard engines, each giving a horsepower of 1250bhp driving the propellers through a 3.1 reduction gear.

MGB 501, the Camper & Nicholson 110ft motor gun boat

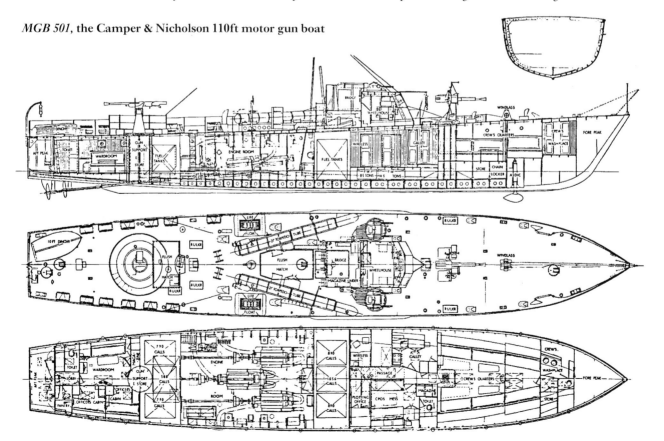

The structure of the boat was as follows;

The main steel frames were web type fitted 3ft 3in to 3ft 5in apart. Intermediate Canadian rock elm frames ¼in x 2in were worked, two between each steel frame. Outside the steel frames, longitudinal stringers 3½in x 2½in spaced about 12½in apart were worked. The planking was double diagonal and was secured to the stringers by screws. The deck was double diagonal mahogany.

The original design provided for a boat which was convertible to a motor torpedo boat, motor gun boat and high-speed anti-submarine boat. Towards the end of the construction it was decided to finish the boat as a motor gun boat and the following armament was fitted:

1-2pdr power-operated mounting forward
1-2pdr hand-operated mounting aft
2 twin .5in power-operated turrets abreast bridge
2-21in torpedoes

On deep displacement of 95 tons the boat attained a speed of 30.3kts.

Motor Gun Boat 501 was followed by *Motor Gun Boats 502* to *509* of similar form but fitted with three Paxman diesel engines. All but two of these craft were completed as cargo carriers, running small valuable cargoes from Sweden, and disguised as far as possible to look like small coasters.

Later craft, *Motor Gun Boats 511* to *518*, were a development of *Motor Gun Boat 501*, but were built to a modified form provided by the DNC. This form had considerable flare forward and a knuckle line running fore and aft about 2ft below the deck edge. The idea of the modified shape forward was to make the fore deck less prone to light spray and thus give the forward guns a better chance of being effective. *Motor Gun Boat 501* was sometime subject to a mist of fine spray when wind and sea were ahead.

The construction was very similar to that adopted for *Motor Gun Boats 501* to *509* but some reduction of scantlings was made.

The arrangement of accommodation was somewhat similar to earlier vessels. A completely enclosed erection covered with protective plating and housing the chart room, radar offices, W/T office was substituted for the wheelhouse. To all intents and purposes this space was a small action information centre. A view plot was fitted to enable the chart to be read from the bridge.

The armament consisted of:

2-6pdr power-operated guns, one forward and one aft
1 twin hand Oerlikon amidships
2 single hand-operated Oerlikon mountings abreast the bridge
4-18in torpedo tubes

Radar type 291 was fitted initially, but was later replaced by type 268.

One of the mercantile conversions of the MGB 502 type. They were used to bring back high-value strategic items like ball-bearings from Sweden and were designed to look as much like small coasters as possible.

Motor Anti-Submarine Boats

It was thought that in event of war some enemy submarines would operate close to the English shores. To cover this possibility, in 1938 a type of fast motor boat fitted with Asdic and armed with a number of depth charges was produced, styled the motor anti-submarine boat. Orders for these boats were placed exclusively with the British Power Boat Company and the boats were built in consultation with the Director of Anti-Submarine Warfare.

Five 60ft motor anti-submarine boats were ordered from the British Power Boat Company in

The original 60ft MA/SB design

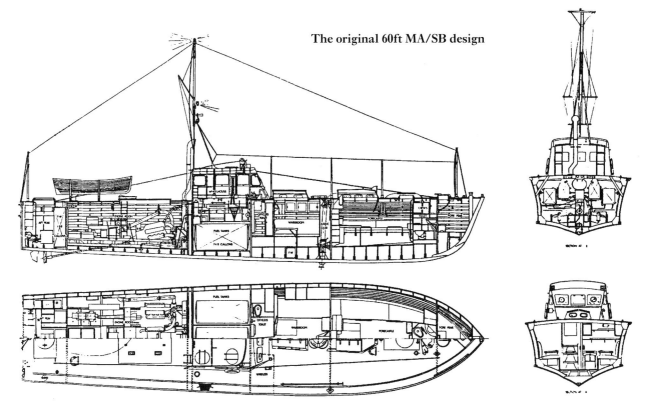

1937. These boats were standard 60ft hulls, exactly similar in form and structure to the 60ft motor torpedo boats built by the company, powered by two Napier Lion engines and having an armament of two twin Lewis guns on scarph ring mountings and eight depth charges carried in chutes.

The Asdic was type 134 and with this Asdic the boat had to be kept head on to the enemy to receive signals. The trial speed was 28½kts.

As a result of experience it was thought that the 60ft motor anti-submarine boats would have limited sea-keeping ability, so the British Power Boat Company put forward a design for a 70ft motor anti-submarine boat, the form and hull structure being exactly similar to the 70ft private venture motor torpedo boat which had been built by the company and powered by three Napier Lion engines.

The boat carried twelve depth charges in chutes, a gun armament of 2-0.5in machine guns on scarph rings and 2156 gallons of petrol.

On trial a maximum speed of 27.8kts was attained and a maximum continuous speed of 25.8kts.

Before *Motor Anti-Submarine Boat 6* had been completed, a further series of boats numbered *7* to *39* was ordered.

The speed obtained by the 70ft *Motor Anti-Submarine Boat 6* was a disappointment, being less than for the 60ft motor anti-submarine boat. In addition, the 70ft boat weighed 34 tons and was,

therefore, more difficult to maintain and slip than the 60ft boat. There had been hopes that in the 70ft boat the A/S gear would give better echoes but trials indicated no improvements. In consequence of the above disappointing performance, the order for 70ft motor anti-submarine boats was reduced and only boats numbers *6* to *21* were completed.

In the meantime, the British Power Boat Company had built for the Union of South Africa a 63ft motor anti-submarine boat which was found to give better Asdic performance. This boat was armed with ten depth charges in chutes, a single twin power-operated machine gun fitted amidships and was powered by three Napier Lion engines.

It was approved to build a number of 63ft motor anti-submarine boats (numbers *22* to *39*) for the Royal Navy. When built they were found to be unsatisfactory from the point of view of anti-submarine and were finally put on air/sea rescue duties. As an experiment, *Motor Anti-Submarine Boat 39* was fitted with two Packard engines and reached a speed on trial of 41kts with a continuous speed of 37.8kts.

Subsequently all the 70ft motor anti-submarine boats were withdrawn from anti-submarine service as being unsatisfactory anti-submarine boats and were converted to motor gun boats. They became *Motor Gun Boats 6* to *21* and were re-engined with Packard engines.

APPENDIX I

General Particulars for Motor Launches

	'A' Type ML	'B' Type ML	HDML
Dimensions			
Length	110ft	112ft	772ft
Beam (max)	17ft 5in	18ft 3in	16ft
Draft (max)	5ft 3in	4ft 11in	4ft 9in
Form	Hard chine	Round bilge	Round bilge
Displacement (with full fuel load)	–	67 tons	54.3 tons
Fuel			
Type	–	–	diesel oil
Normal	1200 gall	2305 gall	1650 gall
Max	–	–	–
Endurance			
Max cont speed (normal fuel)	–	600 N miles at 20kts	–
Cruising speed (full fuel)	–	1500 N miles at 12kts	2000 N miles at 10kts
Machinery			
Make	Hall Scott Defender	Hall Scott Defender	2 diesels
Number of engines	3	2	Gardner 300 or Glennifer 320 or Thornycroft 260
Total bhp	1800	1200	–
Speed			
Maximum	–	20kts	11.5kts
Max continuous	–	17.5kts	10kts
Stability			
GM	1.7ft-2ft	1.7ft-2ft	1.7ft-2ft
Accommodation			
Officers	2	2	2
Men	14	14	8
Total numbers built	12	652	430
Average time to build	6 months	7 months	6-12 months

APPENDIX II

Alternative Arrangements for Type 'B' MLs

Armament	Standard ML A/S	Torpedo Boat	Mine-Laying	Mine-sweeping LL/SA	Oropesa MV*	Rescue MLs	Gun Boats
Forward gun	3pdr Mk V	3pdr Mk I	3pdr Mk I	3pdr Mk I	3pdr Mk V	2pdr Mk XVI	4.5 8cwt Mk II
Amidship gun	Oerlikon Mk IV or VIIA	-	Oerlikon Mk IV or VIIA	Oerlikon Mk IV or VIIA	Oerlikon Mk IV or VIIA	-	Oerlikon Mk XIA
After gun	Oerlikon Mk IIIZ or IX	Oerlikon Mk IIIA	Oerlikon Mk IIIA or IX	Oerlikon Mx IIIA or IX	Oerlikon Mk III or IX	Oerlikon Mk IIIA or IX	2-dr Mk VIII^X
Bridge guns	Sided Twin .303 Vickers GO	Sided Twin .303 Vickers GO	Sided Twin .303 Vickers GO	Sided Twin .303 Vickers GO	Sided Twin .303 Vickers GO	Sided Twin .303 Vickers GO	Sided Twin .303 Vickers GO
Illuminant	2 single 2in rockets	Holman Mk III	-	2 single 2in rockets	2-2 single rockets	-	2 single 2in rockets
'Y' gun	1-Y gun 6-Arbors 6-DCs	-	-	-	1-Y gun 6 Arbors 6-DCs	-	-
DCs in chutes	14 DCs	2 DCs	-	2 DCs	6 DCs	6 DCs	2 DCs
CSA	1-Ml type	2 Type B	Mineload 13,000lb	-	1 ML type	-	2-type B
Displacement	87.2 tons	84.3 tons	83.17 tons	86.6 tons	83.14 tons	81.97 tons	85.4 tons

APPENDIX I

General Particulars for MTBs

	60ft MTBs 1-19	Vosper Prototype MTB 102	PV Boat	1938 Prog. MTBs 22, 29 30	1939 Prog. MTBs 31-34	1939 Prog. MTBs 35-40	1939 Prog. MTBs 41-43	1939 Prog. MTBs 44-48	1939 Prog. MTBs 49-56	1940-1 Prog. MTBs 73-91 201-212 222-245	1942 Prog. MTBs 347-362	Small MTB 105	Experimental Craft MTB 101	Experimental Craft MTB 109	Experimental Craft MTB 103
Dimensions (ft-in) Length c.a.	60-4	68-0	70-0	70-3¼	71-0½	71-0½	72-0	72-0	73-9	71-0½	71-0½	45-0	67-4	43-0	70-0
Beam (max.)	13-10	14-9	19-10	16-5	17-1	17-1	17-1	18-2	16-7	19-2	19-5	10-0	14-6	11-0	18-6
Draft (max.)	3-10⅛	4-10	4-5	4-9	4-6⅛	5-0	4-10½	5-1½	5-4	6-0	4-11½	–	–	–	4-10½
Form	Hard Chine	H.C.	H.C.	H.C.	H.C.	H.C.	H.C.	H.C.	H.C.	H.C.	H.C.	Single step			Hard Chine stepped
Displacement (tons) Full Fuel Load	19.93	31.5	31.0	36.0	41.2	40.0	39.5	42.5	48.4	47.0	44.7	9.5	–	9.05	–
Fuel Type	87 Oct	87 Oct	100 Oct	87 Oct	87 Oct	87 Oct	87 Oct	87 Oct	87 Oct	100 Oct	100 Oct	–	87 Oct	–	–
Normal (gallons)	500	1000	1440	1500	2000	1904	1890	2000	1000	2543	2575	200	1175	180	1500
Maximum (gallons)	740 (incl. Deck Tank)	–	–	1850	–	–	–	–	–	–	–	–	–	–	2200
Endurance Max cont speed (normal fuel)	234nm @ 29kts	240nm @ 35kts	420nm @ 40kts	325nm	410nm @ 39.3kts	310nm @ 25.5kts	430nm @ 25kts	356nm @ 23.5kts	160nm @ 25.6kts	375nm @ 35kts	440nm @ 34kts	–	–	–	–
Cruising speed (full fuel)	493nm @ 20kts	340nm @ 17½	900nm @ 22kts	500nm @ 20kts	500nm @ 22kts					400nm @ 20kts	510nm @ 20kts	–	–	–	–
Machinery Make	Napier Lyons	Isotta	Rolls Royce	Isotta	Isotta	Hall Scott	Isotta	Hall Scott	Thorny-croft RY 12	Packard	Packard	Rolls Royce Martin	Isotta	Packard	Packard
No of engines	3	3	3	3	3	3	3	3	4	3	3	1	3	1	2
Total Bhp	1500	3450	3000	3450	3450	2700	2580	2700	2600	3750	3750	1000	3000	1250	2200
Reduction Ratio	1:1	1:1	1:1	1:1	1:1	1:1	1:1	1:1	1:1	3:2	1:1	–	–	–	1:1
Speed (Kts) Maximum	36	43.7	44.4	42.0	42.0	27.0	29.5	28.4	28.9	38.5	38.8	48.3	–	–	–
Max. Continuous	29	35.5	40.5	40.0	39.3	25.5	25.0	23.5	25.6	35.2	34.2	34.2	–	–	–
Stability GM (ft)	3.677 3.18 with Deck tank	–	–	3.5	3.5	3.5	–	–	6.6	–	–	–	–	–	–
Accommodation Officers	1	2	1	2	2	2	2	2	2	2	2	–	1 anticip- ated	–	1 or 2
Men	7	8	10	7	8	8	8	8	8	8	8	4	7	4	8 7

APPENDIX I

General Particulars for MGBs

	1940 MGBs 50-67	1940 MGBs 6-21	MGBs 74-81	SGB	'C' Fairmile	'D' Fairmile Early Type Direct Drive	'D' Fairmile Early Type Geared Drive	'D' Fairmile Later Type Geared Drive	MGB 501	MGB 502-9	MGB 511-518	MA/SB 1-5	MA/SB 22-39
Dimensions (ft-in)													
Length c.a.	70-0	70-0	71-9	145-8	110-0	115-0	115-0	115-0	117-3	117-3	117-0	60-5	63-0
Beam extreme	19-10	19-10	20-7	23-4	17-5	21-3	21-3	21-3	20-4	20-4	22-2½	13-10	16-6
Draft (max.)	5-5	5-5	5-8	5-3	6-3	5-0	5-0	5-2½	5-7	6-1	5-7	3-4	4-3
Form	H.C.	H.C.	H.C.	R.B.	H.C.	H.C.	H.C.	H.C.	Round Bilge	R.B.	R.B.	H.C.	H.C.
Displacement (tons)													
Full speed load	31.4	36.0	46.0	172.0	72.0	98.0	100.0	118.0	88.0	102.0	100.0	18.0	27.6
With full fuel	–	–	–	202.0	–	108.0	110.0	128.0	95.0	109.0	107.0	–	–
Fuel													
Type	100 Oct	100 Oct	100 Oct	Diesel fuel	87 Oct	100 Oct	100 Oct	100 Oct	100 Oct	Diesel fuel	100 Oct	87 Oct	87 Oct
Normal (gallons)	2232	2156	2733	20 tons	1800	3000	3000	3000	3000	3000	3000	740	1083
Maximum (gallons)	–	–	–	50 tons	–	5000	5000	5000	5000	5000	5000	–	–
Endurance													
Max cont speed (normal fuel)	500nm	430nm	475nm	200nm	300nm	320nm	320nm	270nm	395nm	690nm	372nm	400nm @ 22.8kts	390nm @ 23.6kts
Cruising speed (full fuel)	750nm @ 20kts	490nm @ 20kts	550nm @ 20kts	900nm @ 12kts	500nm @ 12kts	1800nm @ 11kts	–	–	2000nm @ 10kts	2000nm @ 9.75kts	2000nm @ 10kts	–	–
Machinery													
Make	Rolls Royce	Packard	Packard	Steam Turbine	Hall Scott	Packard	Packard	Packard	Packard	Paxman Diesel	Packard	Napier	Napier
No of engines	3	3	3	2	3	4	4	4	3	3	3	2	3
Total Bhp	3000	3750	3750	8000	2700	5000	5000	5600	3750	3000	4200	1000	1500
Reduction Ratio	1:1	1:1	1:1	–	2:1	1:1	2:4:1	2:4:1	3:1	2:1	3:1	1:1	1:1
Speed (Kts)													
Maximum	40.6	43.0	39.8	35.0	26.6	31.0	32.8	29.5	30.4	27.2	31.3	28.4	31.6
Max. Continuous	37.4	38.0	35.0	–	23.6	27.5	27.7	24.3	27.3	25.4	26.3	22.8	23.6
Stability													
GM (ft)	6.0	6.8	4.7	4.5	4.0	–	–	3.3	3.0	3.0	3.5	–	4.5
Accommodation													
Officers	2	2	2	2	2	3	3	3	4	4	3	1	2
Men	11	11	12	21	16	20	20	20	22	24	26	7	8
Total Nos Built	42			7	24	288			18			23	
Average time to build	8 months			13 months	6 months	11 months			12-24 months			8 months	

Particulars of Small Craft

	Mk I Rigid Canoe	*Mk I Folding Canoe*	*SN 1*	*SN 6*	*PD 2*	*Mk II 3 Man Canoe*	*15ft Split Dory*	*18ft Motor Dory*	*18ft Dory MkII*	*MFU Kayak*	*12ft Collapsible Boat*	*16ft Dory MkIII*
Principal dimensions	17'-4" (oa) x 2'-9" x 9⅞" (top of deck at side to bottom of planking)	17'-0" x 2'-5" x 9½" (top of gunwale to USK)	14'-3" (oa) x 5'-0" x 2'-0 mld	20' (oa) x 5'-6" x 2'-2½" mld	13'-6" (oa) x 5'-2" (outside of planking) x 2'-1"	17'-4" x 2'-5" x 1'-7" (bottom of runner to top of coaming erected; ditto collapsed 6")	15' x 3'-9¼" (outside of planking) x 1'-7" (bottom of HOC to top of capping)	18' (oa) x 5'-8" (outside of planking) x 2'-4½" (mld)	18' (oa) x 3'-6" (mld) x 2'-3" (to USK)	19' x 2'-4" x 7½" (dk at side to USK)	12' x 4'-9" x 1'-9" (top of gunwale to top of hog)	16' x 5'-3" x 2'-0"
Weight (light)	100lbs approx.	–	456lb	1605lb	551lb	130lb approx	400lb approx	13cwt	5cwt	60lb	2cwt	5cwt
No of men carried	2	2	–	–	3	3	8 (max seated)	6	8	2	6	8
User & function	CCO	CCO	DDOD(I)	DDOD(I)	DDOD(I)	CCO	DDOD(I) Special for passing through a submarine hatch	CCO	COHQ	DDOD(I) & COHQ	DDOD(I) Special for passing through a submarine hatch	CCO
Type of engine Bhp & Rpm	–	–	–	Stuart Turner 7hp at 1450rpm	Stuart Turner 1½hp at 1500rpm	–	Outboard motor 'British Seagull' 3½hp	Austin 3½hp at 1600rpm	Outboard motor 'British Seagull' 1½hp	–	– –	Outboard motor 'British Seagull' 1½hp
Speed	–	–	–	6kts	4½kts	–	4½kts	6kts	5kts	–	–	4 to 5kts
Fuel	–	–	–	Petrol 3 gallons	Petrol 3 gallons	–	Petrol 3½ gallons	Petrol 12 gallons	Petrol carried in cans on board	–	–	Petrol carried in cans on board
Construction	Stringers 1¼" x ⅝" Gunwale 1" x ½" Obechi skin ⅛" Birch Plywood	Frames ¼" Birch Plywood Stringers ⅝" to ¾" dia. Tubular sectional gunwales Ditto skin rubberised fabric	Timbers 9/16" x 7/16" American Elm planking ⅜" Spruce Garboard & Sheerstrake Mahogany. Deck ¼" Plywood	Timbers ¾" x 9/16" American Elm planking ⅜" Spruce Garboard & Sheerstrake Mahogany. Deck ¼" lywood	Timbers ⅝" x 7/16" American Elm planking ⅜" Spruce Garboard & Sheerstrake Mahogany.	Gunwale 1⅛" x 1" Pine Chines 1¼ x ⅝" Spruce Deck ⅛" Plywood Bottom 3/16" Plywood Strakes - Top & bottom 3/16" Plywood skin & Ply rubberised fabric	Bulkheads 6mm Birch Plywood. Timbers 7/16" x 3/16" planking. Mahogany two thicknesses ⅛" each end diagonally	Longitudinals 1½" x ⅝". Two chines each side ¾" x ⅜" and 2¼" x 1" Columbian pine. Skin 8" plywood.	Keel 2¼" x 2". Hog 3½" x ¾". Timbers ½" x ⅜". Gunwale 1½" x ¾". Skin double diagonal mahogany inner ⅛" out ⅛" (planking 1" wide tongue and grooved.	Timbers 7/16" x ⅛" spaced 1¾" and 2½" timbers on bulkheads ?? x ⅜". Skin 3/32" willow.	Keel 1½" x 1¾" American elm. Hog 2" x 1½" American Elm. Gunwale 1¼" x 1¼" American elm. Stringers 1¼" x 1" American elm. Skin 3ply rubberised fabric.	Timbers 1½" x ⅜" at 3' spacing 1 11/16" x 9/16" in way of bulkheads. Planking double diagonal ⅛" thick 1" wide tongued & grooved. Keel 2¾" mld x 2½" sided (laminated). Hog 4" x ⅜".
No of craft built	–								1 only (prototype)	1 only (prototype)	1 only (prototype)	
Builders	Wates Ltd	Airworks General Trading Ltd	Camper & Nicholson	Camper & Nicholson	Camper & Nicholson	Parkstone Joinery Co	Percy See Fareham	Camper & Nicholson Wates Ltd Minter	Buss & Elston	Percy See Fareham	Tyne Folding Boat Co	Charles Aylard & Co, Buss & Elston Ltd
General notes			Design by DDOD(I) & Camper & Nicholson	Design by DDOD(I) & Camper & Nicholson	Design by DDOD(I) & Camper & Nicholson		Port and starboard sides are separate watertight units each fitted with its own middle-line ballast. The two halves are connected together at keel level by special fittings and at thwart level by toggle clips. The boat can be assembled afloat and in the dark as small luminous buttons are fitted to ensure correct registration of the parts.			Cockpit cover and deck portable for about half length of boat, secured by means of special bolts.	Boat when folded capable of passing through 28in dia circle.	

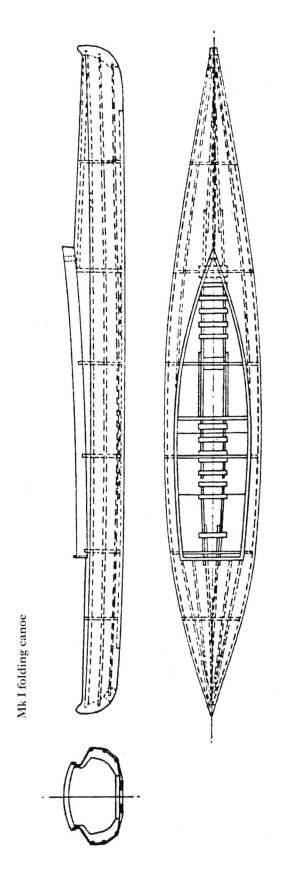

Mk I folding canoe

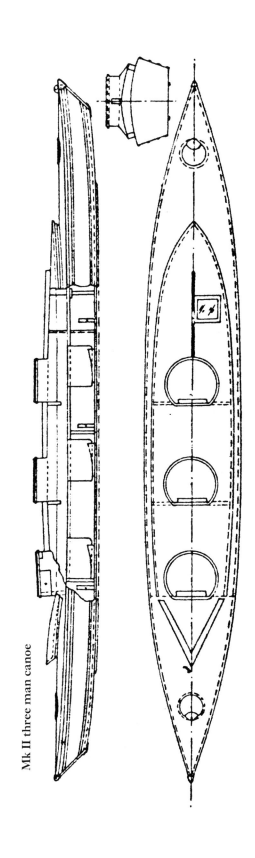

Mk II three man canoe

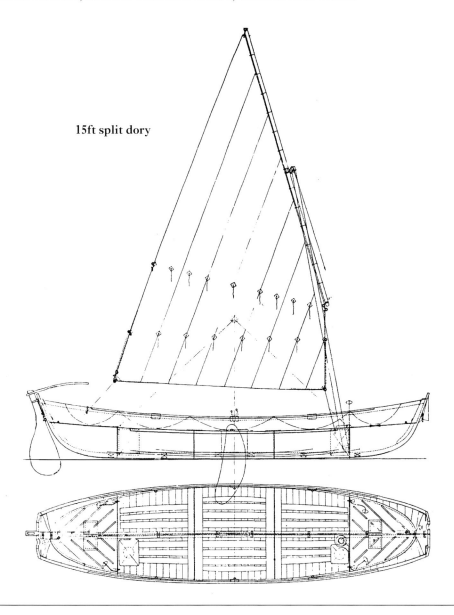

15ft split dory

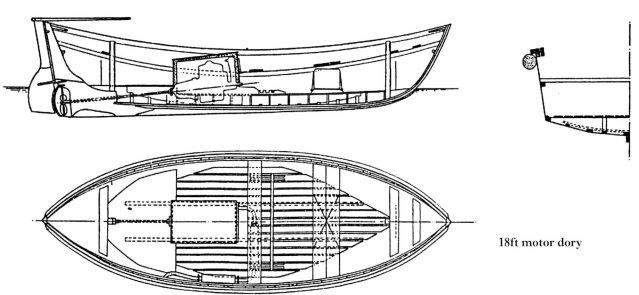

18ft motor dory

CHAPTER 14

Motor Minesweepers

Editorial Note

Though the motor minesweepers are fairly well known, the towing skids which, for a short time were the only counter to the magnetic mine, are less well known.

The 105ft and 126ft motor minesweepers were also designed by W J Holt and, together with the US BYMS formed the basis for his postwar designs of the Ton *class. It is interesting that the original*

wartime requirement was for a 90ft craft, increased at Holt's suggestion to 105ft for seakeeping, and even this length was later found inadequate. This discussion was studied with interest by the editor when developing a small 'utility' minehunter which eventually led to the current Sandown.

Attempts are being made to preserve a 105ft MMS.

Towing Skids and Wooden Minesweepers

Introduction

Soon after the outbreak of war, the Germans put into effect their plan of sowing large numbers of magnetic mines. In some cases, the early efforts to deal with this particular type of mine were in the nature of experiments in many types of sweeps. In other cases the sweep methods were of a temporary nature to tide over the period until minesweepers properly equipped to deal with the new mine could be put into service.

One of these temporary methods was by means of the towing skid. The essence of the towing skid was an electro magnetic coil floated on a raft, the electro magnet being formed of many turns of heavy electric cable wound on a former, the coil being about 16ft internal diameter. The axis of the magnetic coil was vertical. The raft was towed at long span by a special tug fitted with a pulsing

electric generator. An electric cable slung from the towing wire connected the electro magnet on the raft with the pulsing arrangements on the tug. The waxing and waning of the magnetic field due to the electro magnet exploded the mine. The rafts were expendable, but usually it was possible to salve the valuable electric cable composing the coil.

Two types of towing skids were produced. The earlier one was the Mark I towing skid, which was produced in numbers in a great hurry to meet the critical situation which developed following the first sowing of the magnetic mines by the enemy. This was suitable for sweep speeds of 3-5kts. The second type of skid was the Mark II, which was a well-built and well-formed hull capable of sweep speeds up to 25kts.

Mark I Skid

In this form the platform supporting the electro magnet was about 24ft sq and was carried on two

A drifter towing a magnetic minesweeping 'Skid Mark I'. The drifter's name cannot be read with certainty but may be Silver Crest.

Mk II 51ft towing skid

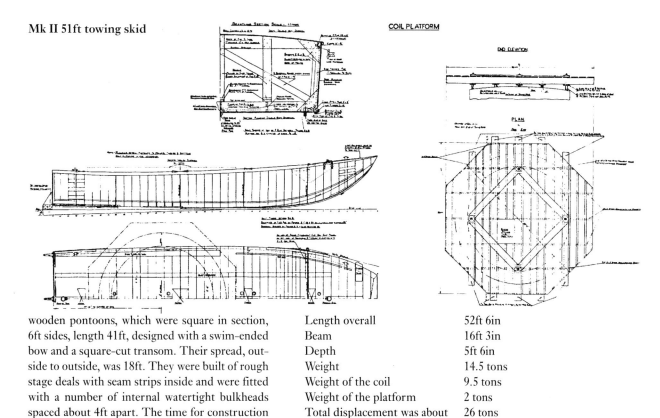

Length overall	52ft 6in
Beam	16ft 3in
Depth	5ft 6in
Weight	14.5 tons
Weight of the coil	9.5 tons
Weight of the platform	2 tons
Total displacement was about	26 tons

wooden pontoons, which were square in section, 6ft sides, length 41ft, designed with a swim-ended bow and a square-cut transom. Their spread, outside to outside, was 18ft. They were built of rough stage deals with seam strips inside and were fitted with a number of internal watertight bulkheads spaced about 4ft apart. The time for construction was about a week to a fortnight.

As has been expected, the pontoons were subject to leakage and a number of barge pumps were supplied to each minesweeping base to enable routine pumping to be carried out to keep the leakage under control. It was found that if one pontoon became leaky the raft was very liable to capsize owing to the great weight of the coil carried on the platform. In later Mark I skids, the compartments were filled with empty herring barrels to keep the skid operational when the pontoons were leaky.

Other particulars of the Mark I skid were as follows:

Displacement of the bare skid without coil and platform	10 tons
Total weight including coil and platform	21.6 tons
Towing wire	2¼ tons FSWR
Length of tow	50 fathoms

Mark II Skid

This skid had the form of a hard chine planing boat with a scow bow. The construction was double diagonal larch or any other clean timber. The bulkheads were also double diagonal. The time of production by a good-class builder was about three weeks.

The skid was very successful from the point of view of design. The main particulars were as follows:

General

The minesweeping skids proved very useful at a critical period. With the advance of the technique in the sweeping of magnetic mines in deep water, skids were soon superseded by trawlers and other minesweepers fitted with the LL sweep. For clearing the magnetic mines dropped in narrow waters the skids continued to be used throughout the war, as it was found that they possessed some advantage in manoeuvrability over the LL for use in these waters.

Wooden Motor Minesweepers

After a period of experiment with various forms of sweep it was established that the LL was the most effective method of clearing up the magnetic mines. The LL minesweepers were used in pairs, each towing one LL cable. A number of trawlers and other small vessels were fitted to take the special pulsing generators, submarine type batteries and the long lengths of buoyant electric cable required by the sweep, but the very large scale on which the mines were sown resulted in an urgent requirement for large numbers of wooden motor minesweepers. The wooden construction was favoured to ensure that the minesweeper itself was, as far as possible, immune from the mine.

In late 1939 the Director of Naval Construction was instructed to prepare a design for a wooden minesweeper about 90ft in length, capable of carrying the LL sweep, and the vessel was to be styled the 'W' class towing vessel. The statement of requirements laid down that the draught should not exceed 8ft, to enable the boat to operate in shallow water, and the construction was to be as robust as possible. The Director of Naval Construction recommended an increase of dimensions and produced a design for a minesweeper of 105ft length between perpendiculars and about 220 tons displacement. The main particulars of this design are given in Appendix I.

The scantlings were more or less in accordance with Lloyd's rules for wooden vessels. The amount of steel and iron used in the construction was kept down to a limit of 50-60 tons including the weight of the engine, which was to be a 500hp diesel engine of stock pattern. This weight of ferrous material used in the construction was considered acceptable from the point of view of immunity from the magnetic mine without resorting to the complication of fitting special degaussing coils. The proposed design was accepted and arrangements were made for production on a large scale and as quickly as possible.

A certain number of motor minesweepers built at Home and in India were of composite construction.

105ft Motor Minesweepers

Production

The production of motor minesweepers was undertaken by a wide variety of boat builders scattered throughout the British Empire. Attempts were made to build minesweepers in places very remote from Britain, eg Singapore, Rangoon, Ceylon. The Far East building was not entirely successful. Hulls on the stocks were captured by the enemy in some of these places. The difficulties attending development of shipbuilding in India were underestimated, which resulted in many uncompleted hulls still on the stocks at the end of the war.

The Home sources of building included fishing-boat builders and yacht yards and saw a most welcome revival of some of the old wood shipbuilding yards. These firms made use of a small nucleus of boat builders (about 5%) and a small army of dilutees, drawn from a number of trades, or coming from no trade at all. One or two firms owed their origin to the sudden spate of building of wooden motor minesweepers.

In the circumstances it was not a matter of surprise that some of the earlier motor minesweepers gave trouble soon after going into service. A statement of some of the troubles experienced is worth putting on record:

1. *Use of Green Timber*
There was no large stock of seasoned timber available and the heavy scantling material could not be artificially seasoned. As time went on and builders received their orders for boats well in advance of starting work on the hull, it was possible to buy large stocks of timber in anticipation and this timber had some chance of slightly drying off before conversion. The use of green timber resulted in a small amount of change of shape as the vessels settled down on

MMS 192 was a 105ft vessel and was a little short for effective open sea work – the editor well remembers helping to haul in the LL sweep in a gregale.

105ft motor minesweeper, general arrangement

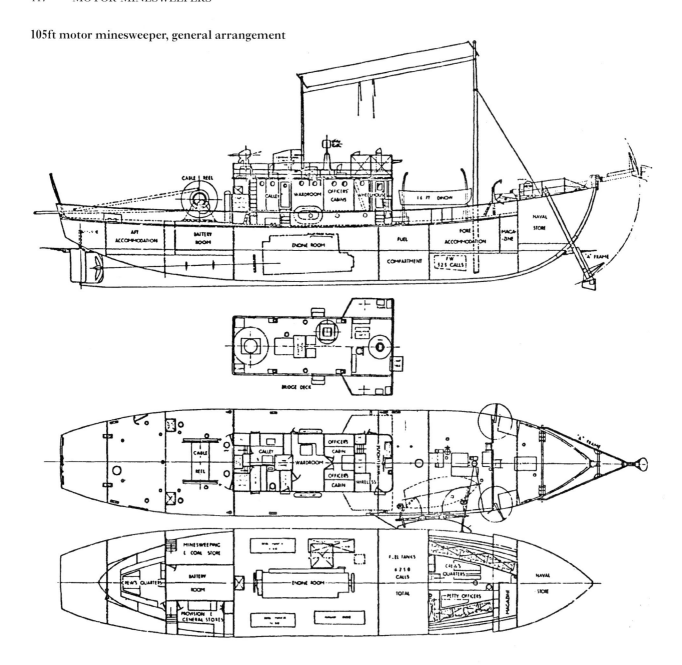

service. Usually the effects of this change of shape 'were not very serious, except that the alignment of the shaft required adjustment from time to time early on in the life of the ship. Another effect of the use of green timber was the rending of the heavy scantling materials, such as heavy beams, carlings, shelves, and so on, as the timber dried out some time after going on service. Usually, the effects were unsightly rather than serious defects of structure. The rending was most marked in those vessels which were sent out to the Mediterranean; after a period of service on this hot station, the heavy scantling material rent as if under the force of a small explosion inside the timber. Steel strapping was generally adopted as the method of repair.

2. *Unsuitable fitting-out berths*
Some of the yards had to make use of fitting-out berths where the hulls grounded at each low water. This was not very objectionable in the case of soft mud berths but, in some cases, in particular Looe, the hulls grounded on hard sand which, owing to the scour of the tides, was by no means level. Hulls fitted out at Looe usually went into service with a keel which was wavy in the vertical plane, due to the keel taking up the form of the sandbank. When the boat went on service, the keel showed a tendency to

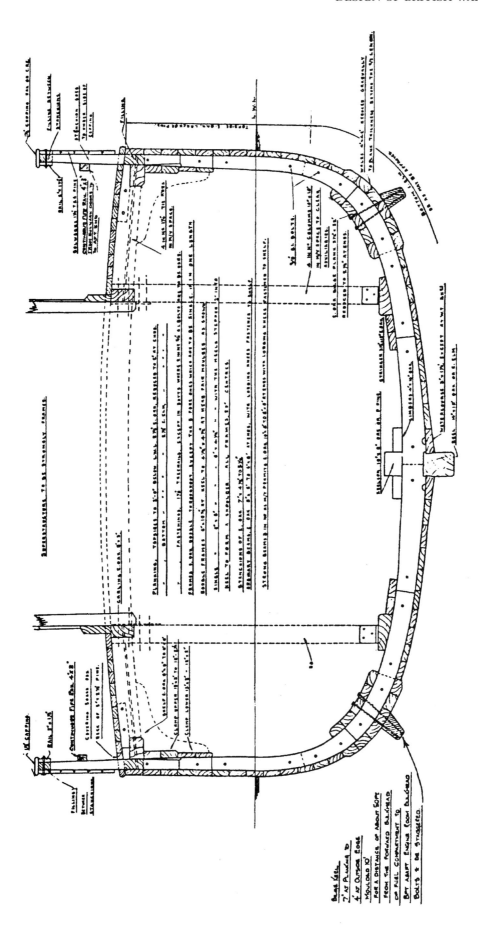

105ft wooden towing vessel, constructional midship section

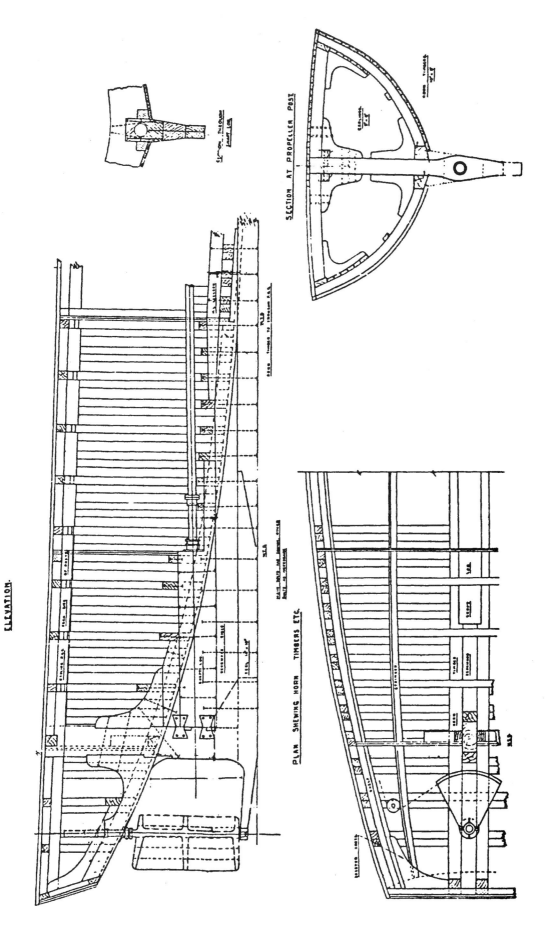

105ft wooden towing vessel, stern timbering arrangement

straighten out and the usual consequence was that the alignment of shafting changed. Unless steps were taken to realign the shafting, trouble developed with the stern tube.

3. *Alignment Troubles*

Two sources of alignment troubles have been outlined in (1) and (2) above. Another source of alignment trouble was the long length of shafting between the engine and the propeller. The engines were situated more or less at the centre of length of the hull and there was no flexible coupling in the shaft between the engine and the propeller. A wooden vessel does not approach the rigidity of a steel vessel and there is appreciable change of shape and alignment as the wooden hull settles down to conditions on service. The usual consequence of lack of alignment was trouble in the fore end of the long stern tube. The lack of straightness in the shaft produced a pumping action up and down or from side to side at the fore end of the stern tube. The bearings ran hot and gradually the stern tube worked loose in the shaft log, when leakage occurred. It was necessary to pay constant attention to alignment and lining up of the shaft was always carried out with the vessels afloat, and in service trim. When they were put in dock, it was necessary to withdraw the bolts in the shaft couplings to prevent straining of the shaft as the wooden keel took up the shape of the docking blocks.

4. *Dilution of Labour*

Some of the troubles with early boats were traceable to the use of diluted labour and general rashness and over-eagerness in building. These troubles soon diminished as a result of the progressive increase of skill of the dilutees. In the long run, the hulls produced in yards where the labour was very heavily diluted were reasonably good examples of wooden shipbuilding and the main criticism of the hulls would have been in respect of the material used rather than the quality of workmanship. The material used was not under control and was dictated by force of circumstances.

Engine

The initial requirement was a 500bhp heavy diesel engine. In order to keep pace with production of hulls, a wide variety of engines was accepted including Harland & Wolff, Mirrlees Crossley, National Gas, Petters, Ruston Hornsby, Newbury, Atlas, Fairbanks Morse (Canadian), Enterprise (Lease/Lend), National Superior (Lease/Lend). Some of these engines were very bulky and the

necessity for withdrawing pistons resulted in a high superstructure. Other engines were of the land variety used in generating stations and were not as well balanced as could have been desired for a marine unit.

In later vessels a 375bhp engine was fitted instead of a 500bhp (obtained by removing one bank of cylinders). The decreased power was acceptable and the reduced number of cylinders in the engine resulted in increased engine production.

Auxiliary Engines

In early boats the pulsing machinery consisted of three 36kW diesel generators. In later boats two 54kW or one 99kW generators were fitted. For ship lighting etc a 7½kW general service diesel generator was fitted, later increased to 12kW.

Batteries

The battery equipment consisted of 200 submarine-type cells.

Acoustic Sweep

Not long after the first 105ft motor minesweepers had been put into production, the enemy began sowing acoustic mines. It was necessary to arrange for the vessels to sweep acoustic mines as well as magnetic mines. The first arrangement fitted was a hammer box carried on an 'A' frame lowered over the bow. The 'A' frame was raised by means of a topping lift carried to a block on the mast and worked from the cable windlass. In later boats a towed box was substituted for the hammer box and 'A' frame. The arrangement with the towed box was for the tow to be taken from an eye plate on the port side of the stem. The box was streamed and recovered by means of a derrick on foremast. Iron sheet sheathing was fitted on the bottom and side in the way of the position for streaming the box to avoid scoring of the wooden hull.

Oropesa Sweep

Towards the end of the war, consideration was given to the fitting of Oropesa sweep Mark V* in addition to the acoustic sweep and magnetic sweeps. It was agreed that the Oropesa sweep could be fitted but the work was never carried out owing to the cessation of hostilities.

Sheathing

In view of shortages of sheathing material and the urgency of minesweeping requirements, some of the early deliveries of motor minesweepers were sent out to the Mediterranean and to Indian waters with bare wooden hulls. These hulls were soon reported as being attacked by teredo and it was necessary to renew some of the planking, chiefly in the neighbourhood of the waterline amidships where the paint had been scored off the bottom by fenders and so on. Later vessels intended for service in Mediterranean and tropical waters were sheathed with copper.[1] As the motor minesweepers were iron fastened, it was necessary to take special precautions against galvanic action between the copper sheathing and the fastenings. This was achieved by fitting a thick layer of tarred felt underneath the copper sheathing. Zinc protectors were fitted in the way of the steel stern skeg and steel rudder fittings.

In an attempt to reduce the amount of galvanic action between the copper sheathing and the stern skeg, instructions were given to apply paint over the sheathing.

Service

The 105ft motor minesweepers were responsible for much of the coastal minesweeping, round the coasts of Britain and elsewhere during the middle period of the war. As the activities of the enemy in the narrow seas were mostly in the direction of minelaying on a very large scale, the degree of genuine service rendered by these small wooden minesweepers can be well appreciated. These small minesweepers also played their part in clearing up mines in advance of the landings on the Normandy Coast. They succeeded in keeping the convoy routes in the North Sea and Channel more or less clear of mines. The operations were rarely spectacular but were continuous, often arduous and always dangerous.

Sea-Keeping Ability

Within the limitations of their size, the 105ft motor minesweepers were good sea boats and were dry. Their high superstructure, lack of draught (dictated by necessity for sweeping in shallow water) and high ratio of beam to draught, made them buoyant but rather prone to rolling.

Stability

The stability of the 105ft motor minesweepers was less than is usual in coastal force craft and more in line with the stability of small trawlers. This decrease of stability range was due to the large additions of topweight involved in fitting acoustic sweep and extra guns. Some boats carried as much as 40ton of ballast to compensate for added topweight. The necessity for ballasting was felt particularly in some of the Indian-built minesweepers which were of particularly heavy composite construction and had teak planking with no compensating increase of size to make up for the extra weight. The usual GM was 1.5-1.7ft and range of stability 60°.

Particulars of 105ft motor minesweepers are given in Appendix I.

[1] It is interesting to note the revival of copper sheathing and, with it, the problems of electrolytic action which plagued nineteenth-century sheathed iron ships.

A mine, probably containing 1100lbs of Torpex, exploding close to a 105ft MMS in a postwar trial.

126ft Motor Minesweepers

The 105ft motor minesweepers were designed primarily to deal with sweeping in estuaries and waters near to the coast. Much of the minesweeping in more exposed positions was carried out by larger minesweepers of the converted trawler type or by specially designed minesweeping sloops such as the *Bangor* class.

In late 1941 it was decided to embark on a programme of building of large wooden minesweepers capable of sweeping in less sheltered and deeper waters and also capable of making ocean passages. To meet this requirement the 126ft motor minesweeper design was prepared by the Director of Naval Construction in January 1942. At the request of the Director of Naval Construction the Naval Staff agreed on a less shallow draught than that insisted upon in the 105ft motor minesweepers. As a result of the relaxation of draught, a very seaworthy design was produced to meet the staff requirements.

Details of the 126ft motor minesweeper design are given in Appendix I. The design embodied experience gained in the production of the 105ft motor minesweepers. The LL cable reel was power driven. The steering gear was electric hydraulic. As a result of leakages in the stern tube experienced in 105ft motor minesweepers, the stern tube was redesigned and a transverse plate

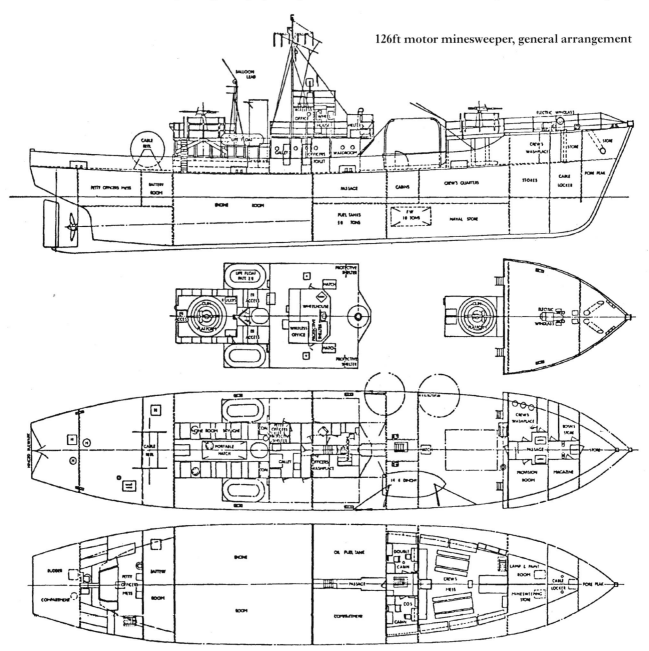

126ft motor minesweeper, general arrangement

The 126ft vessels, such as MMS 1006, were more suitable for open water.

frame fitted for holding the inboard end of the tube. The outboard end of the tube was fitted with a locking nut.

Originally these vessels were designed for sweeping acoustic and magnetic mines only, but later on arrangements were made for fitting an Oropesa sweep Mk V* in addition, although with the end of the war actually only a few were fitted.

A 25kW motor generator was fitted for general purposes. The pulsing power comprised either two 54kW generators or alternatively one 99kW generator.

The structure of the boats was in conformity with Lloyd's rules for wooden vessels, only a few being of composite construction. The structure was strengthened compared with the 105ft motor minesweepers. Extra shelves and extra lodging stringers were fitted and strength riders were worked fore and aft under the deck picking up the carlings to the large engine hatch. With this increase of structure and with the improved building technique, the 126ft motor minesweepers proved to be very free from alignment troubles.

In the main, production of these motor minesweepers was put in the hands of builders who had produced the 105ft motor minesweepers and who were capable of taking on the larger vessels. A number were built in Canada.

The 126ft motor minesweepers were very able seaboats. They possessed an easy motion in a seaway and, with their high freeboard amidships, good sheer and specially high freeboard forward due to the half forecastle, they were very dry boats.

The stability of the 126ft MMS was an improvement on the 105ft MMS, the GM being 2.0ft.

British Yard Minesweepers (BYMS)

The US Navy put into production a very large number of standard wooden minesweepers, length 130ft called Yard Minesweepers. A certain number of vessels from this building programme were allocated to the Royal Navy under the Lease Lend Agreement and were called British Yard Minesweepers to distinguish them from the American-manned vessels.

The design represented a half-way compromise between a trawler and a large motor launch, such as the German R-boat. They were shallow draught vessels (9ft) with moderate displacement of 330 tons, but were high powered, having two 600hp General Motors diesels. The maximum speed was about 14½kts and the endurance about 2500 miles at 10kts.

The boats were fitted for sweeping magnetic, acoustic and ground mines. An electric winch was fitted on the after deck for Oropesa sweep and a power-operated cable reel was fitted for the magnetic sweep. The acoustic sweep was arranged from a single strut fitting, pivoted on the stem, the lower end carrying the hammer box.

The vessels were extremely lively in anything of a seaway. They were dry but the high bridge structure in association with the shallow draught and light displacement resulted in a degree of pitching and rolling.

They were a very interesting contrast to the British designed 126ft motor minesweepers. The latter were of moderate speed - 10kts - and arranged to sweep acoustic and magnetic mines only. Their behaviour in a seaway was reminiscent of a moderate-sized, unusually buoyant and unusually dry trawler.

The hull construction was double skin, each skin being worked fore and aft with shifted edges. The framing was of the bent timber type laminated frame.

Their construction was undertaken by a number of American yacht yards and in many respects the British yard minesweepers design was in the nature of a luxury boat with many fittings not found in British naval craft. Also, the outfit of stores and comforts was on much more generous lines than usual in the British Navy. As a set-off to the many things provided in the British yard minesweepers, the crew accommodation was extremely cramped, with three-tier bunks and inadequate ventilation. The officers' accommodation was fairly generous.

The British yard minesweepers in very large numbers made the Atlantic crossing in safety and, by one route or another, this type of minesweeper found its way to all theatres of operation. The vessels were very seaworthy, but one criticism was that the stern cut-up caused considerable difficulty in keeping vessels on a course. Among subsequent modifications were the fitting of bilge keels and additional flare to the bow at forecastle deck.

In view of the known capacity of the vessels for heavy rolling in a seaway, it was necessary to ensure that there was no encroachment on the moderate range of stability; the GM was 2.3ft and the range was 54°. Ballast was added as necessary to compensate for topweight added in service.

About 150 British yard minesweepers were in service in the Royal Navy. Many of them were allocated to tropical service and it was decided to fit sheathing in the form of pressure creosote-treated wood.

Particulars of British yard minesweepers are given in Appendix I.

Conversion of 75ft Motor Fishing Vessels for Shallow Water Magnetic and Acoustic Sweeps

A requirement arose at the end of 1943 for a method of sweeping magnetic and acoustic mines in rivers and canals. The 105ft motor minesweepers could not be employed for this service as their safe degaussing depth was too great.

Approval was given to convert fifteen 75ft motor fishing vessels to minesweeping, after successful trials on the trawler *Oscar Angelle*, which had been fitted out as a prototype.

Vessels still under construction were selected, to minimise scrapping of completed work. The shallow water magnetic sweep (LLA) consisted of a loop of cable lowered from the stern, with two floats giving an otter effect to spread the loop. The acoustic sweep was a light hinged boom type SA gear (A Mk II). Degaussing gear was fitted so that the magnetic safe depth of the vessel should be as small as possible. A petrol-driven 35kW generator was installed on the upper deck in a steel house for supply of power to the degaussing and SA gear and for charging the batteries provided for pulsing the LAA sweep.

The fish hold foremost was subdivided to provide accommodation, provision room, stores, battery room and fan compartment. The complement consisted of one officer and twelve men. The speed when sweeping was 6½kts, when running free 8½kts.

APPENDIX I

Particulars of Motor Minesweepers

	105ft MMS	126ft MMS	BYMS
Length overall	119ft 0in	139ft 10in	130ft 0in
Length between perpendiculars	105ft 0in	126ft 0in	130ft 0in
Breadth (moulded)	21ft 7in	25ft 6in	24ft 0in
Depth (moulded)	11ft 3in	14ft 9in	12ft 1in
Deep displacement	256 tons	428 tons	334 tons
Deep draughts forward	7ft 8½in	8ft 2½in	8ft 1in
aft	12ft 6in	8ft 1in	8ft 10½in
Horsepower	500bhp	500bhp	1200bhp (2 shafts)
Speed	Free 10kts	Free 10kts	14.6kts
	Sweeping 9kts	Sweeping 9kts	
Endurance	2000 miles at 10kts	4000 miles at 10kts	2500 miles at 10kts
Complement	3 officers, 18 men	3 officers, 23 men	3 officers, 27 men
Metacentric height in deep condition	1.85ft	2.00ft	2.29ft
Maximum GZ in deep condition	1.10ft	1.00ft	0.96ft
Range of stability in deep condition	67½°	65°	54°
Legend of Weights			
Hull	140 tons	272 tons	
Machinery	48 tons	50 tons	
Diesel oil	26 tons	54 tons	–
Fresh water	5 tons	10 tons	
General equipment	37 tons	42 tons	
Total Numbers Built	278	85	About 150 under Lease/Lend
Average time to build	9 months	14 months	–

CHAPTER 15

Admiralty Type Motor Fishing Vessels (MFVs)

Editorial Note

This chapter and the craft described therein is yet another part of W J Holt's prodigious output and, again his enthusiasm is obvious. The chapter seems self explanatory and no footnotes are needed but see *also his paper 'Admiralty Type Motor Fishing Vessels',* Transactions of the Institution of Naval Architects *88 (1946).*

For the purpose of carrying men and stores, a vast number of small craft were required in attendance on ships and men engaged in war operations. In a single port of large size the number of small craft on harbour service duties was usually well over a hundred. When account was taken of all the ports, fleet anchorages, beach heads such as Normandy or Sicily, servicing of outlying establishments in remote positions such as on islands, and the formation of boat pools in recaptured ports, the number of small craft required became very large indeed.

At the outbreak of the war, the Admiralty requisitioned numbers of small motor craft, of types ranging from small fishing craft, such as the steam drifters, seine-net fishing boats and ring-net fishing boats, to passenger launches, pleasure launches and motor yachts.

By the summer of 1940 nearly every small motor craft which could be made to function and which had not been earmarked already for some other essential work had been pressed into service by one or other of the armed forces.

After two years of war the wastage of this heterogeneous collection of requisitioned craft had become very high, especially among the lightly built pleasure launch or motor yacht type of craft. Anyone with experience of some of the windswept fleet anchorages frequented by the British Navy readily appreciated how little suited was the average lightly built pleasure craft to sustain the bumping and banging against ship side or gangway, or shore pontoon, in rough weather, or, again, to meet the demand for continuous running of the engine, day after day, winter and summer, under such conditions of service. On the other hand, war experience had established the entire suitability of the small fishing boat to withstand service conditions.

Reviewing the wastage, and with some foreknowledge of likely requirements for offensive operations, the Admiralty decided in 1942 to embark upon a large programme of building of small craft, and it was further decided that, as the small fishing boat had proved very suitable for Admiralty service, a proportion of the requirements for small craft should be met by the production of motor fishing vessels slightly modified in design to meet service requirements. It was considered that a suitably designed small fishing vessel, in addition to giving good service to the Admiralty during the war, would help to reduce the inevitable shortage of vessels in the fishing industry, if spared from naval service at the end of the war.

The Director of Naval Construction was instructed to prepare a design for a small fishing craft, to meet certain Admiralty requirements and also to be suitable for post-war fishing. In the preparation of the design the Ministry of Agriculture and Fisheries and the Fishery Division of the Scottish Home Department were consulted, and DNC's officers had opportunity of discussing the matter with fishermen and fishing boat builders in ports ranging from the Shetlands to Cornwall. It was soon realized that, quite apart from certain fishing requirements conflicting with Admiralty requirements, there was the problem of variation of fishing requirements between one port and another to be considered. The investigations had brought to light many of the features affecting design which were peculiar requirements of certain ports, and the importance of such local circumstances as the range of tide, type of harbour, nature of the local fishing, and whether the port or fishing ground was exposed or otherwise. It was not possible to design one type of boat to meet all circumstances and to be most suitable

45ft MFV general arrangement

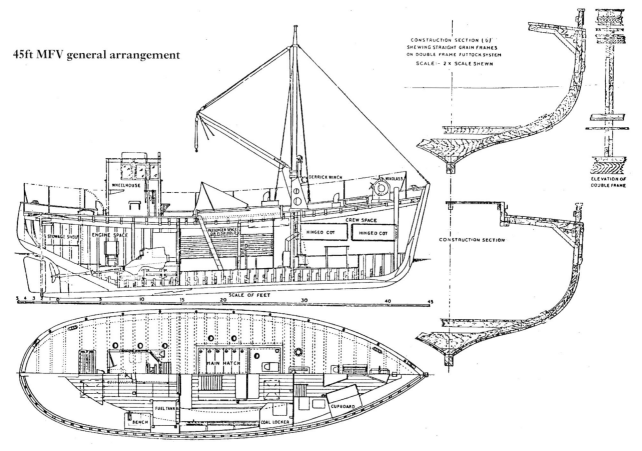

for each particular port, but the attempt was made to consider all circumstances and produce the best one-type boat possible. The design resulting from the investigation was the 61½ft MFV, and it was approved to put this type into production in large numbers.

Late in 1942 the 61½ft MFV seemed likely to be successful for Admiralty service; also by this time the future operational picture was becoming clearer. The Admiralty proposed to extend the production of MFVs to include two further types:
(a) A small type suitable for lifting on to a ship for transfer abroad; and
(b) A large type of good sea-keeping ability and big fuel endurance suitable for making trans-oceanic passages to zones of operations abroad.

The sizes of vessels the Admiralty had in mind were (a) 45ft and (b) 85ft lengths. However, after further consultations with the authorities on fishing, it was established that the Scottish Herring Fisheries required a vessel not more than 75ft in length, whereas the East Anglian Fishery interests appeared to favour a boat about 90ft in length. It was finally approved to build three further types of fishing craft, in addition to the 61½ft MFV:
(a) A boat just under 50ft in length, suitable for ring-net fishing;

(b) A 75ft vessel suitable for East Coast of Scotland ports; and
(c) A 97ft craft for East Anglia (officially called 90ft MFV).

The Director of Naval Construction was instructed to produce the designs.

The 97ft fishing vessel was based on a design for a steel trawler-drifter which had been prepared by Messrs Richards Ironworks of Lowestoft. This design was modified to wood construction, the lines redrafted and the Admiralty requirements embodied. Messrs Richards did most of the work on this particular design.

The main particulars of the four designs are indicated in the tabular statement, Appendix II.

Appendix I gives a statement of scantlings.

Drawings showing the layout of the vessels and details of structure are contained in the figures.

Notes on the Designs

The so-called 45ft, more accurately 50ft, MFV was of the type commonly used for ring-net fishing around the coasts of Britain. There was some difference in type between the boats used around the coast of Scotland and the Northern Islands, and the type common to the south of England and Cornish ports. The Cornish boats were usually fitted with the transom stern and often had an arrangement of two engines, one large, one small. The Scottish boats usually had a scaffie stern in older boats and a cruiser stern in modern boats, one engine, and were very similar to the fishing boats found in Scandinavia, Denmark, North Germany and Baltic fishing ports. The boat designed by the Admiralty was of the Scottish/Scandinavian type, but there should not have been any difficulty in adapting the boat to be suitable for fishing from the Cornish ports.

The 61½ft MFV was generally similar to the seine-net fishing boat, commonly found in the ports on the east and north-east coasts of Scotland. The type was also common to Scandinavia. This size of fishing boat was very suitable for many naval requirements and established a high reputation for sea-keeping ability.

Construction

Many connected with the fishing industry expressed a hope that the MFVs would be given steel hulls, but it was not possible for the designers to balance the relative merits of steel and wood hulls for the MFVs, as circumstances clearly dictated the adoption of wood construction. A wooden hull simplified the problem of avoiding trouble due to magnetic mines. There were numbers of builders who had vacant capacity for building wooden fishing boats, timber for hulls could be

obtained quickly, and the clinching argument was that neither steel nor the steel hull building capacity could be spared for building steel MFVs.

In the main, the building of the boats was entrusted to the firms who had been building wooden motor minesweepers for the Admiralty - work on minesweepers was by this time slacking off. In addition, boat builders whose capacity had been too small to undertake the wooden motor minesweepers, but who normally built fishing boats, were given orders. Leading yacht builders undertook the production of a few hulls.

The design of the hull structure followed existing fishing-boat practice and has been indicated in some detail in the figures at the end of this chapter to form a record of this construction.

The nucleus of boat builders employed on the building of the hulls of the MFVs was heavily diluted with labour of the house-carpenter type. This dilution threw an additional burden on the boat builders and overseers concerned. In general the recruits to boat-building proved to be quick learners and, after gaining experience on a hull or two, the quality of workmanship put into the MFVs was not below the average found in pre-war fishing-boat construction.

The timber used in the hulls was not always in dry condition, and in later boats built it was the practice to coat the timber with copper naphthen-

61½ft MFV general arrangement

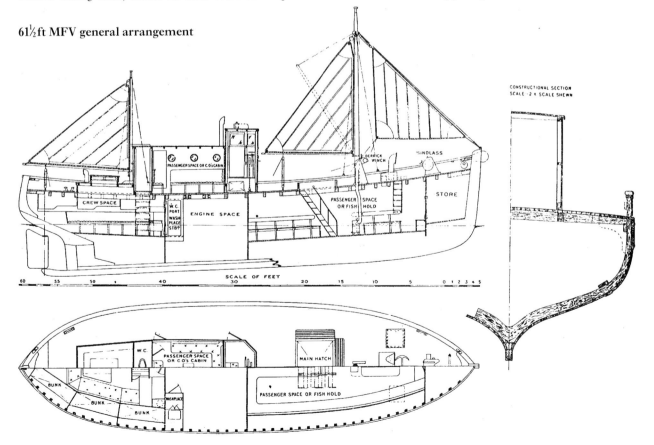

A 75ft MFV.

ate during construction, as a precaution against rot infection.

The frames, stem, keel, hog, stern deadwoods, beams, knees, shelves, bilge stringers, hatch carlings and floors were generally of oak, the frames being grown crooks. Planking was of larch mainly, or Oregon pine, but the thickened bilge strakes and sheer strakes were of oak. English elm or oak was used for the garboard. The majority of the builders in East Anglia used oak for planking exclusively.

One or two builders who had received large orders for MFVs were unable to obtain a sufficiency of grown oak crooks for frames. They were instructed to use a system of straight-grain oak frames on the double frame futtock system. This system of framing, indicated in the accompanying figure was found to be very strong and satisfactory; the main disadvantage was additional weight of framing. It seemed likely that framing on this system was required to be adopted more generally if there was any further bulk building of fishing craft.

A few fishing craft were built using composite construction - steel frames, wood hull - but it was found that this system did not make for quick production in wartime as steel workers were scarce and liable to be deflected to other jobs at short notice; also deliveries of steel were tardy. The composite system of construction would have been favoured in peacetime production of MFVs. It was used in the KFKs, the German equivalent of British MFVs.

Form

All MFVs were given a cruiser-type stern. All northern fishermen consulted were insistent that

the simpler transom stern should not be adopted. The fishermen also required a buoyant stern. On the north-east coast of Scotland there was always the matter of getting back to port in bad weather to exercise its influence on the design of fishing boats. These ports were all on a lee shore in a north-easterly gale, and the design of the stone breakwaters of the harbours resulted in the condition that when entering the ports it was generally necessary for the boat to turn until the sea was almost on the beam - when close inshore and with the waves on the point of breaking - a dangerous condition of affairs which led to disaster on more than one occasion.

Rig

It had been intended that the 61½ft MFVs should be carried abroad on the decks of ships, but when the time came to ship the boats it was found that there was no shipping capacity available. It was decided that the boats should make the ocean passage on their own keels. The flotillas sent abroad were given an outfit of sails before leaving England, to act as steadying sails and also to get the boats to any port to leeward in an emergency. The later-built 75ft and 90ft MFVs were given a small area outfit of sails as part of their initial equipment in preparation for an ocean passage. The rigs of the boats are indicated on the general arrangement drawings at the end of the paper.

Engines

In considering the engine installations fitted in the MFVs, it should be borne in mind that the vessels were built in wartime, when engine-building capacity in Britain was stretched to the limit. Some fishermen wanted to see more engine power in each of the designs. The Admiralty was not in a position to pick and choose over a wide range of possible engines. The best was made of existing circumstances. The main matter for regret was that diesel engines were not obtainable in adequate numbers for fitting in all the 45ft MFVs.

When the engine supply position became easier it would not have been a difficult matter for the new owners of MFVs to remove the existing engine and fit the engine of their choice.

The position of the forward engine-room bulkhead was the subject of criticism by fishermen. In the design every endeavour was made to keep the engine and the bulkhead as far aft as possible, but the engines available imposed a limitation in this respect. In a conversion to fishing and in the event of more suitable engines being available, it would not have been difficult to move the bulkhead further aft to gain extra space in the fish hold.

Trawl Winches

The 75ft and 90ft MFVs were fitted with trawl winches driven off the main engines by means of a belt and jockey pulley arrangement. The winches were double drum, and a pull of two tons could be exerted on each drum concurrently. The hauling speed was 19 fathoms/minute. The stowage capacity of each drum was 250 fathoms 2½in wire rope.

Experience on Service

The four types of MFVs established a reputation for good sea-keeping ability, and they were most useful to the Admiralty. In the spring of 1943 numbers of 61½ft MFVs made the passage to the Mediterranean on their own keels. The forward passenger space was filled with drums of diesel oil as extra fuel, and hand-pumping arrangements were fitted to pump the oil from the drums back into the fuel tanks in the engine room. A number of 2-gallon and 25-gallon tins of water were supplied to enable the crew to use the water at the rate of two gallons per man per day. Thus fitted out, the boats made the long passage - nearly 2000 miles owing to wartime conditions - from Britain to Gibraltar, and reports indicate that they behaved well on the passage.

Sheathing

Experience with the wooden minesweepers and other wooden vessels on service in the Mediterranean in 1942/3 had given clear warning of the degree of upkeep and docking small wooden vessels were likely to receive on war operations in an area deficient in docking capacity. In the early stages of the build up for the Far Eastern operations a party of Admiralty officers was sent out to India to survey the position from the point

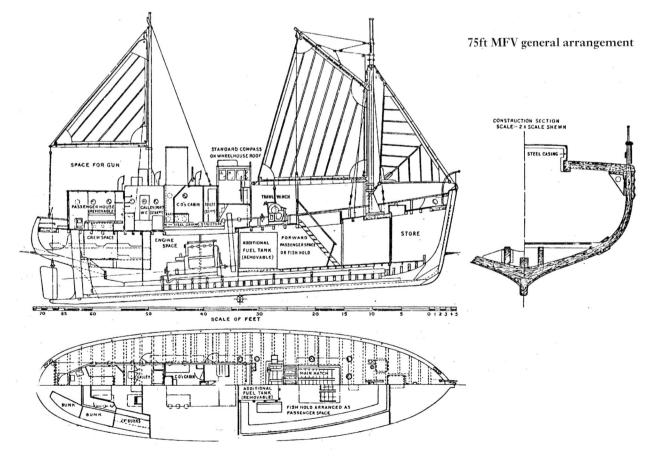

75ft MFV general arrangement

of view of maintenance of harbour craft, MFVs, etc. As a result of investigation, it was decided that, although sheathing of MFVs was expensive of valuable material and labour, and iron-fastened boats were not ideal for the fitting of sheathing such as copper or Muntz metal, it was necessary to sheathe all small craft intended for service in these tropical waters. Alternative methods of sheathing considered were:

(a) Wood sheathing
(b) Muntz
(c) Copper
(d) Iron
(e) Zinc

Iron and zinc were ruled out as they were considered to rust away too quickly. Wood sheathing had been tried by the Americans and Australians and was said to be hopeful and probably the best method of sheathing. From the point of view of the British Admiralty, wood sheathing seemed to offer advantage in that it was not likely to set up galvanic action with the iron fastenings of the MFV.

First of all a number of MFVs were fitted with wood sheathing. The method adopted was as follows:

Long battens of timber 3in x 1in in section were put in a pressure vessel and first subjected to a vacuum. Afterwards the drum was charged with creosote and subjected to a pressure of 120lb/sq in, and the pressure maintained for five to eight hours. It was hoped (a faint hope, it is true) that with this drastic treatment the creosote might penetrate right through the battens and fill all the cells of the timber with creosote. It was known that in the USA common yellow sapwood had been used for the battens, whereas the only timber available in Britain in quantity, Douglas fir, was known to be resistant to creosote treatment. As had been feared, the creosote treatment of Douglas fir was not very satisfactory. The creosote-treated Douglas fir battens were supplied by the Admiralty to all builders of MFVs.

The sheathing procedure was as follows:

(i) The hull of the boat to be sheathed was examined to see that the seams were well caulked.

(ii) The underwater body was afterwards well sludged with tar, and thick tarred felt fitted over the whole of the bottom to be sheathed. Care was taken to see that no gaps were left in the felt covering.

(iii) The outside surface of the tarred felt was given a good sludging of tar.

(iv) The sheathing battens were nailed on top of the tarred felt and fitted closely together so that there would be no gaping seams to invite entry of teredo.

(v) The outside of the sheathing was finally given a good sludging with tar.

The idea of using wood sheathing may have been good - the Admiralty had not had sufficient expe-

90ft MFV general arrangement

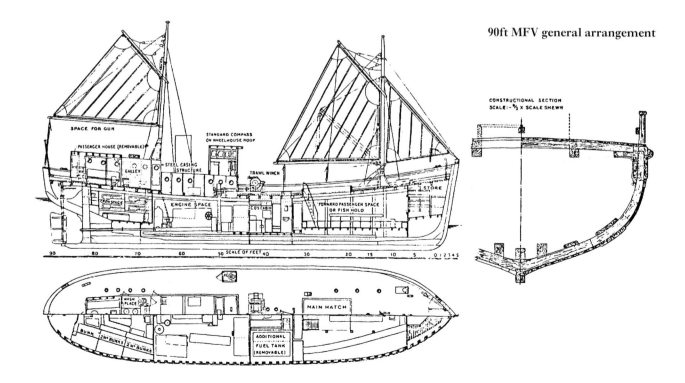

rience to express an opinion – but the method was dropped in later MFVs built because there was considerable doubt whether the Douglas fir battens received sufficient penetration of the creosote to be effective. Also, it was found that the fitting of the battens required good workmanship and the process was slow.

About the time of the Mediterranean landings a few iron-fastened wooden minesweepers had been sheathed with copper, and some months later opportunity was taken when one of these vessels was in dock to strip off a piece of copper sheathing, remove the felt under-sheathing, and knock out some fastenings to see whether there were any signs of eating-away of the heads of fastenings due to galvanic action. It was found that the fastenings were in 'as new' condition. It was decided to drop the scheme of wood sheathing and fit Muntz sheathing instead.

The method of insulating the heads of the iron fastenings from the Muntz sheathing was as follows:

(i)   All heads of fastenings were punched well below the surface of planking and cemented over, and seams of planking were examined and caulked and stopped where defects were revealed.

(ii) The bottom of the boat was then well sludged with tar.

(iii) The bottom was sealed with thick felt, well tarred.

(iv) The Muntz sheathing worked on top of the felt.

(v)   The outside of the Muntz sheathing was given coatings of a composition to kill galvanic action between the sheathing and exposed ironwork such as skegs and rudder fittings.

Conversion to Fishing Craft

As far as possible the superstructures were arranged so that passenger deck houses could be readily removed. The extra fuel tanks carried for Admiralty services could be removed through the hatches. In boats which are still on the stocks, and being brought to the launching stage without engines, the forward engine-room bulkhead has been omitted.

Conclusion

The production of the large numbers of MFVs was only one small section of the vast building effort put forward by the fishing boat, yacht and other builders of wooden craft in Great Britain during the late war. The effort produced the wooden minesweepers, motor torpedo boats and gunboats, motor launches, motor fishing vessels, wooden assault craft, and small boats.

It is to be hoped that some of these craft eventually found their way into the fishing industry.

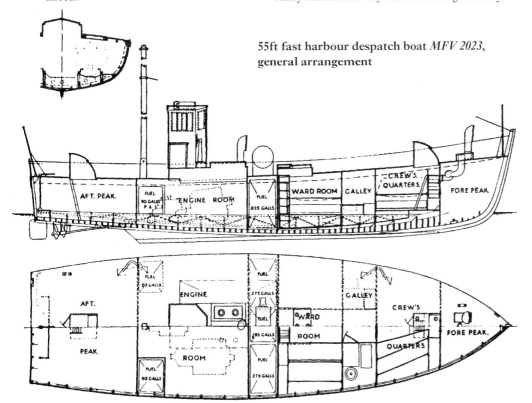

55ft fast harbour despatch boat *MFV 2023*, **general arrangement**

APPENDIX I

Scantlings and Timber Used in Construction of MFVs

Item	Timber	45ft MFV	61½ft MFV Scantlings	75ft MFV	90ft MFV
Keel	oak	sided 6in moulded 8in	sided 6in moulded 9in	sided 9in moulded 11in	sided 10in moulded 14in
Keelson	oak	–	–	10in x 10in	mid. 10in x 11in side 10in x 14in
Hog	oak or elm	4in x 9in	5½in x 9½in	7in x 14in	–
Stem	oak	sided 6in	sided 8in	sided 8in	sided 10in
Apron	oak	sided 10in	sided 8in	sided 15in	sided 10in
Sternport and deadwood	oak	sided 8in	at sterntube 13in	sided 10in swelled at sterntube	sided 12in at sterntube 18in
Framing	oak	grown, single sided 3ins straight grained, double sided 3in	grown, single sided 4ins straight grained, double sided 3in	sided 4½in	sided 4½in double
Hull planking	oak, English elm, larch	thickness 1½in	thickness 1¾in	thickness 2in	thickness 2in
Rubbing strakes	oak, elm larch	four thickness 2in	four thickness 3in	four thickness 3½in	four thickness 4in
Bilge wale	oak	6in x 2½in	8in x 2in	8in x 3½in	8in x 4in four strakes
Bilge stringer	Oregon pine	6½in x 2in	9in x 2in	8in x 2in three strakes	7in x 3½in four strakes
Deep planking	Oregon pine	thickness 1¾in	thickness 2in	thickness 2½in	thickness 2½in
Beams	oak, larch, Oregon pine	thickness 3in heavy 4in	thickness 4½in in way of hatch 5½in	thickness 4½in heavy 6¼in	thickness 6in heavy 7in
Beam shelf	oak or pitch pine	sided 3in	6½in x 5in	main hatch 9in x 7in minor hatches 6in x 5in	7in x 7in rider 10in x 7in
Bulwark stanchion	oak	3in x 3in	4in x 4in	4½in x 4½in	6in x 6in
Capping	oak or English elm	5in x 1½in	7in x 3in	7½in x 3in	8in x 3½in
Belaying rail	oak	4in x 2in	6in x 2in	6in x 2in	6in x 4in
Lodging knee	oak	6in x 2in lodging shelf	thickness 4in	16in x 2½in lodging shelf	20in x 5in lodging shelf
Hanging knee		grown oak or 3in x 3in x ¼in MS bar	oak thickness 4in six each side	MS plate 2½in x ½in	MS plate 3in x ⅞in
Floor timber	oak	sided 3in	long arm 5ft 0in short arm 2ft 6in	sided 4½in	sided 4½in
Frame spacing		13in apart	15in apart	16in apart	20in apart

Fastenings: The keel bolts varied from 5/8in in 45ft MFVs to 1in in 90ft MFVs. The plank fastenings varied from 3/8in dumps and bolts in 45ft MFVs to 5/8in in 90ft craft.

APPENDIX II

Particulars of MFVs

	90ft	75ft	61½ft	45ft
Length				
BP	90ft 0in	69ft 2in	61ft 6in	45ft 0in
OA	97ft 2in	75ft 7in	64ft 6in	49ft 10in
Beam (to outside of plank)	22ft 3in	19ft 8in	17ft 10in	Some 15ft 3in Remainder 16ft 3in
Moulded depth	10ft 9in	10ft 0in	9ft 3in	7ft 10in
Draughts without cargo				
Forward	5ft 6in	5ft 6in	4ft 3in	3ft 3in
Aft	11ft 0in	9ft 6in	7ft 0in	5ft 3in
Displacement at above draughts	200 tons	114 tons	50 tons	28.5 tons
Tonnage				
Gross	115.96	77.42	48.65	27.52
Net		50.80	33.55	23.69 9.06
Machinery				
Makers and fuel	Crossley Diesel	Lister Diesel	Kelvin (D), Gray (D), Widdop (D), Lister (D)	Atlantic (D) Chrysler (D)
Bhp	240	160	88, 106, 120, 120	60, 60
Rpm (engine)	340	600	2.04 : 1 R/G 750, 1600, 400, 600	4.48 : 1 R/G 1000, 1800
Speed (measured)	9¼kts	8½kts	8½kts, 8¾kts, 9kts, 9kts	7½kts, 7½kts
Approximate cargo empty (deadweight)	70 tons	20 tons	15 tons	10 tons
Fuel storage in engine room	12 tons } total 11 tons } 23 tons	7¼ tons } total 4¾ tons } 12 tons	444gal, 444gal, 500gal, 500gal	142gall, 300gall
Endurance (in hours)				
with engine-room stowage	240	200		
with total storage	460	330	111	40. 65
Fresh water	3¾ tons	1½ tons	Nos 1–160 90gal Nos 161 onwards 250gal	50gal
Permanent ballast	9 tons concrete approx	6 tons concrete approx	5 tons concrete approx	3½ tons concrete approx
Sleeping berths fitted	10 in crew space	8 in crew space, 1 skipper's cabin on deck	6 in crew space	4 in crew space
Metacentric height at above draughts	3.67ft	2.4ft	4.76ft	15ft 3in beam – 3.73ft 16ft 3in beam – 4ft 0in

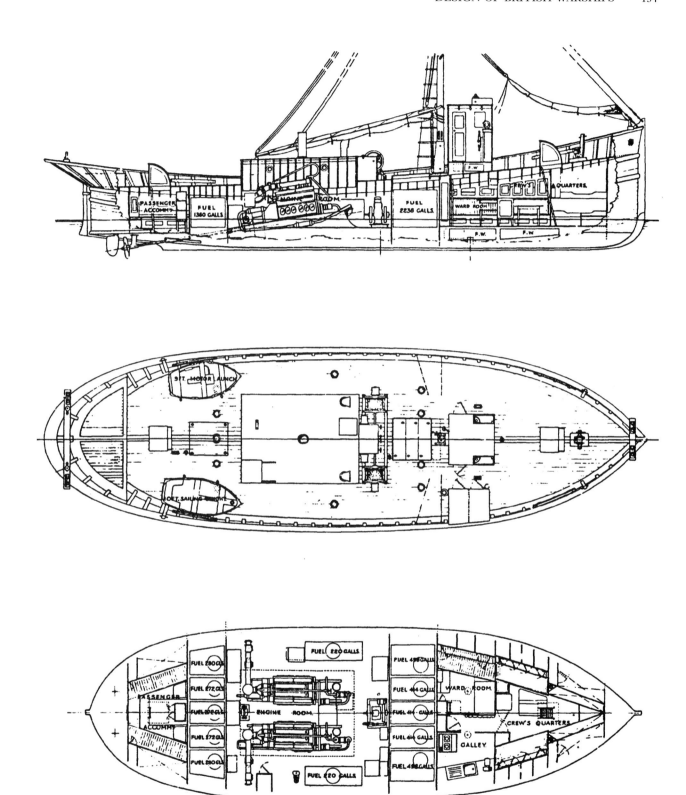

70ft patrol launch *MFV 2029* general arrangement

CHAPTER 16

Depot Ships

Editorial Note

Prior to 1939 the RN had a few old depot ships dating from World War I, together with a few excellent modern ships. Two more depot ships for destroyers and one for submarines were building. The importance of these ships was recognised by not only a heavy defensive armament but an armour deck and extensive torpedo protection which, in the case of Adamant, *added 3000 tons to the displacement. However, it must be doubted if a sandwich only 10ft deep would provide much protection, even against aircraft torpedoes.*

Even in the early years of the war, these were insufficient to maintain the fleet of small ships, often far from a recognised base, and a number of conversions were put in hand. These conversions presented a considerable number of problems, not the least of which was the shortage of suitable merchant ships to convert. Dockyard resources, too, were limited whilst there were all the technical problems of strength and stability described in the text.[1] Note the length of time required for conversion work.

MTB Depot Ships

In 1939 one MTB depot ship was in commission - HMS *Vulcan* - which had been converted in 1937. Approval was given in April 1940 for the conversion of SS *Aberdonian*, owned by the Aberdeen Steam Navigation Company, to an auxiliary MTB depot ship. She was to be capable of maintaining one flotilla of MTBs.

The leading particulars of *Aberdonian* were:

Length overall	275ft 6in
Length between perps	264ft 0in
Breadth moulded	36ft 0in
Depth	19ft 6in
Deep displacement	2575 tons
Mean draught (deep)	15ft 10in
Power	1500shp
Endurance	1400 miles at 12kts
Complement	9 officers, 62 crew

The work of conversion was kept to the minimum necessary to meet the requirements, and compliance with normal Admiralty practice was only called for in details connected with the fighting of the ship and the carriage of ammunition. The existing accommodation was largely utilised for both officers and ratings, except on the lower deck forward, which was stripped and fitted out to usual RN standards. The existing galleys were also stripped and one galley for officers and ratings fitted. A cold room of approximately 400cu ft was fitted.

Minor bulkheads were erected as required to provide store rooms, and watertight bulkheads were fitted in the fore hold to form magazines which were fitted with flooding and spraying arrangements. Stowage was also arranged in the fore hold for twelve torpedoes, twelve warheads, six blowing heads and twenty-four depth charges.

Workshop space was arranged on the lower deck for engineers, coppersmiths, shipwrights and ordnance artificers, and a small number of machine tools were fitted.

A certain amount of protection was fitted in the form of 40lb MS conning shelters at each wing of the bridge, protective plating to the steering engine house and concrete protection to the wheelhouse.

Machinery consisted of a reciprocating engine developing 1500shp and coal-fired boiler; 145ton of coal were carried for fuel. One 36kW steam generator was fitted.

Armament fitted was two 12pdr HA/LA guns and two 0.5in machine guns. These guns were fitted on 40lb MS platforms.

Stability 300 tons of permanent ballast and 98 tons of salt water ballast were carried to give a minimum metacentric height in the light condition of 0.94ft. The metacentric height in the deep condition was 1.64ft.

General
Aberdonian was taken in hand by Messrs Harland & Wolff, North Woolwich, in May 1940 and completed in August 1940. The vessel was released from Naval service and handed over to the Ministry of War Transport in March 1945.

[1] H E Skinner, 'Notes on Depot and Repair Ships', *Transactions of the Institution of Naval Architects* 89 (1947).

MTB depot ship *Vienna* as converted

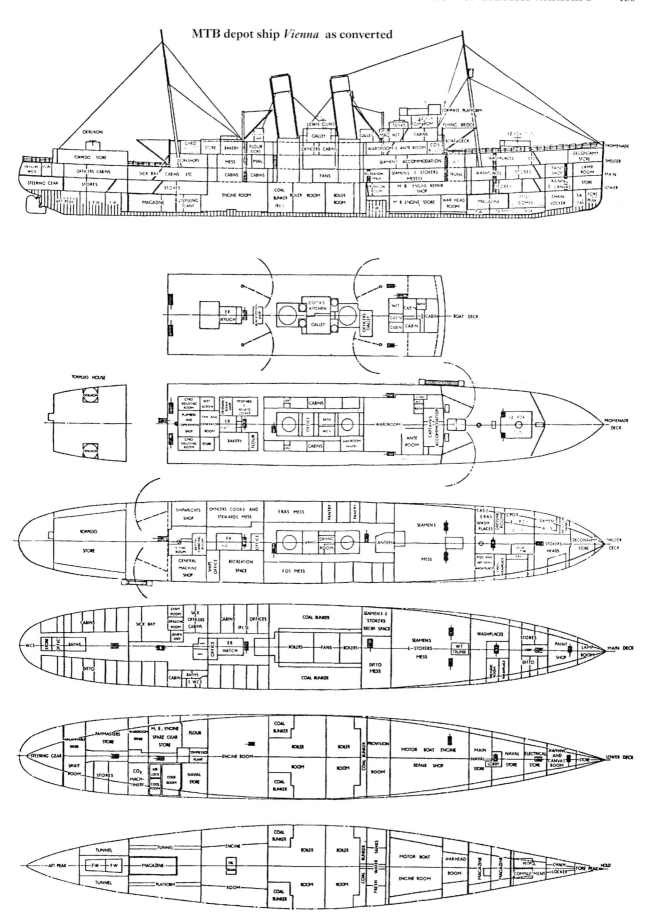

Vienna

In July 1941 approval was given for the conversion of a third vessel for use as an MTB depot ship. The requirements were for a vessel to be capable of maintaining two flotillas of MTBs or one of MTBs and one of SGBs. The LNER cross-channel steamer *Vienna*, then in hand at Portsmouth for conversion to a fast oiler, was selected for the purpose. There was a slight disadvantage in selecting this particular ship in that she was coal-burning, and it was necessary to accept a reduction in requirements as regards endurance.

The leading particulars of the ship were:

Length overall	365ft 0in
Length between perps	350ft 0in
Breadth extreme	50ft 1in
Depth to shelter deck	27ft 0in
Deep displacement	4925 tons
Mean draught (deep)	17ft 8½in
Power	9600shp
Maximum speed	21kts
Endurance	2500 miles at 12kts
Complement	48 officers, 420 crew

Following is a list of structural alterations made during the conversion.

To accommodate workshops, magazines, etc, new flats were built in the hold, portions of the lower deck made watertight and new watertight bulkheads built as necessary. All cargo hatches were plated in and made watertight, one large hatch and trunk being built for access to the MB engine store. Minor bulkheads, deckhouses and gun supports were built as necessary. The first-class accommodation port and starboard on the main deck as stripped to provide bunkerage for an additional 300 tons of coal, and the deck stiffened to support this load. Additional pillars and girders were fitted throughout the ship as necessary.

The following fitting-out work was undertaken: Workshops fitted were: general machine shop; motor boat engine workshop; coppersmiths and plumbers shop; shipwrights shop; ordnance torpedo and electrical shop; gyro adjusting room, duplex pistol test space and battery charging room. Other items such as cold and cool rooms, galleys, storerooms, heads, ventilation and water services, were fitted to Admiralty requirements, existing fittings being utilised as far as practicable. Magazines for depth charges, warheads, 12pdr SA and MTB ammunition, with the usual spraying and flooding arrangements were fitted.

The existing masts, derricks, winches and anchor and cable gear were refitted and retained. Clump and chain paravane arrangements were provided and the vessel was fitted out for Arctic and tropical service.

Protection

60lb NC armour to the crowns and ends of the forward magazines, and to the crowns, ends and sides of the after magazines. Splinter protection was fitted to the bridges, gun positions and steering gear compartment.

Machinery consisted of twin screw geared turbines. Fuel carried was 530 tons coal. Propeller particulars were:

Two 3-bladed propellers	
diameter	10ft 3in
pitch	9ft 3in
developed blade area	42sq ft

The existing steam generators fitted in the ship were considered adequate and were retained. Distilling machinery of total capacity of 100ton/day was fitted.

Armament fitted consisted of one 12pdr HA/LA, two 2pdr pom-poms, four Lewis guns, eight Oerlikons and one PAC outfit.

Stability

Metacentric height in the deep condition was 3.69ft (fl).

General

The bulkhead deck in this vessel was the shelter deck. All watertight doors below this deck and side scuttles below the main deck were blanked watertight to improve the watertight subdivision and so increase protection in the event of bilging.

Accommodation to usual RN standards was arranged, but with the final complement being considerably in excess of the estimate, a lower standard of habitability than normal had to be accepted.

Vienna was taken in hand by Messrs Green & Silley Weir, Royal Albert Dock, London, in July 1941 and completed in July 1942. The vessel was released from Naval service and returned to the Ministry of War Transport in December 1944.

Destroyer Depot Ships

Woolwich

Admiralty policy concerning destroyer depot ships was determined by a committee which considered the matter in 1930 and in 1936. Plans Division stated that the requirement would be for four depot ships in peace and five in war. At that time two destroyer depot ships were in commission, *Greenwich* and *Woolwich*. The *Greenwich* had been purchased whilst building at Swan Hunters

Woolwich, a prewar destroyer depot ship, on 31 October 1940.

during the First World War and *Woolwich*, which was included in the 1932 new construction programme, had been completed in 1935.

The general particulars of *Woolwich* were:

Length overall	608ft 0in
Length between perps	575ft 0in
Breadth on waterline	64ft 0in
Depth (moulded)	44ft 0in
Standard displacement	8750 tons
Mean draught (standard)	14ft 8in
Power	6500shp
Max speed (deep)	17kts
Endurance	5000 miles at 12kts
Oil fuel	1140 tons
Complement (peace)	29 officers, 348 men

Woolwich was equipped for normal repairs of destroyers, but not for the heavier repairs which were intended to be carried out by the fleet repair ships. Workshops included heavy and light machinery shops, foundry, coppersmith's shop, patternmaker's shop, shipwright's shop, plumber's shop, electrical, ordnance and torpedo workshops and boat repair space.

Machinery consisted of four oil-fired watertube boilers in two boiler rooms, with geared turbines driving twin 3-bladed screws at

Propeller particulars:

diameter	10ft 6in
pitch	10ft
developed blade area	27.5sq ft

Four 300kW dynamos were arranged in separate auxiliary machinery rooms, and were of sufficient power to meet the requirements of the ship and to supply power to four destroyers simultaneously.

Armament consisted of:
  4-4in HA guns
  2-.5in machine guns
  8 Lewis guns
The ammunition stowage provided was sufficient for the ship's ammunition and 25 per cent of the ammunition for three flotillas of destroyers.

A magazine was provided for 200 depth charges, while stowage was arranged for 72 torpedoes, with a parting space for 14 torpedoes.

Protection
No special underwater protection was fitted but the ship was given good underwater sub-division, including longitudinal bulkheads 10ft from the ship side port and starboard, abreast machinery spaces and magazines.

The upper deck was 40lb MS, while 2in crowns were fitted to the magazines.

Destroyer depot ship *Tyne*, general arrangement

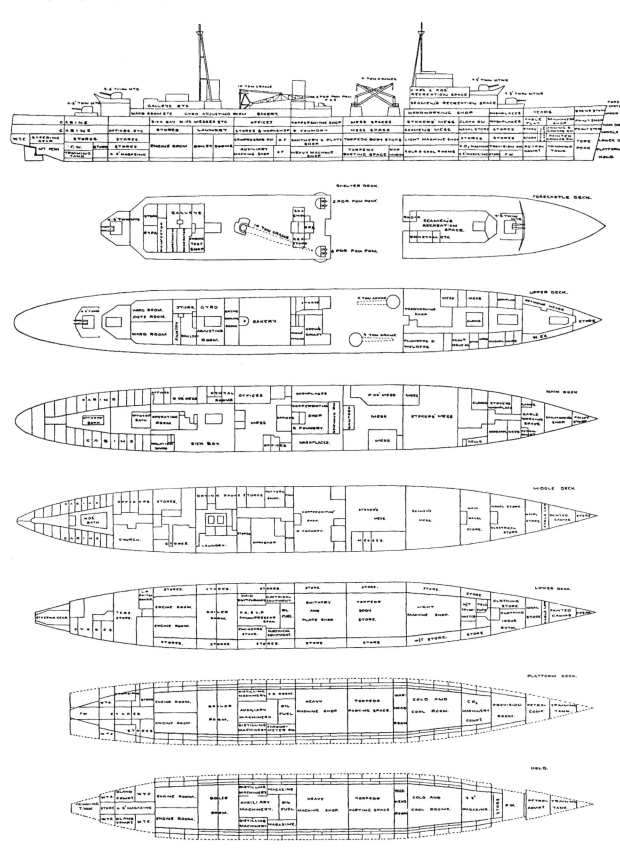

Stability particulars based on an inclining experiment carried out in 1935 were:

	Deep Condition	Light Condition
Metacentric height	5.9ft (fl)	6.7ft
Max GZ	4.9ft	2.7ft
Angle of max GZ	58°	57°
Range	over 90°	82°
Displacement	9500 tons	6700 tons

The standard longitudinal strength calculations gave the following:

	Hogging	Sagging
Maximum bending moment	242,000ton ft	215,000ton ft
Stress in upper deck	6.7ton/in²	5.1ton/in²
Stress in keel	5.7ton/in²	5.9ton/in²
Displacement	9594 tons	10,180 tons

Ship	*Woolwich*
Builder	Fairfields
Laid down	29 May 1933
Launched	20 Sep 1934
Completed	28 Jun 1935

Tyne and *Hecla*

One new construction destroyer depot ship, *Tyne*, was included in the 1937 programme, and a repeat vessel, *Hecla*, in the programme for the following year. The staff requirements for *Tyne* and *Hecla* were generally similar to *Woolwich*, but were modified in detail as a result of experience in *Woolwich*; protection against air and underwater attack was added to the requirements.

The sketch design for *Tyne* was approved by the Board in July 1938. *Hecla* was a repeat of the *Tyne* design except that the 4.5in guns were superimposed on the middle line and a 10ton crane on the middle line substituted for the 20ton sided crane; these alterations were incorporated in *Tyne* during building.

General particulars:

Length overall	621ft 2in
Length between perps	585ft 0in
Breadth extreme	66ft 0in
Depth to upper deck	43ft 0in
Deep displacement (as built)	14,064 tons
Mean draught (deep)	20ft 7in
Power	7500shp
Max speed	17kts
Endurance at 13½kts (6 months out of dock)	4000 miles
Oil fuel	1200 tons
Diesel oil	200 tons
Complement	44 officers, 798 men

Legend Group Weights

Hull	8380 tons
Equipment	1281 tons
Machinery	664 tons
Workshop machinery	367 tons
Oil fuel etc	1693 tons
Armament	445 tons
Fresh water	224 tons
Water in Sandwich protection	470 tons
Extra deep condition	13,524 tons

Equipment

These ships were designed to act as depot ships for one flotilla of *Tribal* class and two flotillas of J or later class destroyers. Stowage was provided for eighty torpedoes and maintenance facilities for 320 torpedoes. The following workshops were fitted: heavy machine shop; light machine shop; coppersmith's shop and foundry; pattern shop; smithery and plate shop; woodworking shop; ordnance, torpedo and electrical shop; welding and plumber's shop; painter's shop; gyroscope adjusting room; sailmaker's shop; impregnating plant room; motor boat engine test shop; motor boat engine workshop and store.

Two 4ton electric cranes were provided for workshops and torpedo handling and one 10ton electric crane for boats etc. Refrigerated stowage for ship and three flotillas for forty-six days, dry provision stowage for ship and one flotilla for thirty days and flour stowage for ship and three flotillas for seventy-six days, were provided. The instructional apparatus for training purposes included that for torpedo attack, asdic attack, etc.

The vessels were fitted as full base W/T ships and for service in Arctic or tropics.

The vessels were built to Lloyd's rules and the oversight of structural work, except the armoured middle deck, was carried out by Lloyd's surveyors.

Protection

A 90lb D1 quality middle deck was fitted over workshops, magazines and machinery spaces (80lb NC in *Hecla*), with 60lb D1 over steering compartment, for protection against air attack.

An underwater protection system was fitted. This extended from stations 52 to 170, ie about 350ft and consisted mainly of an air-water-air sandwich of 10ft maximum breadth; towards the ends of this protection, the three sandwich spaces were replaced by two watertight air spaces. The underwater protection was bounded inboard by a 60lb D1 longitudinal bulkhead. Splinter protection of 15lb D1 HT or 25lb D quality plating was also fitted.

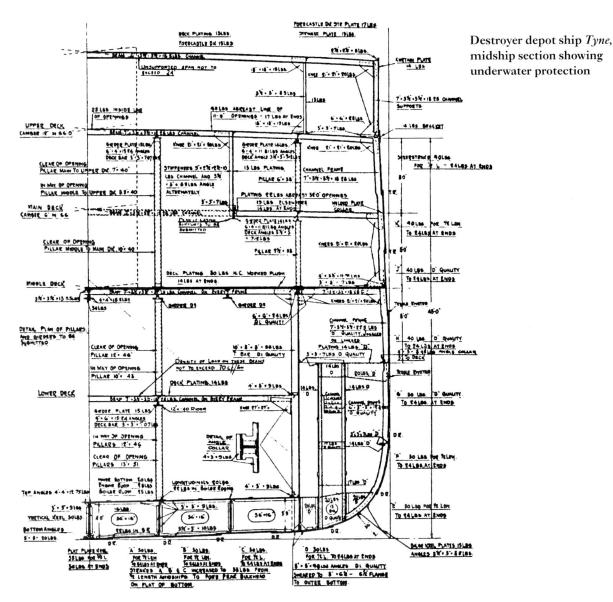

Destroyer depot ship *Tyne*, midship section showing underwater protection

Machinery

The main machinery consisted of four boilers, and geared turbines driving twin screws at 230rpm.

Particulars of propellers:

3-bladed
diameter   10ft 6in
pitch   8ft 6in
developed blade area 31.5ft

The auxiliary machinery fitted included two 300kW turbo-generators and two 300kW diesel generators. In addition to the normal pumping and flooding arrangements two 150ton submersible pumps were fitted for pumping out the large workshop spaces. Distillers with a total capacity of 360ton/day were also fitted.

Radar fitted included types 279, 282 and 285.

Armament consisted of eight 4.5in HA/LA in twin upper deck mountings with fusekeeping clock control system and R/F directors, two 4-barrelled 2-pdr pom-poms, five twin and five single Oerlikons.

Stability Particulars

The following stability particulars were calculated from an inclining experiment carried out on *Hecla* in December 1940 and confirmed by an inclining on *Tyne* in January of the following year.

	Deep Condition	Light Condition
Metacentric height	3.78ft (fl)	2.59ft
Max GZ	4.3ft	2.35ft
Angle of max GZ	50°	48°
Range	over 90°	78°
Displacement	14,103 tons	10,918 tons

Tyne, a destroyer depot ship of the 1937 programme, seen on completion on 3 March 1941.

The standard strength calculation gave the following results:

	Hogging	Sagging
Maximum bending moment	299,890ton ft	268,670ton ft
Stress in upper deck	7.52ton/in²	5.86ton/in²
Stress in keel	5.54ton/in²	5.46ton/in²
Displacement	12,230 tons	12,830 tons

General

A number of modifications were made to this design during building of the ships; included were fitting of the Oerlikons, radar, gun crews shelters, splinter protection to guns, etc.

The ships proved satisfactory in service and no As and As other than minor items and those due to development of equipment were carried out.

Ship	1937 Programme	1938 Programme
	Tyne	Hecla
Shipbuilder	Scotts	John Brown
Laid down	15 Jul 1938	23 Jan 1939
Launched	28 Feb 1940	14 Mar 1940
Completed	28 Feb 1941	6 Jan 1941

Auxiliary Destroyer Depot Shops

Philoctetes and *Blenheim*

In pursuance of the policy regarding depot ships, it became necessary on the outbreak of war to acquire another ship to satisfy the requirement for five destroyer depot ships; this could only be met by a conversion.

Modern destroyer depot ships at that time catered for three flotillas, but as no ship capable of conversion to a three-flotilla depot ship could be made available, approval was given in August 1940 to convert two two-flotilla ships. The two *Holt* liners, *Philoctetes* and *Achilles* (renamed *Blenheim*), had been selected some time previously from the very limited choice available, and the staff requirements had to be reduced from the full requirements to suit these ships.

General particulars were:

Length overall	528ft 6in
Length between perps	503ft 0in
Breadth extreme	63ft 4in
Depth to upper deck	44ft 6in
Deep displacement	16,360 tons
Mean draught (deep)	25ft 5in
Power	7000shp
Max speed (deep)	14¾kts
Endurance at 13½kts (6 months out of dock)	3100 miles
Coal	1450 tons
Complement	33 officers, 565 crew

The major structural items carried out were:

To adjust the deck heights to suit workshops, torpedo stowage etc. parts of the lower deck were removed completely and intermediate WT decks built. Flats were built in holds as necessary, and additional girders and pillaring fitted. The forecastle deck and the superstructure deck were both lengthened, deck houses built as required and minor bulkhead fitted throughout the ship as necessary. All cargo hatches were plated in and made watertight. Gun and director supports were built and WT trunks fitted for transport of stores, material, etc. to storerooms and shops without passing through intermediate spaces.

Workshops fitted were: heavy machine shop; light machine shop; coppersmith's shop and foundry; pattern shop; smithery and plate shop;

woodworking shop; ordnance, torpedo and electrical shop; welding and plumber's shop; painter's shop; gyro adjusting room; sailmaker's shop; impregnating plant; motor boat engine test shop; motor boat engine workshop and depth charge workshop.

The arrangements existing in the ships were utilised as far as possible, but in general the utility of the existing arrangements were limited and practically complete new arrangements were fitted.

The extra storage arrangements fitted allowed cold storage for two flotillas for three months and flour for two flotillas for 120 days.

Protection
In view of the difficulty of obtaining armour, two thicknesses of 60lb mild steel protection were fitted to the crowns and sides of the depth charge and warhead rooms and magazines, with 20lb D1 HT doubling fitted to steering gear compartment, bridges, gun positions etc.

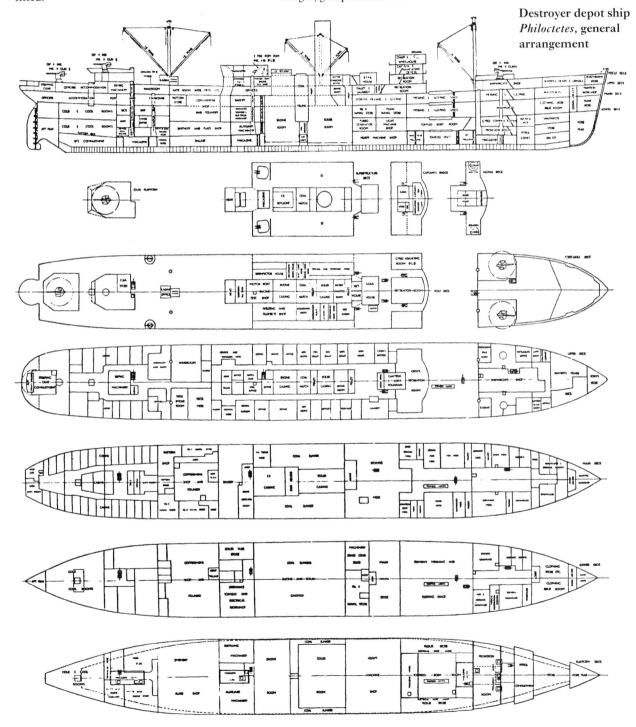

Destroyer depot ship
Philoctetes, general
arrangement

Armament fitted consisted of four 4in HA/LA guns in single mountings with fusekeeping clock control system, four 4-barrelled pom-poms and four single 20mm Oerlikons. Ammunition supply to the guns was by bollard hoists.

Stowage arrangements were provided for sixty 21in torpedoes and 150 depth charges for the destroyer flotillas.

Machinery consisted of twin screw-geared turbines developing 7000shp and three coal-fired double-ended cylindrical boilers.

Distilling machinery with a total capacity of 200 tons per day was fitted, together with four turbo generators each of 300kW. The two 26kW 110 volt generators existing in the ship were retained for the supply of 100 volt power to vessels alongside.

Stability

1500 tons of permanent ballast were fitted and 1000 tons of water ballast carried in DB tanks to reduce freeboard and windage in the seagoing condition, for safer anchoring, and to provide positive stability in the bilged condition.

The bulkhead deck in these vessels was the upper deck but for through access it was necessary to fit WT doors on the main deck. The accommodation was fitted generally on this deck and side scuttles were fitted to these spaces on the main deck and a limited number fitted in the accommodation on the lower deck.

The following stability particulars were calculated from the results of an inclining experiment carried out on *Blenheim*.

	Normal Deep Condition	*Service Light Condition*
Metacentric height	2.31ft (fl)	1.82ft
Max GZ	4.3ft	4.14ft
Angle of max GZ	54°	52°
Range	over 90°	over 90°
Displacement	16,356 tons	13,691 tons

General

The conversions were commenced in August 1940, *Philoctetes* being taken in hand by Messrs Harland & Wolff, Belfast and *Blenheim* (ex *Achilles*) by Messrs Smiths Dock Co, North Shields. Both vessels completed in January 1942.

The estimate for the conversion had been twelve months; delay was caused, however, by the fact that the conversions were not given first priority and by the consequent diversion of shipyard labour to merchant ship repair.

Accommodation for the repair engineer and accountant staff, in addition to depot ships complement, was to RN standards.

Both shops were specified to be fitted with radar and also to be fitted for Arctic and tropical service. To accelerate completion, however, these requirements were relaxed somewhat. Radar was omitted from both ships. *Blenheim* was eventually fitted with radar, and when refitted brought more nearly to the original requirements for service in the Arctic and tropics.

The ships proved generally satisfactory in service and few As and As, other than those due to development of equipment, were necessary. One complaint received from the ship, however, was that due to windage a considerable amount of weather helm was necessary in a beam wind.

In September 1945 *Philoctetes* was released from Naval service.

Submarine Depot Ships

Maidstone and *Forth*

In 1939 there were three new-construction submarine depot ships in commission, in addition to the older and smaller ships *Titania*, *Cyclops*, *Lucia* and *Alecto*, which had been converted during the First World War. The three ships were *Medway*, included in the 1926 building programme and completed in July 1928, *Maidstone* and *Forth*.

The general particulars for *Maidstone* and *Forth* were:

Length overall	531ft 0in
Length between perps	497ft 0in
Breadth extreme	73ft 0in
Depth to upper deck	44ft ½in
Displacement (extra deep)	11,814 tons
Mean draught (extra deep)	20ft 2in
Speed (maximum)	17kts
Power	7000shp
Endurance at 10kts (6 months out of dock)	10,000 miles
Oil fuel	2300 tons
Complement	33 officers, 565 crew

The *Maidstone* and *Forth* designed to act as depot ships for nine 'T' class submarines in peace and twelve in war. The workshops included a heavy machine shop, light machine shop, foundry and coppersmith's shop, plate shop and smithery, pattern shop, welding and plumbing shop, woodworking shop, etc. The main machinery consisted of geared turbines developing 7000shp on twin screws at 170rpm and four oil-fired boilers in two boiler rooms.

Armament originally consisted of four 4.5in HA/LA guns in twin mountings and two 0.5in machine guns, but was increased to eight 4.5in in twin mountings, eight 2pdr pom-poms in quadruple mountings, two single pom-poms, fourteen single Oerlikons and five single Bofors.

The ammunition stowage included a quarter outfit for submarines and 126 torpedoes (10 parting spaces).

Accommodation was provided for a maximum of eighty-nine officers and 617 men (for depot ship) plus 591 men for the attached submarines.

Ship	1926 Programme	1935 Programme	1937 Programme
	Medway	*Maidstone*	*Forth*
Shipbuilder	Vickers	J Brown	J Brown
Laid down	12 Apr 1927	17 Aug 1936	30 Jun 1937
Launched	19 Jul 1928	21 Oct 1937	11 Aug 1938
Completed	6 Jul 1929	5 May 1938	12 May 1939

Adamant

One submarine depot ship was included in the 1938 new construction programme. The staff requirements were generally similar to *Maidstone* and *Forth* except that protection against air and underwater attack was required – this resulted in an increase in displacement of about 3000ton over *Maidstone*.

The sketch design was approved in November 1938 and the design was completed and laid down at Harland & Wolffs in May 1939. She was named *Adamant*.

The ship was designed to act as a depot ship for twelve 'T' class submarines in war, accommodation being provided for the crews of nine 'T' class submarines and two spare crews in addition to the depot ship's complement. Stowage for 117 torpedoes and maintenance facilities for 309 torpedoes were provided.

The following workshops were fitted: heavy machine shop; light machine shop; tool room, diesel valve test shop; smithery and plate shop; coppersmith's shop and foundry; welding and plumber's shop; pattern ship; ordnance torpedo and electrical shop; woodworking shop; motor boat engine shop; motor boat engine test shop; gyro adjusting room; impregnating plant shop; painter's shop; DSEA workshop and periscope examination and repair shop. One 2ton and one 6ton electric cranes were fitted for workshop and torpedo handling, and one 10ton electric crane for boats etc. Refrigerated space for ship and fourteen submarines for forty-five days, and dry provision

Forth with three unidentified submarines in October 1942.

stowage for this number for 120 days were provided. The vessel was fitted as a full base W/T ship.

The leading particulars of *Adamant* were:

Length overall	658ft 0in
Length between perps	620ft 0in
Breadth extreme	70ft 6in
Depth to upper deck	45ft 0in
Deep displacement	16,497 tons
Mean draught deep	21ft 3in
Power	8000shp
Maximum speed (standard)	17kts
Endurance (6 months out of dock)	4000 miles at 13½kts
Oil fuel stowage (total)	2476 tons
Complement	36 officers, 1174 ratings

Titania, *one of the mercantile conversions to submarine depot ships carried out during the First World War*

The first of the post-Great War purpose-built submarine depot ships was the Medway, *seen here on builder's trials*

Legend Group Weights

Hull	8124 tons
Protection	1750 tons
Machinery	756 tons
Equipment	1181 tons
Workshop machinery	321 tons
Oil fuel	1250 tons
Oil fuel for submarines	1226 tons
Armament	566 tons
RFW	80 tons
Fresh water	110 tons
Water in protection	694 tons
	16,178 tons

Protection

A 2in NC armour deck was fitted over workshops, magazines, torpedo stores and machinery spaces; this was considered sufficient protection against a 250lb dive bomb. The steering gear was protected by 1½in 'D' quality plating.

The underwater protection system fitted consisted of the standard air-water-air sandwich, and extended approx 294ft of the ship's length with an average width of about 10ft.

The water jackets contained 650ton water protection when full. This underwater protection, together with the 55lb D1 longitudinal bulkhead, was designed for protection against 18in aircraft torpedo attack.

Splinter protection was also fitted to bridges, guns, etc.

Armament

Armament fitted consisted of eight 4.5in HA/LA in twin upper deck mountings with fusekeeping clock control system and R/F directors, four 4-barrelled pom-poms, six 20mm Oerlikons and eight machine guns.

The ammunition stowage accommodated a total of 2000 rounds for the ship and a quarter outfit for the twelve submarines.

Torpedo stowage was arranged for 117 21in submarine torpedoes.

Machinery consisted of geared turbines, 8000shp powered by four oil-fired boilers situated in two boiler rooms.

Propeller particulars:

2 3-bladed propellers at 240rpm	
diameter	10ft 6in
pitch	8ft 9in
developed blade area	34.5ft^2

Auxiliary machinery included two 800kW and two 400kW turbo-generators, and two 300kW diesel generators, each dynamo being in a separate watertight compartment. The distillers fitted had a total capacity of 360ton/day and, in addition to the normal pumping arrangements, two 150ton/hour submersible pumps were fitted for pumping out the large workshop spaces.

Radar fitted included types 282, 285 and 79.

Stability

Based on an inclining experiment carried out in January 1942, the following stability particulars were calculated:

	Extreme Deep Condition	Light Condition
Metacentric height	6.2ft (fl)	4.49ft
Max GZ	5.89ft	3.24ft
Angle of max GZ	52°	47°
Range	over 90°	80°
Displacement	16,497 tons	12,307 tons

The longitudinal strength of this ship was not calculated by use of the standard longitudinal strength calculation, but an estimate was made with the formula WL/K using values of K calculated for *Tyne* viz 23.8 for hogging and 28.0 for sagging.

	Hogging	Sagging
Max bending moment	369,550ton/ft	342,800ton/ft
Stress in upper deck	7.79ton/in^2	6.4ton/in^2
Stress in keel	6.15ton/in^2	6.46ton/in^2
M1 of section	609,480in^{2}ft^2	612,600in^{2}ft^2
Displacement	14,186 tons	15,484 tons

A number of amendments to the design were made during building of the ship. Included were: omission of signal guns and fitting of Oerlikons, radar, guns crews shelters, splinter protection to guns, etc.

It is of interest to note that after enemy action at Belfast in May 1941 which caused considerable dislocation of the shipyard facilities, the ship's own cranes and workshop machinery were used to assist in the fitting out and completion of the vessel.

1938 Programme

Ship	*Adamant*
Builder	Harland & Wolff
Laid down	18 May 1939
Launched	30 Nov 1940
Completed	28 Feb 1942

Conversions to Submarine Depot Ships

Montclare and *Wolfe*

Two submarine depot ships were included in the 1941 conversion programme and approval was given for the conversion of the two CPR ships - *Montclare* and *Wolfe* (ex *Montcalm*) - then serving as armed merchant cruisers. The full requirements for submarine depot shops at that time were reduced to suit these two ships, the main reductions were that accommodation for eleven submarine crews was to be provided instead of sixteen, and that an endurance of 5000 miles at 11½kts was acceptable; some reduction in the torpedo stowage was also necessary to provide sufficient torpedo parting space.

The leading particulars of these ships were:

Length overall	575ft 0in
Length between perps	546ft 0in
Breadth extreme	70ft 3in
Depth to shelter deck	43ft 3in
Deep displacement	21,499 tons
Mean draught (deep)	27ft 8in
Power	13,500shp
Maximum speed	15kts
Endurance	5000 miles at 11½kts
Fuel	949 tons + 810 tons for submarines
Complement	93 officers, 707 men (for depot ship) + 563 men for (attached submarines)

The major structural work included the following items:

To adjust deck height to suit workshops etc, portions of the lower, main and superstructure decks, together with one main WT bulkhead, were removed completely, and other flats built as necessary and one new main WT bulkhead fitted. Additional pillars and girders were fitted and all cargo hatches plated in and made watertight. Minor bulkheads were fitted throughout the ship as required and gun and director supports built. Trunks were fitted for transport of stores, materials, etc to storerooms and shops without passing through intermediate spaces. Cofferdams to separate oil stowages from fresh water and ballast tanks were built.

The following workshops were fitted: heavy machine shop; light machine shop; tool room; coppersmith's shop and foundry; pattern shop; smithery and plate shop; woodworking shop; ordnance torpedo and electrical shop; welding and plumber's shop; painter's shop; gyro-adjusting rooms; periscope examination room; optical repair shop; DSEA workshop; diesel valve test shop; impregnating plant shop; MB engine test and workshop.

Other items such as galleys, storerooms, heads, ventilation, water services, etc, were fitted to Admiralty requirements, the existing arrangements being utilised as far as practicable. Magazines for 4in pom-pom, Oerlikon and SA ammunition, and for 4in and 3in submarine ammunition with the usual spraying and flooding arrangements, were fitted.

Full base W/T equipment was fitted and the vessels were made suitable for service in the Arctic or tropics.

The converted submarine depot ship Montclare, *seen in October 1953.*

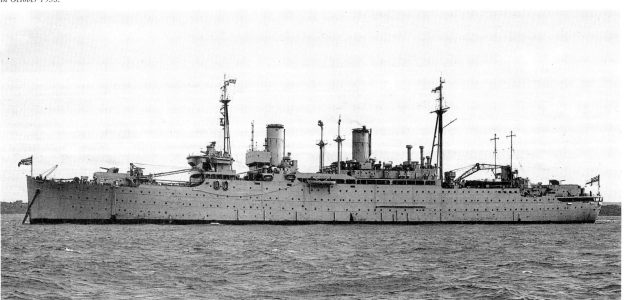

Submarine depot ship *Wolfe*, general arrangement

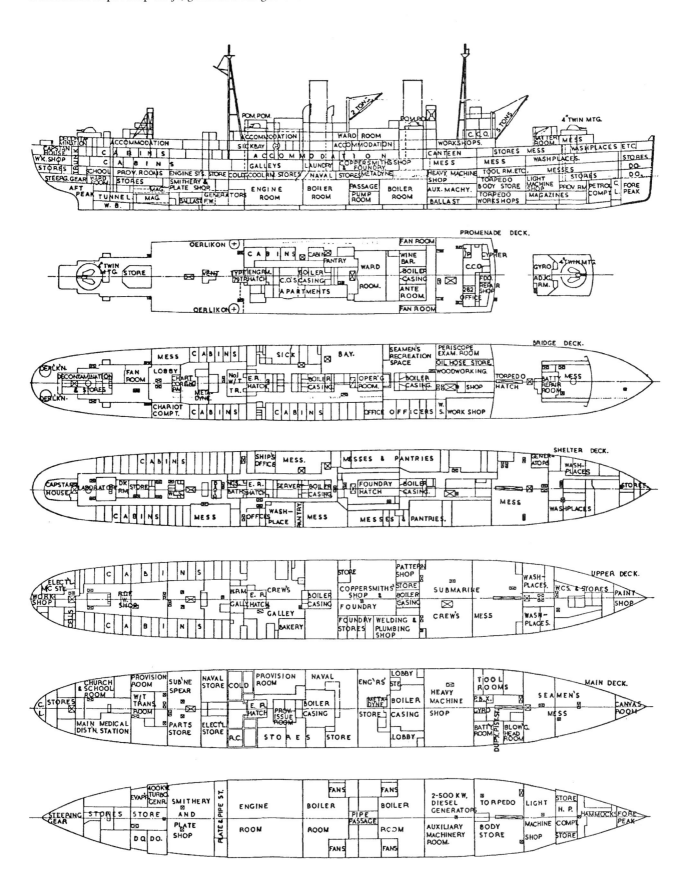

Protection

The protection fitted was not extensive and consisted of 80lb NC armour protection to crowns, ends and sides of the magazines (120lb MS in *Wolfe*) and splinter protection to steering gear compartment, bridges, guns, etc.

Armament consisted of four 4in HA/LA guns in twin mountings, four 4-barrelled pom-poms, eighteen single Oerlikons and two twin Oerlikons (six twin and ten single Oerlikons in *Wolfe*).

Ammunition for six full outfits for 'A' class submarines was also stowed in addition to that for the ship's armament. Seventy-two torpedoes were also carried as replacements for submarines.

Machinery

The main machinery consisted of two sets of turbines driving twin screws, and ten cylindrical Scotch boilers at 215lb/in working pressure.

Propeller particulars:

2 3-bladed propellers at 100rpm	
diameter	18ft
pitch	17ft 3in
developed blade area	82sq ft

The auxiliary machinery originally installed in *Montclare* included three 175kW turbo generators and two 150kW diesel generators; this was supplemented by the fitting of an additional 300kW diesel generator. *Wolfe* was fitted with two 500kW alternators.

The distilling capacity of each ship was 360ton/day.

Radar fitted included types 79, 291, 285 and 282.

Stability particulars based on an inclining experiment carried out on *Wolfe* in 1943 were:

	Deep Condition	Light Condition
Metacentric height	1.97ft (fl)	1.79ft
Max GZ	3.96ft	3.98ft
Angle of max GZ	53°	55°
Range	over 90°	over 90°
Displacement	21,845 tons	19,205 tons

General

The bulkhead deck in these ships was the shelter deck, but as accommodation was generally fitted on the upper deck, side scuttles were fitted at this level and a limited number on the main deck. Accommodation was to usual RN standards for both ship's complement and for the eleven submarines crews.

'X' Craft Depot Ship

Bonaventure

The title 'X' craft was the name given to midget submarines developed during the early years of the war. These craft were 51ft 7in in length overall, 5ft 9in pressure hull diameter and 35ton surface displacement, including two side cargoes or explosive charges weighing 4ton each, carried out board on the craft and capable of release from within the pressure hull.

In August 1942 the development of 'X' craft had progressed so far that their early active employment in war operations was envisaged; staff requirements were then formulated for the conversion of a merchant ship to an 'X' craft depot ship. The depot ship was originally required to transport twelve craft with their crews from base to base, to maintain the craft and to transport and launch six craft as near the scene of operations as possible. The requirements were primed to enable the ship to be completed by December 1942, and the ship was fitted as a depot ship for eight 'X' craft.

The ship offered by Ministry of War Transport for conversion was a shelter deck type then under construction by Greenock Dockyard Company for the Clan Line steamers. She was named *Bonaventure*.

The leading particulars of this ship were:

Length overall	487ft 8in
Length between perps	457ft 0in
Breadth extreme	63ft 0in
Depth to upper deck	40ft 9in
Deep displacement	12,110 tons
Mean draught (deep)	22ft 3in
Power	8300ihp
Maximum speed	16kts
Endurance (6 months out of dock)	5,000 miles at 15kts
Fuel	953 tons oil fuel and 950 tons of coal
Complement	54 officers, 454 crew

The conversion work commenced early in September 1942, while the ship was still on the building berth and approaching readiness for launching. The major structural work necessary included moving the whole bridge structure and lengthening No 2 hatchway to allow 'X' craft to be lowered into the hold and stowed; plating up the 4 hatchway to provide stowage space for 'X' craft on the upper deck. All other large cargo hatchways were plated in and minor bulkheads built to provide store rooms, workshops accommodation etc. Longitudinal bulkheads were also built in No 4 hold and magazines fitted for the side 'cargoes', 4in gun and small arms.

The workshops fitted included: ordnance and electrical shops; periscope, shipwright, smithery and plate shops; coppersmith's; plumber's and welder's shops; radar and machine shops and an engine test room.

The cold and cool rooms being fitted for the vessel as a merchant ship were adequate for RN requirements and were retained, but other items such as additional accommodation, store rooms, ventilation, water services and oil fuel filling arrangements etc were fitted to Admiralty requirements.

Two of the 'X' craft carried were stowed in the hold, and stowages were arranged for the other six craft on the upper deck, two under the forward 50ton derrick and four under the after 40ton derrick.

Protection

As armour protection could not be obtained in the required time, the equivalent mild steel protection was fitted to magazines etc on the following scale; the crowns of the 4in magazine, small arms and side 'cargo' magazines were fitted with 80lb mild steel, while the longitudinal bulkheads and trunked hatch to side 'cargo' magazines were 40lb mild steel. The Macauking hatch covers fitted to the side 'cargo' magazines were 15lb D1 HT steel.

Bridge structure was fitted with plastic armour protection.

X Craft depot ship *Bonaventure*, general arrangement

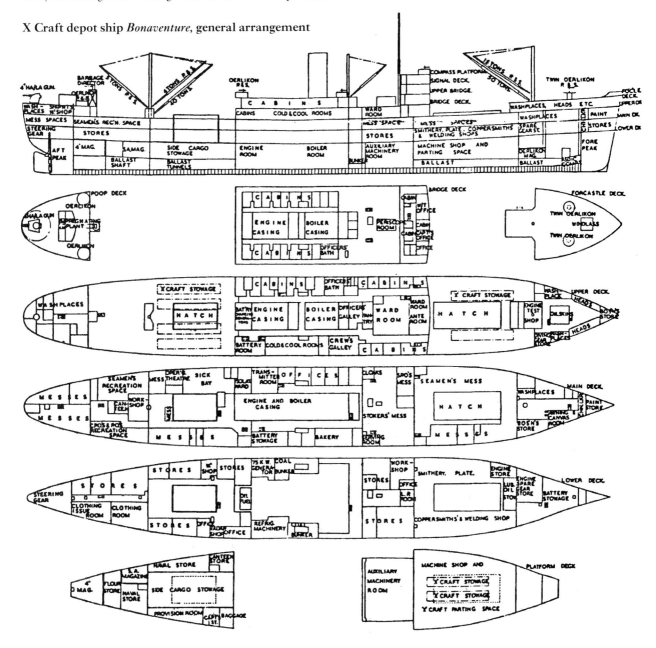

Armament consisted of one 4in twin mounting, two power-operated twin Oerlikon mountings and eight single Oerlikons. It was originally intended to fit a second twin 4in mounting, but the two power-operated twin Oerlikon mountings were eventually fitted in its place.

Machinery

Twin screw reciprocating steam engines with Bauer-Wach low-pressure exhaust turbines developing a total of 8300ihp. The boilers were coal or oil fired.

Propeller particulars:

2 3-bladed propellers
diameter   9ft 6in
pitch   12ft 0in
developed blade area   57sq ft

The auxiliary machinery fitted included three generators each of 70kW in addition to two diesel generators, each of 30kW for charging the 'X' craft batteries. During conversion two additional diesel generators were fitted, one 100kW and one 75kW.

The distilling capacity of the ship as designed was increased to 130ton/day.

Stability

1430ton of slag ballast were provided to reduce freeboard and windage for a better seagoing performance, and to provide positive stability in the bilged condition.

The stability particulars for the ship in the deep condition were:

Metacentric height   4.12ft (fl)
Max GZ   5.2ft
Range   over 90°

Accommodation

The crew's accommodation, originally based on approx 25sq ft/man was ultimately somewhat crowded due largely to increases in complement. Staff requirements called for accommodation for fifty-four officers and 300 ratings; this was increased to 370 ratings when the scheme of complement was issued. A further increase to 450 ratings took place while the ship was on service. Some improvement was effected by building additional messes at the expense of certain recreation spaces.

The crew's accommodation was fitted generally on the main deck; as the bulkhead deck was the upper deck no side scuttles were fitted below. Complaints were received on the inadequacy of the ventilation of the messes and additional fans were fitted.

General

Early experience with this ship showed that she consistently dragged anchor. It was therefore decided to fit two 11,000lb anchors in lieu of the 82cwt Merchant anchors fitted and increase the available length of cable from 300 fathoms to 375 fathoms. No further reports of dragging of anchors were received.

The ship was stated to steer well.

Early in 1945 *Bonaventure* sailed for the Far East carrying six 'XE' craft which formed the 14th Submarine Flotilla. These 'XE' craft were about 2ft longer than the original 'X' craft.

After the conclusion of the war with Japan the Flotilla was paid off in September 1945, the craft dismantled and *Bonaventure* became an independent command employed with British Pacific Fleet for transport of stores and personnel.

Index